photograph: carolyn cowan

Welcome to the Baby Directory: 8th Edition

My first pregnancy was an exciting time - full of anticipation and trepidation about the little person I was about to bring into the world. Setting out on a fact gathering exercise my husband and I came across The London Baby Directory, and as we thumbed through the categories our eyes were opened to an entirely new world.

London is an exciting and vibrant place for young children, and a great place to have a baby. No other city has such a diversity of products and services on offer and there is nowhere better to find them than in The Baby Directory. Our researchers have uncovered some of London's best secrets to give you the inside knowledge on all things related to babies and young children.

I constantly refer to my Baby Directory for my two children (Georgia $4^1/_2$yrs and Max 2yrs) and countless testimonies from customers confirm that mothers and fathers use it religiously. We hope you will enjoy finding the original and exceptional things on offer.

Clare Flawn-Thomas

Clare Flawn-Thomas, Editor
editor@babydirectory.com

Edited, designed and published by
The Baby Directory Limited
7 Brockwell Park Row
London SW2 2YH
Tel +44 (0)20 8678 9000
Fax +44 (0)20 8671 1919
www.babydirectory.com

Editor	Clare Flawn-Thomas
Deputy Editor	Sue Carpenter
Researchers	Kirsty Vind, Karen Ip & Krista Lowe
Designer	Johanni Loubser
Website	Cyberscreen
Printers	AntidoteFM

Disclaimer

While every effort and care has been made to ensure the accuracy of the information contained in this publication, the publisher cannot accept responsibility for any errors, inaccuracies or omissions it may contain. Inclusion in the Directory does not imply an endorsement of the service of product.

All rights reserved throughout the world. No part of this publication may be reproduced or transmitted in any form, or by any means, electronic, mechanical, photocopying, recording or otherwise, or stored in any retrieval system, without prior written permission of the publisher.

The Data Protection Act requires that we inform you that if your company or service is listed in the Directory, it is on our computer. Data Protection Register No: PX 4379316

Copright © The Baby Directory Limited. All rights reserved.

ISBN: 1-903288-12-6
Eighth Edition: Updated 2004

The Baby Directory is an invaluable reference guide for mothers-to-be" **The Times**

"Forget about wading through the local paper for mother and baby contacts - The Baby Directory has done it for you"
Pregnancy & Birth

"Indispensable and essential" **Practical Parenting**

"A mine of useful information" **The NCT**

Your pregnancy calendar

These pages enable you to plan your pregnancy in phases of 4 weeks. You can write the dates or names of the months in the spaces next to the week headings to personalise the calendar to your own pregnancy. Then you can follow the suggestions for each month and also make your own notes in the relevant spaces.

Weeks 1-4

Things to do:

- Buy and borrow books on pregnancy.

- Start taking a daily amount of folic acid (400mg).

- Avoid smoking and taking any drugs or medication.

- Week 4: get home pregnancy kit or visit your doctor to calculate your estimated due date.

Notes:

Weeks 5-9

Things to do:

- Get in touch with local hospitals and see what facilities they have, or research home birth.

- Keep a note of everything you read in pregnancy books and magazines.

- Consider complementary therapies to keep morning sickness under control (see aromatherapy, pg 10 and reflexology, pg 19).

- Start looking for pregnancy exercise classes (see pg 12, yoga, pg 19).

Notes:

Weeks 10-14

Things to do:

- You will be offered a 12 week scan - the first time you see your baby.

- After the scan is when most people tell close friends and family the exciting news.

- Consider booking a maternity nurse or doula - popular ones get booked very quickly so contact agencies now for a list of candidates (see pg 78).

Notes:

Weeks 15-19

Things to do:

- If your clothes are feeling uncomfortable, start ordering the maternity wear catalogues and visiting the stores (see pg 43).

- Book antenatal/parenting classes as they get booked up (see pg 1).

Notes:

Weeks 20-24

Things to do:

- 20 week fetal anomaly scan.

- 22 weeks: half way there!

- Think about decorating the nursery (see murals, pg 50 and nursery furniture/interiors, pg 60).

Notes:

Your pregnancy Calendar

Your pregnancy calendar

Weeks 25-29

Things to do:

- If you would like one last trip abroad, now's the time to go. Some airlines won't let you fly after 28 weeks. Also check that your travel insurance covers pregnancy. Most will cover to 32 weeks for the date of return.

- Think about whether you'll be returning to work, and make arrangements with your employer. You can take maternity leave from week 29

- If you are thinking of returning to work, register with your local nursery school - popular ones can have up to 1 year waiting lists (see pg 107).

Notes:

Weeks 30-34

Things to do:

- Order some of the larger items you will need when your baby arrives (such as prams, cots and car seats), as they can take 6 weeks to order (see cribs and cots, pg 36 and prams and pushchairs, pg 68).

- Treat yourself to a pregnancy massage (see pg 15).

- Consider body painting, life casting and pregnancy photography (see pg 3).

Notes:

Weeks 35-39

Things to do:

- Sort out all the things you need if you are having a home birth (see waterbirth pool hire, pg 8).

- Organise TENS hire (pg 6).

- Prepare your list of friends and family for sending birth announcement cards (see pg 22).

- Organise your Stem Cell collection kit (see pg 6).

Notes:

Weeks 40-42

Things to do:

- Stock your larder and freezer and get online with home delivery companies (see pg 37).

- Don't get too fed up if your baby arrives after the estimated date. Use the time to relax, see friends and generally organise yourself (see clutter clearing, pg 197).

Notes:

---

contents

pregnancy & birth 1

Antenatal Classes
Antenatal Tests & Scans
Breastfeeding
Body Painters
Hospitals (NHS)
Hospitals (Private)
Sex Choice
Stem Cells
TENS machines
Waterbirth Pool hire

health 2

Acupuncture
Alexander technique
Aromatherapy
Baby Research
Chemists, late opening
Complementary Health
First Aid & safety
Exercise: pre & post-natal
Health Clubs with Creches
Homeopathy
Hypnotherapy
Immunisations
Infertility
Massage
Medical Advice
Nutrition
Osteopathy & Cranial Osteopathy
Craniosacral Therapy
Physiotherapists
Post natal support & info
Reflexology
Yoga

shopping 3

Baby Accessories
Baby Equipment Hire
Baby Showers
Birth Announcements
Bookshops for Children
Bookclubs
Car Safety
Carriers, Slings & backpacks
Car Seats
Castings: Hands & Feet
Christening Gifts
Christening Gowns
Clothing Shops
Department Stores
Cribs, Cots & First Beds
Dressing Up
Food (organic)
Garden Toys
Gifts: Personalised
Gifts for Newborns
Hairdressers
Highchairs
Linens & Sleeping Bags
Lotions & Potions (natural)
Maternity Wear
Maternity Bra Specialists

Magazines
Monitors
Murals
Name Tapes
Nappies, Cloth
Nappy Laundry
Nearly New
Nursery Furniture
Nursery Goods
Nursery Goods: mail order
Nursery Interior design
Photographers & Portraits
Prams
Pushchairs
3-Wheelers
Pram & Buggy repairs
Rocking horses
Shoes & Shoe Shops
Swimwear & Sun Stuff
Toy shops
Toys: mail order
Travel Cots

childcare 4

Au pair agencies
Babysitters
Childminders
Doulas
Maternity Nannies & Nurses
Midwives: Independant
Nanny Agencies
Nanny Share
Nanny Payroll Services

travel 5

UK Hotels & Holidays
Overseas travel
Camping
Home Swaps
Family villages & resorts
Family Skiing

parties 6

Party Food
Party Ideas
Party Entertainers
Party Equipment
Party Organisers
Party Shops
Party Venues

nurseries 7

Nurseries
French Nursery Schools
Spanish Nursery Schools
Schools, pre-prep
Gifted Children
Learning Difficulties
Left-handedness
Speech Therapy
Tuition (extra)

toddler activities 8

Adventure playgrounds
Art Workshops
Baby Research
Chess
Ceramic Cafes
Cookery
Cycling & Scooters
Dance
Drama
Foreign Language classes & clubs
Football
Gyms – mini
Holiday Activities
Indoor Playcentres
Libraries
Model Agencies
Music Groups
Paddling Pools
Parks & Playgrounds
Riding
Swimming Classes
Swimming Pools
Swimming Pools: Outdoor
Tennis

Days Out 9

Art Centres & Galleries
Castles & Soldier
Circus
Farms: City
Farms: Out of town
Ice Rinks
Museums
Parks & Gardens
Pubs with gardens & playrooms
Restaurants:child-friendly
Theatres
Theme Parks
Trains
Zoos

good advice 11

Adoption
Councils
Expat Advice
Fatherhood
Financial Advice
Helplines
Naming Ceremonies
Parenting classes & courses
Paternity Testing
Working Opportunities
Useful Tradesmen

antenatal classes

For this category we have selected London's top antenatal teachers who help prepare mother and father for labour, birth and life with a new baby. Also provides opportunities to meet other mums-to-be who live near you and have a similar due date. Important to book early as these classes are extremely popular

EAST

Arlene Dunkley Wood   020 8923 6452
154 King's Head Hill, E4 7NU
An active birth teacher.

Bridget Baker   020 7249 3224
116 Forest Road, E8 3BH
Childbirth preparation classes - group or individual sessions

Jeyarani Gentle Birth Programme 020 8530 1146
34 Cleveland Road, South Woodford, E18 2AL
www.jeyarani.com
Self-hypnosis, reflexology, craniosacral therapy and yoga.

NORTH

Trish Ferguson   020 7354 5228
56 Morton Road, N1 3BE

Diana Parkinson   020 8347 8521
6a Landrock Road, N8 9HP

Debra Sequoia: Birth Body   020 8365 3545
info@birthbody.info
Hypnotherapist and childbirth educator

Jill Benjoya Miller   020 8445 1159
144 Hampden Way, N14 5AX

Karen Patrick   020 8882 5996
16 Conway Road, N14 7BA
Active birth teacher covering Watford and North London

Yogahome   020 7249 2425
Bliss Studios, 11 Allen Road, N16 8SB
Pregnancy yoga classes.

Active Birth Centre   020 7281 6760
25 Bickerton Road, N19 5JT
www.activebirthcentre.com

Yvonne Moore Birth Preparation 020 7794 2056
77 South Hill Park, NW3 2SS
Antenatal yoga classes in North London.

Julie Krausz   020 8459 2903
77 Hardinge Road, NW10 3P
Active birth and yoga teacher.

SOUTH

Albany Midwifery Practice   020 7525 4995
Peckham Pulse, 10 Melon Road, SE15 5QN

Lesley-Anne Kerr   020 7564 3316
16 Hawk House, SW11 2NN

Sue Lewis Grad DP MCSP SRP
Obstetric & Gynaecological Physiotherapist

ANTE-NATAL
♦ Daytime Ladies or Evening Couples Classes
♦ Meet other Mums-to-be
♦ Prevent Pregnancy Aches and Pains
♦ Prepare for Labour including Pain Relief
♦ Relaxation and Breathing Techniques
♦ Positions for Labour
♦ Coffee and Informal Discussion

POST-NATAL
♦ Pilates based exercises to regain your figure
♦ Meet other New Mums
♦ Strengthen Abdominal & Pelvic Floor Muscles
♦ Prevent Incontinence and Back Pain
♦ Advice on Life with a New Baby
♦ Creche for Babies — Coffee for Mums
♦ Informal Discussion

PLUS
♦ Advanced Post-Natal & Pilates-based exercise class
♦ Baby Safety Courses
♦ Breast Feeding Sessions
♦ Baby Massage Workshops
♦ Refresher Courses for 2nd and 3rd Time Mums
♦ Individual Treatments for
  - Ante-Natal Obstetric Problems
  - Post-Natal Gynaecological Problems
♦ Books, Videos and Equipment to Borrow or Buy

Tel 020 8946 8561 for further details
65 Vineyard Hill Road Wimbledon SW19 7JL
www.suelewisantenatal.co.uk

BirthBody

Group and Private
Birth Preparation

info@birthbody.info
www.birthbody.info

07951 21 59 84

"Prepare yourself for motherhood - not just for birth"

Our course will prepare you for childbirth and also guide you through those first essential weeks after the baby is born.

• Ante-natal for new mums
• Couples course
• Refresher courses
• Baby & child first-aid
  Courses held in Wandsworth
  & Marble Arch
Call us on 020 7751 1152
www.newbabycompany.com

NEW *BABY*
COMPANY

professional, practical, personal advice and help during and after pregnancy

antenatal classes (cont.)

Babyprep　　　　　　　　　　**020 8877 0378**
116 Fawe Park Road, Putney SW15 2EQ
Antenatal classes on a one-to-one basis or in a group

Val Orrow　　　　　　　　　　**020 8789 8885**
31 Howards Lane, SW15 6NX
Pregnancy yoga/active birth exercises, positions, breathing, relaxation for labour

Kathleen Beegan　　　　　　　**020 8769 3613**
41 Stanthorpe Road, SW16 2DZ

Mama-Rhythms　　　　　　　　**020 8879 7081**
Wimbledon, SW19

Sue Lewis　　　　　　　　　　**020 8946 8561**
65 Vineyard Hill Road, SW19 7JL
Small classes in preparation for birth and refresher courses for existing mothers. *(See advert on page 1)*

Heather Guerrini　　　　　　　**020 7352 0245**
30 Redesdale Street, SW3 4BJ

The Zita West Clinic　　　　　**020 7224 6091**
144 Harley Street, W1
www.zitawest.com
One-to-one sessions and group classes at the Harley Street clinic

Portland Hospital　　　　　　　**020 7390 8160**
234 Great Portland Street, W1N 6AH
www.theportlandhospital.com

National Childbirth Trust (NCT)　　**0870 444 8707**
Alexandra House, Oldham Terrace, W3 6NH
www.national-childbirth-trust.org.uk

Sarah Bradley　　　　　　　　**020 8994 0966**
11 Fielding Road, W4 1HP

Christine Hill Associates　　　**020 8994 4349**
Strand End, 78 Grove Park Road, W4 3QA

The Ladbroke Rooms　　　　　**020 8960 0846**
8 Telford Road, W10 5SH

Lolly Stirk & Rose Ryan　　　　**020 8674 6997**
St John's Church, Ladbroke Grove, W11 2NN

WEST

Ella Van Meelis　　　　　　　　**020 8537 9258**
ellavanmeelis@btconnect.com
Prepare with antenatal yoga exercises for birth. Also postnatal and baby massage classes after birth.

New Baby Company　　　　　　**020 7751 1152**
8 Souldern Road, W14 0JE
www.newbabycompany.com
Professional, practical, personal advice and help during pregnancy *(see advert on page 1)*

antenatal tests & scans

The following are private antenatal testing services which offer a range of scans and blood tests not necessarily available to you on the NHS without referral. Alternatively you may have missed a scan, or require the comfort of a 5-10 week fetal viability scan

Antenatal Screening Service　　**020 7882 6293**
The Wolfson Institute, Charterhouse Square, EC1B 1EB

Baby Echos　　　　　　　　　**01270 255 201**
Hear and record the sounds of your unborn baby in the privacy of your own home

Babybond　　　　　　　　　　**01572 823 888**
4D video imaging of your baby via a private ultrasound appointment. Studios in Ashford, Uppingham and Paris

Clinical Diagnostic Services　　**020 7483 3611**
27a Queen's Terrace, NW8 6EA

Doctor's Laboratory　　　　　**020 7460 4800**
55 Wimpole Street, W1M 8LQ
Including Cystic Fibrosis carrier test. and a home test for Group B Strep

Foetal Medical Centre　　　　　**020 7486 0476**
137 Harley Street, W1G 6BG
www.fetalmedicine.com

Leeds Antenatal Screening　　　**0113 262 1675**
3 Gemini Park, Sheepscar Way, LS3 3JB
www.leeds.ac.uk/lass

Ultrasound Diagnostic Services　　**020 7486 7991**
113 Harley Street, W1G 6AP

Women's Ultrasound Centre
53 Parkside, Wimbledon SW19　　**020 7636 6765**
86 Harley Street, W1　　　　　　**020 7636 6765**
Full range of ultrasound scans including nuchal screening for Down's syndrome

breastfeeding

If you are trying to breastfeed and find it difficult (or your baby finds it difficult), then it is best to turn to people who really know how to help. The following breastfeeding counsellors can either come to your home or help you over the telephone and have considerable experience in sorting out problems or alleviating anxieties. The organisations also offer support and advice. For recommended breast pumps see the Shopping section

Assoc. of Breastfeeding　　　　**020 7813 1481**
Mothers
A charity offering a network of local breastfeeding counsellors around the country

Vicki Scott -
Baby Confidence   **07960 611 987**
www.babyconfidence.co.uk
Experienced midwife offering up-to-date practical help and
advice. Also troubleshooting and baby routines

Clare Byam-Cook   020 8788 8179
Private home visits

Suzanne Colson   020 8341 7394

Esame Diyan   07944 349571
Newborn consultant

Ellen Glover   020 8871 4654

Geraldine Miskin   07939 820 651

Active Birth Centre   020 7281 6760
Regular breastfeeding classes at the centre.

Breastfeeding Network   **0870 900 8787**
www.breastfeedingnetwork.org.uk
This charity aims to provide support for mothers via a free
national helpline and a comprehensive website offering
advice, product recommendations and chat

Jane's Breastfeeding Resources
www.breastfeeding.co.uk
Website with many useful articles, FAQs, help and support for
breastfeeding mothers

La Leche League   **020 7242 1278**
www.laleche.org.uk
Information and support including those in special situations
eg multiple births, premature babies, cleft or soft palate

National Childbirth Trust   **0870 444 8708**
www.nctpregnancyandbabycare.com
The Trust provides trained counsellors who are available via
their breastfeeding helpline (8am – 10pm). Also a register for
mothers and babies with special situations eg, multiple birth,
feeding a toddler and newborn at the same time, feeding
after breast surgery (see advert on page 8)

body painters

Julia Laderman: Body Painter
for Pregnant Women   **07803 121 923**
www.embody.org.uk
Become a canvas for the day and remember your pregnancy
forever

Carolyn Cowan   **020 7701 3845**
www.mooncycles.co.uk
Portraits with a fusion of photography and body painting
(See advert on page 63)

Celebrate Your Pregnancy

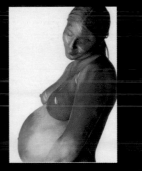

Body Painting
for
Pregnant Women

Become a canvas for the day and remember your pregnancy forever
For more information contact:

Julia Laderman

07803 121923   www.embody.org.uk   info@embody.org.uk

hospitals: NHS

In case of emergency call 999

E1
Royal London Hospital   020 7377 7000
Whitechapel

E9
Homerton Hospital   020 8510 5555
Homerton Row

E11
Whipps Cross Hospital   020 8535 6861
Whipps Cross Road

E13
Newham General Hospital   020 7476 4000
Glen Road, Plaistow

EC1
St Bartholomew's Hospital   020 7377 7000
West Smithfield

Moorfields Eye Hospital   020 7253 3411
City Road

EN2
Chase Farm Hospital   020 8366 6600
The Ridgeway

EN5
Barnet Hospital   020 8216 5218
Wellhouse Lane

HA1
Northwick Park Hospital   020 8864 3232
Watford Road, Harrow

KT2
Kingston Hospital   020 8546 7711
Galsworthy Road, Kingston-upon-Thames

N18
North Middlesex Hospital   020 8887 2000
Sterling Way

N19
Whittington Hospital   020 7288 5249
Highgate Hill, Archway

NW1
Western Ophthalmic Hospital   020 7886 6666
171 Marylebone Road

NW3
Royal Free Hospital   020 7794 0500
Pond Street, Hampstead

NW10
Central Middlesex Hospital   020 8965 5733
Acton Lane, Park Royal

SE1
Guys & St Thomas's Hospital   020 7922 8012
Lower Bridge Road

SE5
King's College Hospital   020 7737 4000
Denmark Hill, Camberwell

SE10
Queen Elizabeth Hospital   020 8836 6000
Vanbrugh Hill

SE13
Lewisham University Hospital   020 8333 3000
Lewisham High Street

SW6
Charing Cross Hospital   020 8846 1234
Fulham Palace Road

SW10
Chelsea & Westminster Hospital   020 8846 7903
369 Fulham Road

SW15
Queen Mary's University Hospital   020 8789 6611
Roehampton Lane

SW17
St George's Hospital   020 8672 1255
Blackshaw Road

TW7
West Middlesex Hospital   020 8560 2121
Twickenham Road, Isleworth

UB1
Ealing Hospital   020 8967 5000
Uxbridge Road, Southall

W1
Middlesex Hospital   020 7636 8333
Mortimer Street

W2
St Mary's Hospital   020 7886 6666
Praed Street

W12
Hammersmith Hospital   020 8383 1000
Du Cane Road

Queen Charlotte's and
Chelsea Hospital NHS Trust   020 8383 1000
Du Cane Road

WC1
University College Hospital   020 7387 9300
Elizabeth Garrett Anderson, Huntley Street &
Grafton Way

Hospital for Sick Children   020 7405 9200
Great Ormond Street

Action for Sick Children   0800 074 4519
1st floor, 300 Kingston Road, Wimbledon

hospitals: private

These hospitals offer first-class birth and postnatal facilities which far outweigh those provided by NHS labour wards. Some NHS hospitals offer private postnatal care at around £300 per day

NW8
Hospital of St John & St Elizabeth 020 7286 5126
Grove End Road

SW17
The Birth Centre   020 7498 2322
37 Coverton Road, Tooting
www.birthcentre.com
Give birth at home, in hospital or in their purpose-designed Birth Centre

W1
The Portland Hospital   020 7390 8492
205-209 Great Portland Street

W2
The Lindo Wing   020 7886 1465
St Mary's Hospital, South Wharf Road

W6
Sir Stanley Clayton Ward 020 8383 3569
Queen Charlotte's Hospital

PREGNANT?

*Let us provide you
with the maternity care of your dreams.*

- Free initial consultation
- Your personal midwife available 24/7
- Convenient appointments
- Birth at our Birth Centre
- Birth in hospital
- Birth at home
- Privacy
- Active and water births
- Up to six weeks after-care

THE BIRTH CENTRE LTD

Director - Caroline Flint
For brochure & information
020 7498 2322

Midwife Led Delivery Service
Give birth the natural way

- 24 hour continuity of care by dedicated Midwives
- Specialists in normal pregnancy and birth
- Medical back up if required
- Individual, flexible service
- Convenient antenatal appointments
- Choice of labour from a natural birth, water birth to an epidural with the first contraction!
- All inclusive package (please ask for details)

The Portland Hospital, London W1

T 020 7390 8492 / 6103
F 020 7390 8198
E marketing@portland.hcahealthcare.co.uk

www.theportlandhospital.com

you can't wrap them up in cotton wool, but you can help protect their future health

FUTURE HEALTH

Family Cord Blood Stem Cell Bank

To find out more please contact
Future Health, Unit 3 Faraday Building, Nottingham Science and Technology Park, Nottingham, NG7 2QP
Phone: 00 44 (0) 115 907 8610

Or visit our website www.futurehealth.co.uk

SE1

Nuffield House	020 7922 8025
Guy's Hospital	

SW3

The Kensington Wing	020 8746 8616
Chelsea & Westminster Hospital	

sex choice

Materna S.A.	020 7225 3234
PO Box 21947, London SW3 2ZU	
www.babychoice.com	

stem cells

For the treatment of many terminal childhood illnesses you can have your baby's stem cells collected at birth and stored for any necessary medical treatments in the future. With a monthly payment schedule to cover the costs, what price would you put on a potentially life-saving opportunity? The collection of stem cells is from the placenta and umbilical cord and is totally painless. Your midwife or consultant will perform the collection immediately after the birth of your baby in accordance with procedures set out by these companies

Cells 4 Life	**01273 234 676**

Sussex Innovation Centre, Science Park Square, University of Sussex, Falmer BN1 9SB
www.cells4life.co.uk
Stem cell collection and umbilical cord blood storage to use in potentially lifesaving cases of serious childhood illnesses.

Future Health Technologies	**0115 907 8610**

3 Faraday Building, Nottingham Science & Technology Park, University Boulevard NG7 2QP
www.futurehealth.co.uk

Smart Cells	**020 7486 4686**

60 Marylebone High Street, London, W1U 5HU
www.smartcells.com.

TENS machines

Pain relief without drugs. An effective form of pain relief in labour, the TENS machine (Transcutaneous Electrical Nerve Stimulation) consists of four electrodes taped to your back which give a tingling sensation as a current passes through.

Ameda Egnell	**01823 336 362**

4 week TENS hire £25 inc p&p plus free extension and cancellation within notice period.

"if those cells are there when you need them, you will never regret your decision"
Sunday Times

"it takes about 3 minutes and cannot affect either mother or baby"
Daily Mirror

SECURE YOUR CHILD'S HEALTH LONG INTO THE FUTURE

1,000s of mothers in the UK have chosen to have their new-born baby's umbilical cord blood collected and the stem cells stored. The use of stem cells is important in the treatment of many childhood diseases such as leukaemia.

Parents realise that storing their baby's stem cells with SMART CELLS (formerly Cryo•Care) could secure their child's health against many diseases long into the future.

For more details on how to preserve your baby's stem cells, telephone our **CARELINE on 020 7486 4686** or apply online at **www.smartcells.com**

WHY SMART CELLS?

- Full twenty five (25) years storage
- No additional cost for retrieval
- Amplification of your stem cells if required
- Storage and processing in accordance with MHRA regulations
- The longest established stem cell storage company within the UK
- Fully qualified stem cell advisory board
- Worldwide CliniCall assistance

SMART CELLS

MIRACULOUS POSSIBILITIES

SMART CELLS INTERNATIONAL
60 Marylebone High Street London W1U 5HU

Cells4Life

Stem cell collection and storage

Potentially lifesaving in cases of serious childhood illness

- Non-invasive procedure at birth
- Full blood sample testing and reporting
- Whole blood storage
- UK storage facility
- Variable storage options
- 12-24 hour freezing time

A safeguard for my baby's future

☎ +44 (0)1273 234676
🖷 +44 (0)1273 234677
✉ info@cells4life.co.uk
🌐 www.cells4life.co.uk

TENS machines (cont.)

BabiTENS   01491 578 446
www.babitens.com
Drug free, safe and effective pain relief during pregnancy and labour. 4 week hire £27.50 inc p&p plus free extension period with notification.

Babycare TENS   020 8532 9595
4 week hire from £22 with one week extension free.

Mama TENS   020 8547 1999
PO Box 43537,London, SW15 3XF
www.mama-tens.info
Mama TENS helps you through the birth of your baby more effectively. For more informtion ring their helpline.

Nature's Gate   01256 346 060
6 week hire starts at £22 inc p&p

ObTENS   0117 924 1982
6 week hire £19 and then 50p for each day thereafter

Pulsar Sembly Medical   0800 515 413
www.pulsar-tens.com
Pulsar TENS for effective drug-free pain relief during childbirth. Recommended by NHS and NCT.

Septrim Medical   0500 710 071
6 week TENS hire £20 inc p&p or you can buy

Trust TENS   020 8546 1616
5 week TENS hire £25 and £5 per week thereafter

water births: pool hire

If planning a hospital delivery, check with your local hospital for their facilities and policies on water birth (see hospitals: NHS and hospitals, private). For useful information visit www.waterbirth.org

Active Birth Centre   020 7281 6760
www.activebirthcentre.com

Aqua Birth Pool Hire   01202 518 152

Baby Bliss   020 8568 4913
www.baby-bliss.com

Birthworks   01227 730 081
www.birthworks.co.uk

Gentle Water Birthing Pools   01273 474 927
www.gentlewater.co.uk

Splashdown Water Birth Services   020 8422 9308
All shapes supplied as well as inflatables. Waterbirth workshops also run for mums-to-be and couples

---

Baby on the way?
New to being a mum or dad?

The National Childbirth Trust offers support in pregnancy, childbirth and early parenthood. We aim to help all parents enjoy an experience of pregnancy, birth and early parenthood that enriches their lives and gives them confidence in being a parent.

The National Childbirth Trust
Alexandra House, Oldham Terrace
London, W3 6NH
www. nctpregnancyandbabycare,com
E: enquiries@national-childbirth-trust.co.uk
Registered charity 801395

THE UK's biggest support group for parents-to-be and new parents.

- A network of parents across the UK with places to go and other parents to meet.
  Or get in touch with friends you have lost touch with
  www.nctparentsconnect.co.uk

- Courses on birth, breastfeeding and coping as a new parent 0870 444 8707

- Breastpump and valley cushion hire, nearly new baby goods 0870 444 8707 and maternity bras 0870 112 1120 www.nctms.co.uk

- Breastfeeding helpline 0870 444 8708 open 8am-10pm 365 days a year and information on pregnancy, labour, birth, babycare and toddler development www.nctpregnancyandbabycare.com

- To support our charity, become a member £36 for the first year.
  Phone the membership hotline 0870 990 8040.

acupuncture

(see also complementary health)

Recommended for morning sickness, tiredness and bleeding during pregnancy. In children sometimes used for recurrent colds, poor appetite and hay fever

British Acupuncture Council 020 8735 0400
63 Jeddo Road, W12
www.acupuncture.org.uk
Members (MBAcC) have all completed a 3yr training course and are bound by the BAcC code of conduct. The website lists practitioners by postcode

**British Medical
Acupuncture Society   01925 730 727**
Royal London Homeopathic Hospital
Greenwell Street, W1W 5EP
www.medical-acupuncture.org.uk
Central London Clinic and also a list of London GPs and doctors who have completed the 3yr diploma

EAST
Alison Courtney MBAcC   07790 264 515
Clockwork Pharmacy, 398-400 Mare Street, E8
Back to Back, 78 Chatsworth Road, E5

NORTH
Alison Courtney MBAcC   07790 264 515
Mackenzie Road Practice, 125 Mackenzie Road, N7

**Meredith &
Wainwright Churchill**   **020 8444 1007**
49 Woodland Gardens, N10 3UE
Specialising in pregnancy, children and also infertility/recurrent miscarriage

Sarah Moon MBAcC   **020 8969 1506**
30 Linden Avenue, NW10 5RE

Anne Lewthwaite MBAcC   **020 7267 9995**
Courthope Road, NW3 2LE

SOUTH & CENTRAL
The Zita West Clinic   **020 7224 6091**
144 Harley Street, W1
www.zitawest.com
Specialists in the use of acupunture for improved fertility and a healthier pregnancy

Traditional Acupuncture Clinic   **020 7928 8333**
75 Roupell Street, SE1 8SS

Southfields Clinic   **020 8874 4125**
41 Southfields Road, SW18 1QW

Chi Centre for Children   **020 7233 5566**
1 Lower Grosvenor Place, SW1W 0EJ

Alternative Therapy Clinic   **020 7224 3387**
140 Harley Street, W1 1AH

WEST
The Ladbroke Rooms   **020 8960 0846**
8 Telford Road, W10 5SH

Liu Clinic   **020 8993 2549**
13 Gunnersbury Avenue, W5 3XD

Chiswick Acupuncture Clinic   **020 8747 4816**
251 Acton Lane, W5 5DG

alexander technique

Useful both during pregnancy for improving the awareness of good posture and relieving the uncomfortable compression of internal organs. Also used in labour to help facilitate a natural birth

STAT   **020 7284 3338**
www.stat.org.uk
Society of Teachers of the Alexander Technique. Registered teachers (MSTAT) have 3yrs training including working with pregnancy. List of practioners available

EC2
Alexander Technique Centre   **020 7749 7246**
82 Great Eastern Street

NW6
Ilana Machover MSTAT   **020 8969 5356**
5 Milman Road
Specialises in small classes for pregnant women

SW6
Jackie Coote MSTAT   **020 7731 1061**
27 Britannia Road, Fulham SW6
jackiecoote@alexandertec.co.uk
Learn how to look after your back during and after pregnancy

SW12
Karen Wentworth MSTAT   **020 8673 3853**
6 Ravenslea Road

W1
Alexander Studio   **020 7629 1808**
16 Balderton Street

W14
Harriet Evans MSTAT   **020 7603 2337**
19 Caithness Road

WC1
**Bloomsbury
Alexander Centre**   **020 7404 5348**
80a Southampton Row
www.alexandertechniquelondon.co.uk

aromatherapy

(see also complementary health and massage)

In pregnancy often used to relieve tiredness, nausea, fluid retention as well as pain and anxiety during labour. For baby the oils can be used for gentle massage or in the bath

ISPA   **01455 637 987**
www.the-ispa.org
International Society of Professional Aromatherapists. List of local practitioners available online or by request

Tabitha Robertson   **020 8960 8476**
31 Dundonald Road, NW10

Micheline Arcier   **020 7235 3545**
7 William Street, SW1

The Ladbroke Rooms   **020 8960 0846**
8 Telford Road, W10

RETAIL
Earth Mother   **020 8442 1704**
59 Muswell Avenue, N10

Neal's Yard Remedies
68 Chalk Farm Road, NW1   020 7284 2039
32 Blackheath Village, SE3   020 8318 6655
15 Neal's Yard, WC2   020 7379 7222
9 Elgin Crescent, W11   020 7727 3998
6 Northcote Road, SW11   020 7223 7141
15 King's Street, Richmond, TW9   020 8948 9248
www.nealsyardremedies.com

Verde
15 Flask Walk, NW3   020 7431 3314
75 Northcote Road, SW11   020 7924 4379
www.verde.co.uk
Chamomile Baby Balm, Bizzy Kids Bathtime Oil

MAIL ORDER

Absolute Aromas   **01420 549 991**
www.aboslute-aromas.co.uk

A. Nelson & Co   **020 7495 2404**
www.nelsonbach.com

Aromakids   **01278 434 440**
www.hippychick.com

Blue Moon   **020 8346 1400**
www.bluemoonaromatherapy.com

Jurlique   **0870 770 0980**
www.jurlique.com.au
Organic essential oils also available as water sprays, massage & bath oils

Tisserand   **01273 325 666**
www.tisserand.com

Vital Touch   **01803 840 670**
www.vitaltouch.com
Organic armoatherapy products for pregnancy, labour and new parenthood

Wanted
Baby Scientists!

How do babies learn? How do they recognise faces? How do they develop language? We want to answer such questions. We are recruiting babies (birth – 18mo.) to take part in fun studies at our Babylab. You are with your baby at all times. We provide a black taxi if you live within 5 miles of our Centre, or we refund your travel expenses. If you would like to discover how babies learn, please phone Jane at the Babylab.

The Babylab
Birkbeck College
32 Torrington Sq.
London WC1E 7BR
Tel: 020 7631 6258
Website: www.cbcd.bbk.ac.uk

baby research

The Babylab   **020 7631 6258**
Centre for Brain & Cognitive Development, FREEPOST, 32 Torrington Square, WC1E 7BR
www.cbcd.bbk.ac.uk
Together with your baby you can have fun making discoveries about brain development

chemists, late opening

Not only do these chemists stay open late for medication such as Calpol and Children's Nurofen, they are also well stocked with nappies, bottles and a range of baby foods

NW6
Bliss Chemists   **020 7624 8000**
50-56 Willesden Lane, NW6
9am-midnight

NW11
Warman Free Pharmacy   **020 8455 4351**
45 Golders Green Road, NW11
8.30am-midnight

W1
Bliss Chemists **020 7723 6116**
5-6 Marble Arch, W1
9am-midnight

SE24
Fourway Pharmacy **020 7924 9344**
12 Half Moon Lane, Herne Hill, SE24
9am-7pm

SW5
Zafash Pharmacy **020 7373 3506**
233-235 Old Brompton Road, SW5
24-hr, 365 days a year

complementary health

These centres and therapists offer a range of
complementary treatments for pregnant women,
babies and young children. Treatments include
acupuncture, hypnotherapy, osteopathy, cranial
osteopathy, reflexology, massage, homeopathy,
reiki and counselling

Natural Mother **0709 202 2020**
www.naturalmother.co.uk
A specialist service bringing natural therapies and treatments
to your home. No travel, no stress. London wide

CENTRAL
The Hale Clinic **020 7631 0156**
7 Park Crescent, W1B 1PF

**Harley Street
Complementary Care** **0870 241 4025**
19 Gloucester Place, W1

Natureworks **020 7355 4036**
16 Balderton Street, W1Y 1TF

Neal's Yard Therapy Rooms **020 7379 7662**
Covent Garden, WC2

The Portland Hospital **020 7390 8061**
234 Great Portland Street, W1W 5QT
www.theportlandhospital.com
Treatments include Bowen therapy, massage, reflexology and
osteopathy

NORTH
Active Birth Centre **020 7272 7003**
25 Bickerton Road, N19 5JT
www.activebirthcentre.com

Muswell Healing Arts **020 8365 3545**
169 Avenue Mews, N10 3NN

**Clissold Park Natural
Health Centre** **020 7249 2990**
154 Stoke Newington Church Street, N16 0JU
Large centre with around 30 therapists

Women and Health **020 7482 2786**
4 Carol Street, NW1

Chatsworth Clinic **020 8451 4754**
4 Chatsworth Road, NW2 4BN
www.ihms.co.uk

Pregnant   Post Natal   Trying to conceive

naturalmother

A specialist service just for you
Natural therapies in your home

Reflexology
Massage
Baby Massage
Yoga
Acupuncture
Hypnotherapy
Aromatherapy
Homeopathy
Reiki....& more

**Shorter labour
Increased fertility
Reduced pain
Sympton relief**

Expert guidance, one to one
No travel, no stress, London wide

www.naturalmother.co.uk 0709 202 2020
Gift Vouchers make a great maternity present

Viveka **020 7483 0099**
27a Queen's Terrace, NW8 6EA

SOUTH
Awareness in Pregnancy **020 8856 8797**
16 Balderton Street, SE3 0NE

Clapham Common Clinic **020 7627 8890**
151/3 Clapham High Street, SW4 7SS

The Vale Practice **020 8299 9798**
64 Grove Vale, SE22 8DT
www.thevalepractice.co.uk

Family Natural Health Centre **020 8693 5515**
106 Lordship Lane, East Dulwich, SE22 8HF

The Karuna Healing Centre **020 8699 4046**
103 Dartmouth Road, Forest Hill, SE23

Living Centre Clinic **020 8946 2331**
32 Durham Road, Raynes Park, SW20 0TW

**Newlands Park Natural
Health Care Centre** **020 8659 5001**
48 Newlands Park, Sydenham, SE26 5NE

Putney Natural Therapy Clinic **020 8789 2548**
11 Montserrat Road, SW15 2LD

The Vitality Centre **020 8871 4677**
Alexander House, 155 Merton Road, SW18 5EQ

**South London
Natural Health Centre** **020 7720 8817**
7a Clapham Common Southside, SW4

Westover House	020 8877 1877
18 Earlsfield Road, SW18 3DW	
www.westoverhouse.com	

WEST
BushMaster	
Natural Health Practice	020 8749 3792
204 Uxbridge Road, W12 7JD	
Craven Clinic	020 8563 8133
54 Cambridge Grove, W6 0LA	
Equilibrium	020 8742 7701
150 Chiswick High Road, W4 1PR	
Life Centre	020 7221 4602
15 Edge Street, W8 7PN	
Millennium Clinic	020 8846 7539
Richford Gate Primary Care Centre, W6 7HY	
The Ladbroke Rooms	020 8960 0846
8 Telford Road, W10 5SH	
www.theladbrokerooms.com	

first aid & safety

These small-group courses offer practical tuition and peace of mind for parents and carers wanting to know the principal causes of accidents and how to prevent them, including resuscitation (after a fall, choking or drowning) and general first aid (burns, breaks and poisoning)

ChildAlert   **020 7384 1311**
PO Box 29961, London, SW6 6FT
www.childalert.co.uk
Childalert provides advice relating to child safety including a child proofing home safety survey, safety products and parenting courses including first aid

Marie Askin   **020 7603 8103**
maire-askin@freenet.co.uk
Classes for parents. Small groups in your own home.
Registered nurse

My Nanny Network   **0870 220 2657**
www.mynannynetwork.co.uk
A website for parents and nannies including job adverts, cv posting and a range of training courses

The Parent Company   **020 7935 9635**
6 Jacob's Wells Mews, W1U 3DY
www.theparentcompany.co.uk
Paediatric nurses teach first aid classes in your own home.
London and Surrey

Safe & Sound   **020 8449 8722**
www.safe-and-sound.org.uk
Safe & Sound trainers are all experienced medical professionals dedicated to promoting high quality paediatric first aid training

. theparentcompany

First Aid for Babies and Children
Classes for up to 6 people in your own home

All courses taught by paediatric nurses

0207 935 9635 info@theparentcompany.co.uk

MNT

Maternity & Nanny Training

TRAINING COURSES FOR PARENTS & NANNIES

0870 2202657

DO YOU WANT TO LEARN MORE ABOUT CARING FOR YOUR CHILDREN?

• Paediatric 1st Aid
• Anaphylactic Shock/Epi-Pen
• Baby Massage
• Post Natal Depression
• BabyCare for Parents & Nannies
• Care of Multiples

ARM YOURSELF WITH THE KNOWLEDGE TO BE ABLE TO COPE WITH ANY SITUATION ...

www.mynannynetwork.co.uk

Tinies Paediatric
First Aid course   **020 7384 0322**
Unit 14 Block A, 126-128 New Kings Road, SW6 4LZ
Certified course for parents and carers focused upon baby & child resuscitation. Learn enough to save your child's life

exercise pre & post-natal

We have selected these classes because they have programmes specifically designed to help mothers regain their shape after pregnancy. Exercise classes during pregnancy can help you improve posture, maintain circulation to prevent varicose veins, control your weight gain and improve your stamina and energy levels

London Academy of
Personal Fitness   **0870 442 3231**
www.lapf.co.uk
Complete ante and post-natal programmes including yoga and pilates

Wonder Women Fitness   **07989 831 256**
www.wonderwomen.co.uk
Exercise classes and personal training for mums and mums-to-be

Revolution Health   **07958 464 770**
appleson5@aol.com
Pre and post-natal personal training to keep in shape

Judy Difiore   **020 8931 2085**
Specialist ante and post-natal fitness consultant

The Portland Hospital   **020 7390 8061**
234 Great Portland Street, W1W 5QT
www.theportlandhospital.com
Yoga and pilates classes especially for pregnant ladies.
Postnatal exercise classes also available.

Jocelyn Hughes   **07977 384 390**
Ante and post-natal pilates on a one-to-one basis in your
own home. Based from SW18

Wonder Women Fitness

Build stamina for birth   Exercise Classes &
Speed up recovery   Personal Training
Get those flat abs back   For Mums &
Great value   Mums-to-be

07989 831 256   www.wonderwomen.co.uk

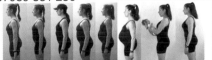

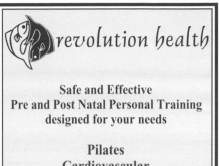

revolution health

**Safe and Effective
Pre and Post Natal Personal Training
designed for your needs**

**Pilates
Cardiovascular
Strength
Stamina
Relaxation
Nutrition**

Call Karen for a consultation
07958 464770
N/NW/W and Central London Only
Fully insured and member of Fitness Professionals
And Pilates FoundationUK

EXPERT PERSONAL FITNESS TRAINING

The London Academy of Personal Fitness
(Est. 1989)

Expert One to One fitness training
in your own home from *the best trainers* in London

We look at all aspects of health and long term fitness
- The latest work-outs and information on reshaping after birth.
- Trainers will motivate you to achieve your goals with varied work-outs and equipment.
- Constant motivation and assessment.

Limited vacancies for those who want to shape up & get fit fast.

Call Chrissie and set your goals
0870 4423231
or visit us on: www.lapf.co.uk

THE FASTEST ROUTE TO EXTRA ENERGY!

health clubs with creches

(see also leisure centres, swimming pools)

Local authority sports centres often provide crèches to supplement their sports activities. We have not listed the big chains, such as Holmes Place and Canons which also offer children's facilities

N10
Dragons Health Club   020 8444 8212
Hillfield Park

Manor Health & Leisure Club 020 8883 0500
140 Fortis Green

N16
Sunstone Health and Leisure Club 020 7923 1991
16 Northwold Road, Stoke Newington

NW3
Lingfield Health Club   020 7483 6800
81 Belsize Park Gardens

NW4
The Laboratory   020 8201 5500
Hall Lane

SPORTS ◆ CLUB

**Welcome to
JAGS Sports Club**

JAGS Sports Club is a private members club offering an excellent variety of facilities for families and children at very competitive prices.

◆ JAGS Kids Club   ◆ JAGS Activity Days
◆ Swimming Lessons from age 0 and up!
◆ Football Club   ◆ Tennis Lessons
◆ Street Dance Classes

While your children are being entertained, why not use our State-of-the-art gym and swimming facilities.
So come on down and check it out for yourself!

Phone us now on **020 8299 4286** or visit us at 144 East Dulwich Grove, London
(enter from Red Post Hill)
www.jagssportsclub.co.uk

SE22
JAGS Sports Club   020 8299 4286
144 East Dulwich Grove, SE22 8TE
www.jagssportsclub.co.uk
Private members club offering excellent facilities for families and children

SE26
LA Fitness   020 8778 9818
291 Kirkdale

SW15
Roehampton Club   020 8480 4200
Roehampton Lane

SW19
Tots Spot   020 8542 1330
Wimbledon Leisure Centre, Latimer Road

Esporta Health and Fitness Club 020 8545 1700
21-33 Worple Road

SW6
Lillie Road Fitness Centre   020 7381 2183
Lillie Road

Harbour Club   020 7371 7700
Watermeadow Lane

W3
The Park Club   020 8743 4321
East Acton Lane

W4
Riverside Health Club   020 8987 1800
Duke's Meadows, Riverside Lane

W5
**Ealing YMCA
Health & Fitness Centre**   020 8799 4800
25 St Mary's Road

WC1
Central London YMCA   020 7343 1700
112 Great Russell Street
Crèche on Saturday

homeopathy

Used during pregnancy to treat conditions such as nausea, heartburn, thrush, cramps and emotional distress during labour. In children used for building up overall health and immunity to common colds. The practioners and clinics listed below all have specialist knowledge of treating pregnant women and children

CENTRAL
**Royal London
Homeopathic Hospital**   020 7837 8833
Great Ormond Street, WC1

NORTH

Homeopathy Allergy Centre   020 7483 1640
15 Westbourne Road, N7

SOUTH

Liz Whitehead   020 8488 2027
2 Desensons Road, SE21 7DN

The Vale Practice   020 8299 9798
64 Grove Vale, SE22 8DT

Dr Charles Innes   020 7589 6414
The Health Partnership, 12a Thurloe St, SW7 2ST

Olga Lawrence Jones   020 7737 1294
10 Stockwell Park Crescent, SW8 0DE

Acute Homeopathic Clinic   020 8877 1877
at Westover House, 18 Earlsfield Rd, SW18 3DW
www.westoverhouse.com

WEST

Homeopathic Children's Clinic   020 8741 9264
Brackenbury Natural Health Centre,
30 Brackenbury Road, W6 0BA

Dr Max Deacon   020 7602 1006
63 Rowan Road, W6 7DT

hypnotherapy

Below you will find hypnotherapy associations and
therapists who offer hypnotherapy and self-
hypnosis for birth

Joe Lacey   **020 8567 7028**
joelacey@btconnect.com
Practising in London W7. Member of the NCH, practising
hypnotherapy and NLP for all aspects of modern living

General Hypnotherapy Register   01590 683 770
www.general-hypnotherapy-register.com

Hypnotherapy Association   01257 262 124
www.thehypnotherapyassociation.org

UK Hypno Birth Register   020 8442 0105
info@hypnobirth.info

Debra Sequoia: Birth body   **07951 215 984**
Hypnotherapist and Childbirth Educator (see advert on page 3)

The Ladbroke Rooms   020 8960 0846
8 Telford Road, W10

immunisation

(see also medical advice)

NHS Immunisation Information
www.mmrthefacts.nhs.uk
Free literature available to help inform parents who have
concerns about childhood vaccinations

Immunisation checklist   Source: NHS

Age	Protects against	How it is given
2 mths	polio	by mouth
	meningitis C	1 injection
	Hib haemophilus influenza B DPT - diphtheria, pertussis (whooping cough) and tetanus	1 injection
3 mths	same as for 2 months	
4 mths	same as for 2 months	
12-15 mths	MMR	I Injection
3-5yrs	polio	by mouth
	DTaP - diphtheria, tetanus & accellular pertussis	1 injection
	MMR	1 injection
10-14yrs	BCG - tuberculosis then injection if needed	skin test
13-18yrs	Td-tetanus and diphtheria	1 injection
	polio	by mouth

Direct Health 2000   0870 2000 999
6-7 Grove Market Place, Court Yard, SE9 5PU

JABS   020 8442 0105
www.jabs.og.uk
Website provids details of local doctors who provide single
vaccinations formeasles, mumps and rubella

The Portland Hospital   **020 7390 8312**
234 Great Portland Street, W1W 5QT
www.theportlandhospital.com
Private vaccinations service (single MMR vaccinations not
available)

National Autistic Society
www.nas.org.uk
Information pack available on MMR vaccinations and a
statement about the society's position

Vaccinations - Yes or no?   **0870 720 0067**
www.vaccinations-yesorno.co.uk
A must-have unbiased book for parents facing the dilemma
of MMR and other childhood vaccinations

If you know someone struggling to conceive then these organisations can provide couples with help and advice

CHILD   **01424 732 361**
PO Box 107, Bexhill, TN40 1AZ
The National Infertility Support Network

Natural Mother   **0709 202 2020**
www.naturalmother.com
Specialised therapies to help you conceive. Treatments at home. No travel, no stress. London wide.
(see advert on page 11)

The Zita West Clinic   **020 7224 6091**
144 Harley Street, W1
www.zitawest.com
Natural treatments and programmes designed to increase your chances of success with IVF

massage

Massage during pregnancy is a luxury everyone should treat themselves to. Easing tension and boosting energy levels are some of the benefits. Newborns and babies, who are too young to play, benefit mentally and physically from regular massage. It is both a communicative experience for parents and can settle a baby prior to sleep. With some tuition you can learn to use more complex strokes as your baby grows. These practitioners hold local classes or come to your home

Baby Massage with
Amber White   **07799 077205**
81 Pert Close, N10 2RZ

Natural Mother   **0709 202 2020**
www.naturalmother.co.uk
Expert pregnancy, postnatal and baby massage, Aromatherapy at home. No travel, no stress. London wide
(see advert on page 11)

Baby Play   **07989 384 641**
Babyplay, massage and sensory fun for under ones. Best teacher, best venues, best class (Kensington Gate Hotel, Clapham Soho Hotel and coming soon to Chelsea and Hampstead)

Baby Massage with
Clare Mundy   **020 7639 2397**
36 Juniper House, Pomeroy Street, SE14 5BY
www.blissfulbaby.co.uk
Small group sessions with a friendly experienced teacher; home visits in South London

Catherine Owens   **020 7351 0919**
Ifield Road, SW10   **07976 803 886**
cs_owens@hotmail.com
"The finest pregnancy massage therapist in London" according to Harpers & Queen 2002.

The Vale Practice   **020 8299 9798**
64 Grove Vale, SE22 8DT

The Portland Hospital   **020 7390 8061**
234 Great Portland Street, W1W 5QT
www.theportlandhospital.com
Antenatal and postnatal massage for mothers. Baby massage technique taught as part of postnatal mother and baby workshop

Massage for Mums   **07946 268 217**
Simply invite some fellow Mums over for coffee, lunch, or tea and enjoy a relaxing massage while your little ones are looked after. If the kids are at school, why not just have a get-together?

medical advice

(see also antenatal testing, immunisation)
NHS Direct   **0845 46 47**
The 24hr NHS helpline is extremely useful and comforting when you are concerned about your child's health. Initially your details are taken and then within a short period of time a trained nurse will call back and help you decide what further action should be taken. The number, although short, is correct

Direct Health 2000   **0870 2000 999**
6-7 Grove Market Place, Court Yard, SE9 5PU
Private Doctor service provided Mon-Fri. Price £45

Doctorcall   **07000 372255**
16 Wimpole Street, W1
24 hr call out service. Price around £85 for central London depending on postcode. Private clinic Mon-Fri

Doctors Direct   **020 7751 9701**
73 –77 Britannia Road, SW6 2JR
24hr call out service. Price around £90 during week out of hours, depending on postcode. Private clinic Mon-Fri

Minor Injuries Treatment Centre   **020 8355 3002**
Queen Mary's Hospital, Roehampton Lane, SW15 5PN

The Gynae Centre   **020 7935 7525**
93 Harley Street, W1N 1DF
Private gynaecological clinic. Price £80; no referrals required

SOS Doctors Direct   **020 7751 9701**
24hr doctor call out service. Price around £80 depending on time and postcode

Westover House   **020 8877 1877**
18 Earlsfield Road, SW18 3DW
www.westoverhouse.com
Private general practice with visiting consultant specialist and in-house complementary therapists

The Portland Hospital   **020 7390 8312**
234 Great Portland Street, W1W 5QT
www.theportlandhospital.com
Private appointments for children with specialist consultant Paediatricians. Urgent referral appointments available.

nutrition

The Zita West Clinic　　**020 7224 6091**
144 Harley Street, W1
www.zitawest.com
Straightforward help and reassurance for modern couples

The Vale Practice　　**020 7277 6963**
64 Grove Vale, East Dulwich, SE22 8DT
Optimum nutrition for pregnant women and little ones

The Ladbroke Rooms　　**020 8960 0846**
8 Telford Road, W10 5SH
www.theladbrokerooms.com
Nutritional and naturopathic support for pregnancy, mothers
& babies

**The Centre for Nutritional
Medicine Ltd**　　**020 7907 1660**
43 Devonshire Street, W1G 7AL
www.nutritionalmedicine.co.uk
A medically supported nutrition service with an expertise in
pregnancy

osteopathy & cranial ost.

Osteopathy is a hands-on therapy that combines
soft-tissue massage and manipulation and spine-
cracking. Osteopathic treatment may relieve back
pain in pregnancy and aid recovery post natally. In
babies, cranial osteopathy has been used for
sleeplessness, colic, sticky eye, teething and
earache

International Cranial　　**020 8367 5561**
Association
List of practitioners who have completed a recognised
training programme

**British College of
Naturopathy and Osteopathy 020 7435 7830**
6 Netherhall Gardens, Hampstead, NW3 5RR

**Docklands Children's
Osteopathic Clinic**　　**020 7536 0004**
8b Lanterns Court, Millharbour, E14 9TU

British Osteopathic Council　　**020 7357 665**
www.osteopathy.org.uk

Grania Stewart-Smith　　**020 7286 2615**
31 Grove End Road, NW8 (opposite of St. John &
Elizabeth Hospital)
Treatment of pregnant women

**Fulham
Osteopathic Practice**　　**020 7384 1851**
769 Fulham Road, SW6 5HA
Cranial osteopathy for mothers & babies. 3 minutes from
Parsons Green tube

Martien Jonkers　　**07748 938 299**
BSc (Ost) Hons, DO, Dip/Ot
Neals Yard, 9 Elgin Crescent, W11　020 7727 3998
Active Birth Cenre, N19　　　　　　020 7272 3003
Tufnell Park, N7　　　　　　　　　020 7609 8973
Experienced in treating women during and after pregnancy
and cranial osteopathy for babies.

**Maxine Hamilton
Stubber,** BSc Ost (Hons)　　**020 7730 7928**
Wilbraham Place Practice, 9a Wilbraham Place,
(off Sloane Square), SW1X 9AE

ZITA WEST

*Good nutrition for fertility,
pregnancy, birth and recovery*

A superb range of multi-vitamins
and minerals formulated by
the Harley Street
fertility and pregnancy consultant

www.zitawest.com
Tel 0870 166 8899

F ULHAM
O STEOPATHIC
P RACTICE

• Cranial Osteopathy
• Gentle treatment for mother and baby

3 Minutes from Parsons Green Underground
☎ 020 7384 1851　769 Fulham Road SW6 5HA

Westover House　　　　**020 8877 1877**
18 Earlsfield Road, SW18 3DW
Structural and cranial osteopathy. Specialising in pregnancy
and children

Kane & Ross Clinics
9 Upper Wimpole Street, W1　　**020 7486 9588**
28 Knightsbridge Court, SW1　　**020 7235 8300**
www.kaneandrossclinics.co.uk

Nik Casse　　　　**020 8542 4455**
Albany Clinic, 277 The Broadway, 1st floor,
Wimbledon, SW19

Osteopathic Centre for Children　**020 7486 6160**
109 Harley Street, W1N 1DG

**The Battersea
Osteopathic Practices**　　**020 7738 9199**
2b Ashness Road, Webb's Road entrance,
SW11 6RY

The College Practice　　**020 7267 6445**
60 Highgate Road, NW5 1PA

The Hale Clinic　　　**020 7631 0156**
7 Park Crescent, W1N 3HE

The Maris Practice　　**020 8891 3400**
13 Baylis Mews, Amyand Park Road,
Twickenham, TW1 3HQ
A team of osteopaths and homeopaths experienced in the
treatment of children and babies

The Vale Practice　　**020 8299 9798**
at The Vale Practice, 64 Grove Vale,
East Dulwich, SE22 8DT

Tideswell Road Clinic　　**020 8788 5761**
7 Tideswell Road, Putney, SW15 6LJ

Total Care　　　**07748 938299**
30 Fortis Green, East Finchley, N2 9EL
Colic, sleep disturbance, constant crying,
neurodevelopmental problems, etc. We can help

West London Osteopaths　**020 8749 0581**
65 Vespan Road, W12 9QG

craniosacral therapy

Trained for at least 2 years, therapists work with
babies who have suffered some trauma during birth

**Craniosacral Therapy
Association**　　　**0700 078 4735**
www.craniosacral.co.uk
Members (RCST) are required to maintain ongoing training
with pregnant women and babies

Florence de Crevoisier-Fedder RCST
Physio for All, 40 Webbs Rd, SW11　020 7228 2141
Eden Medical Centre, SW3　　　020 7881 5800

The Vale Practice　　020 8299 9798
64 Grove Vale, SE22

Physio For All　　　020 7228 2141
40 Webbs Road, SW11

Physiotherapists

Kiki's Clinic　　　**020 7207 4234**
133 Thurleigh Road, SW12 8TX
www.kikisclinic.com
Physiotherapy & occupational therapy for babies and children
using neuro-developmental therapy and play to stimulate
movement and the ability to learn

Physio for All　　　**020 7228 2141**
The Battersea Practice, 40 Webbs Road, SW11 6SF
www.physio4all.com
Back pain, sports injuries, incontinence, cranio-sacral
therapy, chest infection

Physio for All　　　**020 7351 9918**
The Chelsea Practice, 186 Fulham Road, SW10 9PN
www.physio4all.com
Back pain, sports injuries, pelvic floor and incontinence
problems

Physio for All　　　**020 7591 1910**
The South Ken. Practice, 21 Thurloe Place, SW7
www.physio4all.com
Back pain, sports injuries, pelvic floor and incontinence
problems, chest infections

**The Chartered Society
of Physiotherapists**　　**020 7306 6666**
14 Bedford Row, WC1R 4ED
Contact for details of qualified physios in your area

The Portland Hospital　　**020 7390 8061**
234 Great Portland Street, W1W5QT
www.theportlandhospital.com
Physiotherapy and complementary healthcare for pregnancy
including treatment for back pain. Rehabilitative
physiotherapy also available for children following medical
referral.

post-natal support & info

The Portland Hospital　**020 7390 8492/6103**
234 Great Portland Street, W1W5QT
www.theportlandhospital.com
Postnatal group for mother and baby including baby
massage and first aid techniques. Specialist postnatal pelvic
floor treatment available.

reflexology

Reflexology has been around for thousands of
years, but the modern form was established in the
early 20th century when system of massage
through reflex points on the feet, hands and head
was developed and used to relieve tension and

treat illness in the corresponding zones of the body. In pregnancy reflexology can allieviate morning sickness, constipation and rid the body of excess catarrah and stubborn colds. Postnally, the therapy is said to boost energy levels and increase breastmilk supplies

British Reflexology Association　01886 821207
Monks Orchard, Whitbourne, WR6 5RB

Andrea Allardyce BA, MIFR, ITEC　020 8995 5037
4a Oxford Road North, W4 4DN

Feet First　07956 684 455
feetfirst@pavilion.co.uk
Louise Sanders specialises in reflexology and holistic massage during pregancy and postnatally

Denise Cameron　07769 656 008
Home visits in South and West London Denise offers pre and postnatal reflexology to restore the body's vital energy (SW10, SW3, SW7, W8, W11, SW11, SW12)

Natural Mother　0709 202 2020
www.naturalmother.co.uk
Expert treatments during pregnancy, postnatally with baby massage and aromatherapy at home. No travel, no stress. London wide (see advert on page 11)

The Healing Company　07958 396956
32 Heathfield Road, Wandsworth, SW18 2ZZ
www.thehealingcompany.com
Treatments for stress, pregnancy, baby colic

The Ladbroke Rooms　020 8960 0846
8 Telford Road, W10 5SH
www.theladbrokerooms.com
Treating the whole body via the feet

The Portland Hospital　020 7390 8061
234 Great Portland Street, W1W5QT
www.theportlandhospital.com

yoga

Yoga classes are particularly recommended during pregnancy as they are less energetic, but build and maintain strength as your body changes shape. Recommended from 12 weeks (see also antenatal teachers for antenatal and yoga classes)

Iyengar Yoga Institute　020 7624 3080
223a Randolph Avenue, W9 1NL
www.iyi.org.uk
Pre/post natal yoga classes and yoga for children (7yrs+). 'I can't recommend the classes highly enough,' reader's comment

Kundalini Yoga　020 7701 3845
www.southernlightyoga.com
Karta Kaur teaches antenatal yoga classes for mothers-to-be and post natal classes (mothers and babies from 8 wks) in llocations across South London. (The Yoga Studio, Peckham: Globe house, London Bridge; Goose Green, East Dulwich and St Barnabas, Dulwich Village)

Kundalini Yoga

A series of DVD's from CAROLYN COWAN

Yoga for Pregnancy
Specialising in: Pain in labour and Fear in pregnancy

Yoga for Empowering Women
Fantastic for post-natal! (Not for pregnant women)

Available on DVD from: www.devotion.org.uk
For Carolyns yoga class details see www.southernlightyoga.com

Relax Kids　020 8208 8303
www.relaxkids.com
Relaxation courses, books and CDs

The Grove Health Centre　020 7221 2266
182-184 Kensington Church Street, W8 4DP

The Ladbroke Rooms　020 8960 0846
8 Telford Road, W10 5SH
www.theladbrokerooms.com

The Life Centre　020 7221 4602
15 Edge Street, W8
www.thelifecentre.com

Triyoga　020 7483 3344
Erskine Road, Primrose Hill, NW3

Whyoga　020 8874 3858
170a Garratt Lane, SW18 4DA
www.whyoga.com

Yoga For Pregnancy　020 8788 0372
369 Fulham Road, SW6
Private tuition or small group classes

Yoga for Pregnancy and Birth　020 8287 5411
Mostyn Road, SW19
hargrave.family@virgin.net
Annabel Hargrave teaches gentle yoga, using breathing and relaxation techniques for preparation of labour

Yoga Junction　020 7263 3113
The Whittington Park Community Centre,
Yerbury Road, N19 4RS

Yogabananas　020 8874 3858
170A Garratt Lane, SW18 4DA
www.yogabananas.com

Yogahome　020 7249 2425
11 Allen Road, N16 8SB

Yoga Therapy Centre　020 7419 7195
60 Great Ormond Street, WC1N 3HR

Yvonne Moore Birth Preparation　020 7794 2056
South Hill Park, NW3
Antenatal yoga based exercise classes in North London

The Portland Hospital　020 7390 8061
234 Great Portland Street, W1W 5QT
www.theportlandhospital.com

What I need to buy Checklist

✓ Items	Buy from...	Borrow from...	Gift from...

For the nursery

☐ cot and mattress

☐ moses basket/crib

☐ linen (sheets, blankets, etc.)

☐ changing mat/table

☐ wardrobe

☐ chest of drawers

☐ playmat

☐ babybath

Clothing

☐ 6 cotton sleepsuits

☐ 3 x sleeping bags

☐ 4 cotton vests

☐ 1-2 two-piece outfits

☐ 2-4 cardigans

☐ 4-6 pairs socks/bootees

☐ 1 pair gloves/mittens (for winter)

☐ 1 snowsuit (for winter)

☐ muslin cloths/ bibs

☐ 1 hat

☐ 1 pair soft shoes/ booties

Essential supplies

☐ disposable or washable nappies

☐ baby wipes, cotton wool

☐ nappy bags

☐ barrier cream, vaseline

☐ breast pump

☐ bottles

☐ sterilizer

For travelling

☐ pram/pushchair

☐ rain cover and cosytoes

☐ car seat

☐ baby carrier/sling

☐ travel and changing bag

☐ travel cot

baby accessories

These suppliers have designed unique and stylish products that really offer something hugely practical with a great sense of style

Bagtalk   020 8673 0400
www.bagtalk.com
Create your own photo tote bag

Couverture   020 7795 1200
www.couverture.co.uk
Chelsea boutique selling luxurious accessories for the home and children via mail order catalogue. Range includes linens, gifts and nightwear.

Crawlers   020 8346 5558
www.crawlers.ltd.uk
Knee pads for avid crawlers – saves having to sew patches on trousers

Ezee-Reach   01908 565 001
www.ezee-reach.com
Stay-Put Cutlery defies gravity and assists the early development of baby's eating skills. Watch this website for new products!

Favourite Things   01932 355 603
www.afavouritething.co.uk
Unique baby quilts, fleece blankets and wooden toys

Goo-Goo   07002 466 466
www.goo-goo.com
Accessories for babies and kids (shoes, merino wool outfits and Sposh swimwear)

Kate Samphier   01835 824742
www.katesamphier.com
Knitted accessories and blankets

Mili Mouse   0870 112 4882
www.milimouse.co.uk
Personalized duffel bags for babies & children

The Sleepover Company   0870 300 2010
www.sleepovercompany.com
Get organised for sleepovers with this innovative mail order company.

Tyrrell Katz   020 7372 6696
www.tyrrellkatz.co.uk
Linens, coathangers and lampshades in the traditional Tyrrell Katz designs.

White Rabbit England   020 8961 8856
www.whiterabbitengland.com
China night lights

ZPM   020 8288 1091
www.zpm.com
Funky range of bibs, bags, aprons, sponge bags and changing mats

baby equipment hire

Chelsea Baby Hire   020 8789 9673
www.chelseababyhire.com
A personal and reliable service offering top brand equipment for long and short term hire.

Lilliput
255-259 Queenstown Road, SW8   020 7720 5554
100 Haydons Road, SW19   020 8542 3542
www.lilliput.com

Little Stars   020 8621 4378
8 Anselm Road, Hatch End, HA5 4LJ
www.littlestars.co.uk
We hire and sell a full range of nusery and baby equipment - based in Hatch End in Middlesex.

Nappy Express   020 8361 4040
www.nappyexpress.co.uk

baby equipment

(see 'nursery goods' on page 57)

baby showers

Baby Babble   020 8386 7046
www.babybabble.co.uk
Good selection of gifts (including named gifts) for newborns and baby showers

Storkparty   01279 465 048
www.storkparty.co.uk

birth announcements

There is great choice as to how you circulate news to friends and family about your new arrival, and since it's a one-off event we think it is worth making the effort. The following companies offer a range of cards in different styles to suit all tastes and budgets, as well as putting images of the new baby on a specially designed website for family who live abroad or can't visit

Announce It!   **020 8286 4044**
www.announceit.com
Your beautiful baby, introduced in a gorgeous range of birth announcements mailed within 3 days

Chatterbox Cards   **020 8650 8650**
www.chatterboxcards.com
Exclusive personalised birth announcements and christening invitations. Delivered in 3 days

Cute as a Button   **01461 337 427**
www.cuteasabutton.co.uk
Unique wooden heart birth announcements, the perfect keepsake to celebrate the birth of your baby

Happyhands   **020 8671 2020**
7 Brockwell Park Row, SW2 2YH
www.happyhands.ws
Your baby's hand and foot prints on cards. Ingenious ink-free kit provided

Heritage Personalised   **01256 861 738**
Stationery
Western Patrick House, Western Patrick, RG25 2NT
www.heritage-stationery.com

Historystore   **020 7976 6040**
29 Churton Street, Pimlico, SW1V 2LY
www.historystore.ltd.uk
Special stationery for a very special person

Hyperbubba   **07932 447 752**
www.hyperbubba.com
Calling all trendy bubbas! Stylish, personalised and colourful birth announcement cards, virtual and printed.

Minor Mail   **01952 275 426**
www.minormail.co.uk
Stylish birth announcements, embroidered christening keepsakes and hand-crafted cards.

Monkey Sites
www.monkeysites.co.uk
Online - only service to create your own baby website in a few easy steps.

Stork News   **01279 731 230**
www.storknews.co.uk
The online birth announcement and baby website service. Gift certificates and keepsake disks available.

bookshops for children

All these bookshops are either specialist children's bookshops or those who have a specialist children's department. The majority also offer audio books, children's music CDs and tapes for travelling. In addition to those listed below the major chains such as Books etc, WH Smith and Waterstones have stores throughout London.
The Baby Directory team are passionate about children's books, and we review new titles monthly on the www.babydirectory.com website. We also have a recommended reading list featuring classics that should be in all family bookshelves and ideas for parents on ways to inspire their children towards a lifelong love of reading. *Stockists of the London Baby Directory are coloured red*

CENTRAL
Selfridges   **0870 837 7377**
400 Oxford Street, W1

Hatchards   **020 7439 3932**
187 Piccadilly, W1

Penguin Books   **020 7010 3000**
80 Strand, WC2

EAST
Eastside Books   **020 7247 0216**
178 Whitechapel Road, E1

Centerprise Bookshop   **020 7254 9632**
136-138 Kingsland High Street, E8

Newham Bookshop   **020 8552 9993**
745-747 Barking Road, E13

Hammicks   **020 8521 3669**
259 High Street, E17

NORTH
The Bookshop
Islington Green   **020 7359 4699**
76 Upper Street, Islington, N1

Angel Bookshop   **020 7226 2904**
102 Islington High Street, N1

Highgate Bookshop   **020 8348 8202**
9 Highgate High Street, N6

Word Play   **020 8347 6700**
1 Broadway Parade, Crouch End, N8

Prospero's Books   **020 8348 8900**
32 The Broadway, Crouch End, N8

Muswell Hill Bookshop   **020 8444 7588**
72 Fortis Green Road, N10

BIRTH ANNOUNCEMENTS CARDS & PERSONALISED STATIONERY

Michael and Annabella
are delighted to announce the birth of their daughter
Charlotte Helena Louise
on Friday 27th April 2001
7lbs 10oz / 3.48kg
a sister for Amelia

6 Eastview Mansions
London SW15 1PF   020 8741 3589

- Exclusive
- Top Quality Board
- Traditional Printing
- Excellent Value
- Hand Ribboned
- Delivered in Days

View our products and order online at:
www.heritage-stationery.com

HERITAGE PERSONALISED STATIONERY
01256 861738

Congratulations

from Historystore.
We would be delighted
to design your
Birth Announcement &
Christening Invitations.

Call Claire on 020 7976 6040

historystore.ltd.uk

happyhands™

The ultimate birth announcement or thank
you cards

"Ingenious idea" *Pregnancy & Birth*
"Simply Irresistible" *Prima Baby*

Your own baby's foot prints
on personalised cards

An easy to use inkless footprint kit is provided

Call us on **020 8671 2020**
www.happyhands.ws

announce it!

*for birth announcements,
wedding invitations, christenings,
parties, moving house, anything...*

We offer a wide range of beautiful cards and gifts
personalised with your own message, including
ribbons or photographs if required and a free proof.
Our new range of photograph albums and
keepsake boxes are perfect as a gift.

Come and browse or have a chat at our new shop
99 Station Road Hampton TW12 020 8286 4044

Visit our web site **www.announceit.co.uk**
or call **020 8395 5228** for a free brochure

Children's Bookshop 020 8444 5500
29 Fortis Green Road, N10

Stoke Newington Bookshop 020 7249 2808
159 Stoke Newington High Street, N16

NORTH WEST
Primrose Hill Bookshop 020 7586 2022
134 Regents Park Road, NW1

Daunt Books 020 7794 4006
193 Haverstock Hill, NW3

Karnac Books 020 7431 1075
118 Finchley Road, NW3

Owl Bookshop 020 7485 7793
211 Kentish Town Road, NW5

West End Lane Books 020 7431 3770
277 West End Lane, West Hampstead, NW6

Kilburn Bookshop 020 7328 7071
8 Kilburn Bridge, Kilburn High Road, NW6

Willesden Bookshop 020 8451 7000
Willesden Green Library Centre,
95 The High Road, NW10

Bookworm 020 8201 9811
1177 Finchley Road, NW11

SOUTH EAST
Riverside Bookshop 020 7378 1824
Hay's Galleria, SE1

Words Worth Books 020 7277 1377
Butterfly Walk Shopping Centre, Denmark Hill, SE5

Arcade Bookshop 020 8850 7803
3-4 The Arcade, Eltham, SE9

Ottakar's 020 8853 8530
51 Church Street, Greenwich, SE10

Bookseller Crow on the Hill 020 8771 8831
50 Weston Street, Crystal Palace, SE19

The Bookshop
Dulwich Village 020 8693 2808
1d Calton Avenue, SE21

Dulwich Books 020 8670 1920
6 Croxted Road, West Dulwich, SE21

Kirkdale Bookshop 020 8778 4701
272 Kirkdale, Sydenham, SE26

SOUTH WEST
Harrods
Children's Book Department 020 7225 5721
4th floor, Harrods, Knightsbridge, SW1

John Sandoe 020 7589 9473
10 Blacklands Terrace, SW3

Daisy & Tom 020 7352 5000
181 King's Road, SW3

Young Book Trust 020 8516 2977
Book House, 45 East Hill, SW18 2QZ
www.booktrusted.com

Nomad Books 020 7736 4000
781 Fulham Road, SW6

Ottakar's Science Museum 020 7942 4481
Exhibition Road, South Kensington, SW7

The French Bookshop 020 7584 2840
28 Bute Street, SW7

Pan Bookshop 020 7373 4997
160 Fulham Road, SW10

Ottakar's 020 7978 5844
70 St Johns Road, SW11

Bolingbroke Bookshop 020 7223 9344
147 Northcote Road, SW11

My Back Pages 020 8675 9346
8-10 Balham Station, SW12

Beaumonts 020 8741 0786
60 Church Road, Barnes, SW13

Bookstop 020 7228 9079
375 Upper Richmond Road West, East Sheen, SW14

Ottakar's 020 8780 2401
6-6a Exchange Centre, Putney, SW15

Beckett's Bookshop 020 8672 4413
6 Bellevue Road, SW17

Golden Treasury 020 8333 0167
29 Replingham Road, Southfields, SW18

Langton's Bookshop 020 8892 3800
44-45 Church Street, Twickenham, TW1

Kew Bookshop 020 8940 0030
1-2 Station Approach, Kew, Richmond, TW9

WEST
Bookcase 020 8742 3919
268 Chiswick High Road, W4

Pitshanger Bookshop 020 8991 8131
Pitshanger Lane, W5

Children's Book Company 020 8567 4324
11 The Green, W5

Children's Book Centre 020 7937 7497
237 Kensington High Street, W8

Early Bird Books 020 8579 0076
Daniel Department Store, 96 Uxbridge Road, W13

bookclubs

www.BooksForChildren.co.uk   020 7760 6500
Online discounted book club for children

www.bookstart.co.uk   020 8516 297
A book starter pack initiative run in conjunction with some local authorities, usually given to parents at the 8 month check.

The Book People   0870 607 7740
www.thebookpeople.co.uk
A discounted range of books is available fromthis mail order and online company.

car safety

For car seat fitting, seat belt adjusting or fixing ISOFIX anchorages. Autosafe actually come to you for a very modest fee (within M25)

Autosafe   020 7372 3141
www.auto-safe.co.uk
Seatbelt specialists supplied and fitted

Halfords   0845 7626 625
www.halfords.com
Car seat fitting and seat belt adjusting

Kwik-Fit   0800 757 677
www.kwik-fit.com

carriers, slings & backpacks

Baby Bjorn and Wilkinet are the best-known brands in this category, with Bill Amberg being the priciest, but there is good choice and style depending on how heavy your baby is, when you want to use the carrier (quick walk to the shops or long walk on the beach) and comfort. See www.babydirectory.com for product reviews.

Baby Backpacs   01872 270 213
www.babybackpacs.co.uk
Online retailer of carriers and accessories including Bushbaby, Hippychick, Kelty Kids and Karrimor.

Baby Bjorn   0870 120 0543
www.babybjorn.com

Babyhut   01273 245 864
www.babyhut.net
Experts in cotton baby slings and baby hammocks. Award winning and praised by health professionals, Babyhut provides natural, quality and practical products for babies and parents.

Bill Amberg   020 7727 3560
10 Chepstow Road, , W2 5BD
www.billamberg.com

CARS • MINIBUSES • WELFARE VEHICLES • COACHES
SEATBELT SPECIALISTS (SUPPLIERS & FITTERS)

Seat belt too short?
Seat belt not working properly?
Problems fitting your baby seat into the car?
Want to replace a lap belt with a cross diagonal?

CENTRE BELT

PHONE US ....
We can advise you on the correct products for your needs

020 7372 3141
www.auto-safe.co.uk

Bushbaby   0161 474 7097
www.bush-baby.com
Baby carriers and baby outdoor clothing from 0-3yrs.

Hippychick   01278 434 440
www.hippychick.com
Innovative back-supporting belt with integral seat for carrying children (6mths-3yrs). Endorsed by osteopaths

Hauck   0870 840 6727
www.hauckuk.com

Huggababy Natural   01874 711629
Baby Products
www.huggababy.co.uk
Designed by a mother, this double-thickness cotton twill sling is favoured by many other mums, and tough enough to last baby from birth to 2 or 3 yrs

Kelty Kids   01395 443 789
www.kelty.com

Wilkinet Baby Carrier   01239 841 844
www.wilkinet.co.uk
Very comfortable, hands-free carrying. The unique wraproud tying ensures even weight distribution.

Please say you saw the advert in The Baby Directory

The new generation of car seats have greater side-impact protection than in previous years as well as "head huggers" which stop your newborn's head from wobbling around. The Group 0+ size is normally outgrown by 9mths, so consider buying a Group 0+1 which lasts up to 4yrs

Jane
Matrix 'Lie Flat'

An award winning car seat can be used like a carrycot or as an upright car seat. With 4 position backrest and fully padded harness/crotch flaps.

- Group 0+
- Head hugger
- Deluxe mattress
- 4 positions
£110
www.johnstonprams.co.uk
Stockists: 0289077 0779

Maxi-Cosi
Cabrio

Good side protection and a built-in seat adjuster, this car seat can become part of a travel system. Ergonomically designed handle and nappy/wipes storage compartment.

- Group 0+
- Seat flattens
- Washable cover
- Good carry handle
£80
www.maxi-cosi.com
Stockists: 020 8236 0707

With this car seat you fit the base first, then simply lock the car seat in place – saving considerable time and comfort as your baby gets heavier

Graco
Auto Baby
Safety Plus

- Group 0+
- Head hugger
- Newborn comfort liner
- Base not always required
£99
www.graco.co.uk
Stockists: 0870 909 0501

Very padded side impact wings and a fully reclining seat for newborns and 5 different positions for toddlers. Rear or forward facing ;suitable up to 4yrs.

Britax
First Class

- Group 0+1
- Ergonomic carry handle
- Washable cover
- Many fabric designs
£80
www.britax.co.uk
Stockists: 01264 386 034

Bebe Confort
Elios Safe Side

Big side impact protection and a self locking carry handle which fits onto a Bebe Confort travel system.

- Group 0+
- Head hugger
- Semi-lying position
- Washable cover
£80
www.bebeconfort.co.uk
Stockists: 020 8236 0707

Mothercare
Auto Route
Deluxe

This comes with a newborn head hugger and can be used rear or forward facing from birth.

- Group 0+1
- 3 seat positions
- washable cover
- 5 point one pull harness
£70
www.mothercare.co.uk
Stockists: 0845 330 4030

Chicco
Shuttle

Longer lasting car seat with integral footrest for forward facing position. 5 point one pull harness. Deep side impact protection.

- Group 0+1
- 4 seat positions
- Soft padded seat
- 5 point one pull harness
£99
www.chicco.co.uk
Stockists: 01623 750 870

Mamas & Papas
Primo Viaggio

Deep side impact protection and a simple one-lock mechanism fits to the Surefix Base or to chassis for compact travel system.

- Group 0+
- 3 shoulder height positions
- Rear facing
- Easy to use buckle
£110
www.mamasandpapas.co.uk
Stockists: 0870 830 7700

castings: hands & feet

A cast or print of your baby's hands and feet is a must to remember how small they once were. Most mothers regret that they never got round to taking their baby's hand or foot prints, or struggled with a tube of paint and made something strange on a piece of paper. But the art has moved on and the companies below offer a range of styles (casts, prints and imprints) to suit all budgets

First Impressions   **020 8346 8666**
263 Nether Street, N3 1PD
www.firstimpressions.org.uk
Original hand and foot castings in bronze, silver, gold and resins. (See advert on page 28)

Golden Hands,   **020 8290 4091**
Silver Feet Ltd
www.goldenhands.co.uk
Hands and feet cast in bronze, brass, aluminium or stone. And pregnant mums can have their full torso cast

Hands & Feet by   **020 8723 5378**
Gillian Wood Ceramics
Create timeless imprints of your children's hands & feet in clay

Happyhands   **020 8671 2020**
7 Brockwell Park Row, SW2 2YH
www.happyhands.ws
Your baby's hand and footprints on ceramics. Ink-free kit provided for taking prints at home

Imprints
John Lewis Brent Cross	020 8202 6535
John Lewis Kingston	020 8547 3000
John Lewis Oxford Street	020 7629 7711
John Lewis Watford	01923 244 266
Peter Jones	020 7730 3434

www.imprints.org
Original fired clay impressions. By appointment at John Lewis Stores.(See advert on page 28)

Lifestone Ltd   **0800 917 8964**
www.lifestone.com
Imprints the new way - no mess, no stress, just press. Castings in glass, bronze and cast stone.

Sarah Page Sculpture   **020 7731 8789**
www.sarahpagesculpture.co.uk
Immaculate and sensitive fine and applied castings from babies' and children's hands and feet. (See advert on page 28)

Wrightson & Platt   **0845 226 5775**
www.wrightsonandplatt.com
Perfect castings in silver, bronze, glass, resin and plaster. Local representatives can visit you for a home casting visit.. (See advert on page 29.)

Sarah Page Sculpture
FINE CASTINGS IN BRONZE, SILVER, GLASS & PLASTER
020 7223 8399
Immaculate and sensitive fine casting from your little treasures
www.sarahpagesculpture.co.uk

happyhands™
Your own baby's hand or foot prints on framed ceramic tiles

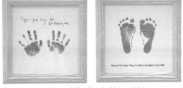

An easy to use inkless footprint kit is provided

"Simply irresistible – here's a lasting memory that makes a perfect present for friends and relatives."
Prima Baby Magazine

Call us on **020 8671 2020**
www.happyhands.ws

first impressions™

020 8346 8666

www.judywiseman.com

Precious casts in bronze, silver & glass of you & your baby to treasure for ever

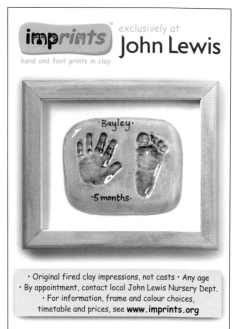

imp*rints*™ exclusively at
John Lewis
hand and foot prints in clay

·Bayley·

·5 months·

• Original fired clay impressions, not casts • Any age
• By appointment, contact local John Lewis Nursery Dept.
• For information, frame and colour choices,
timetable and prices, see **www.imprints.org**

Hands & Feet Prints
Preserve your children's precious early years forever

**Create expert imprints of your children's
hands and feet in clay. Perfectly safe for
babies from 6 weeks old.**

• **Ideal gift for grandparents**
• **Family/sibling imprints are available**
• **Home visits available**

*Babies grow very fast, don't let this
opportunity pass. Call Gillian on
0208 7235 378 or 07931 884 673*

*precious today,
priceless tomorrow*

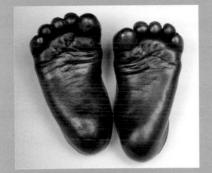

your child's hands & feet in silver,
bronze, glass, resin & plaster

call

0845 226 5775

for a brochure or appointment
www.wrightsonandplatt.com

Baby Heirlooms

www.babyheirlooms.co.uk 020 7630 7103

happyhands™

The Perfect Christening Gift

*The gift box entitles the
recipient to either one framed
Happyhands tile or 25 cards*

*An easy to use inkless
footprint kit is provided*

Their own baby's hand & foot prints

Call us on **020 8671 2020**

www.happyhands.ws

christening gifts

There is now such a plethora of items suitable for godchildren, we have selected those companies which we think offer the highest quality, originality and personalised service at the right price. See also gift ideas, gifts for newborns, and gifts, personalised

Asprey & Garrard   020 7493 6767
167 New Bond Street, , W1S 4AR
www.asprey-garrard.com
Cups, spoons, plates and yo-yos - engraved with initials or name

Baby Heirlooms   020 7976 5158
13 Churton Place, , SW1V 2LN
www.babyheirlooms.co.uk
A wonderful range of antique and traditional silver gifts beautifully gift wrapped and delivered to your door. Many affordable presents for girls and boys with a hand engraving service for special messages and baby names.

Braybrook & Britten   020 8993 7334
www.braybrook.com
A large range of silver gifts for children from £30 upwards - most can be personalised. "Silversmiths by Post", they can receive orders from anywhere in the UK.

Happyhands   020 8671 2020
www.christening-gifts.com
Gift box for hand and foot imprints on ceramic packaged in a red box with white ribbon. Price £35

Heirlooms UK   020 7738 1868
www.heirlooms.uk.com
Personalised cushions, ring cushions, shawls and decorative pictures using words and images you provide.

Heritage Personalised Stationery 01256 861 738
www.heritage-stationery.com
Personalised leather photograph albums (very reasonably priced)

Junior Traditions   01884 860 063
www.juniortraditions.co.uk
Chairs and chests for children 1-6 years made from oak and walnut for exceptional christening gifts.

Purple Heart   020 7328 2830
www.purple-heart.com
Hand painted, personalised china (name and date) by Claudia Meynell

Tiffany & Co   020 7409 2790
25 Old Bond Street, W1S 4QB
www.tiffany.com
Items in sterling silver start from around £100. Everything can be engraved and comes wrapped in their trademark box. Also at 145 Sloane Street, London, SW1X 9AY (020 7409-2790); and The Royal Exchange, The Courtyard, EC3V 3LQ (020 7409 2790

christening gowns

If you are starting from scratch and don't have a family heirloom christening gown, then a trip to Christening Gowns, is well worth a visit. Otherwise there are a few expert retailers in London who stock a small selection alongside other children's clothes

Anna's Christening Centre   020 8807 5961
2 Market Parade, Winchester Road, N9 9HF

Christening Gowns   01536 515 401
35 Derwent Crescent, NN16 8UH
www.christeningoutfits.co.uk
Over 500 gowns, dresses and romper suits in stock. Accessories including personalised bibs. Mail order throughout the UK.

Christening Stuff   0870 777 0285
www.christeningstuff.co.uk

Gale Classic Clothes   01249 712 241
All items made to order: christening gowns, matinee jackets, smocked dresses and romper suits. Free catalogue.

Heirs Wears   020 8809 7160
Mail order traditional and contemporary Christening gowns, bonnets, shoes and bootees.

Little Darlings   01604 846 655
www.littledarlings.co.uk
Visit the website to view their full christening and fashion ranges.

Patrizia Wigan Designs   020 7823 7080
19 Walton Street, SW3 2HX
www.patriziawigan.com
Refined gifts, babywear, christening, bridesmaid and pageboy outfits.

Thimbelina   01865 872549
Hand-smocked heirloom gowns, outfits and accessories handmade to order

clothing shops

We have covered this category pretty comprehensively, so you may find it hard to wade through all that's on offer. But if your once-favourite pastime has diminished now that you can't browse at leisure, many brands have good catalogue and online purchasing routes

BOUTIQUE

EAST LONDON

Baby This 'n' Baby That   020 8527 4002
359 Forest Road, E17 5JR

Bambini   020 7474 3591
317 Barking Road, E13 8EE

Diverse Kids   020 8539 2821
792 High Road, E10 6AE

Chi   020 8510 9000
251 Graham Road, E8 1PE

Kool Kids   020 7247 2878
9-11 New Goulston Street, E1 7QD

Jakss   020 8981 2233
463 & 469 Roman Road, E3 5LX

Tiddlywinks   020 8981 7000
414 Roman Road, E3 5LU

NORTH LONDON

American Collections   020 8806 0702
41 Oldhill Street, N16 6LR

Buckle My Shoe Head Office   020 8445 3111
1230 High Road, N20 0LH

Early Clothing   020 8444 9309
79-85 Fortis Green Road, Muswell Hill, N10 3HP

Hobby Horse Riders   020 8348 9782
50-52 Crouch End Hill, N8 8AA

Kiddie Chic   020 8880 1500
19 Amhurst Parade, Stamford Hill, N16 5AA

Igloo Kids   020 7354 7300
300 Upper Street, N1 2TU

Notsobig   020 8340 4455
31a Highgate High Street, N6 5JT

Rubadubdub   020 7263 5577
198 Stroud Green Road, N4 3RN

Shoe and Fashion Boutique   020 8806 5581
28 Stamford Hill, N16 6XZ

Teddy Bear Childrenswear   020 7502 2238
93 Dunsmure Road, Stamford Hill, N16 5HT

Thoe Tho   020 8442 0419
55 Fortis Green Road, Muswell Hill, N10 3HP

Trendys   020 7837 9070
72 Chapel Market, N1 9ER

Za Trendy Kids   020 8365 8382
Wood Green Shopping City, High Road, N22 6YQ

NORTH WEST LONDON

Adam & Eve Children's Boutique   020 8455 8645
5 The Market Place, Hampstead Garden Suburb, NW11 6LB

Charly's   020 7723 6811
71 Church Street, NW8 8EU

Daphne & Mum   020 8458 7095
7 Belmont Parade, 838 Finchley Road, NW11 6XP

Dynasty   **020 8731 8521**
1-2 Russel Parade, Golders Green Road, NW11 9NN

Humla   **020 7794 8449**
13 Flask Walk, NW3 1HJ

Look Who's Walking   **020 7433 3855**
78 Heath Street, Hampstead Village, NW3 1DN

Purple Heart   **020 7328 2830**
13a College Parade, Salusbury Road, NW6 6RN

Tartan Turtle   **020 8959 9938**
52 The Broadway, Mill Hill, NW7 3LH

Tiddlywinks   **020 7722 3033**
23 St Johns Wood High Street, NW8 7NH

Trotters   **020 8202 1888**
Brent Cross Shopping Centre, NW4 3FP

SOUTH EAST LONDON

Bunny London   **020 7928 6269**
Unit 1, 22 Oxo Tower Wharf, Bargehouse Street, SE1 9PH

Peppermint for Kids   **020 7703 9638**
321-323 Walworth Road, SE17 2IG

Biff   **020 8299 0911**
43 Dulwich Village, SE21 7BN

SOUTH WEST LONDON

Agnes b   **020 7225 3477**
111 Fulham Road, SW3 6OL

Barney's   **020 8944 2915**
6 Church Road, SW19 5DL

Bonpoint   **020 7235 1441**
35b Sloane Street, SW1X 9LP

Brora   **020 7352 6397**
344 King's Road, SW3 5UR

Bug Circus   **020 8741 4244**
153 Church Road, SW13 9HR

Caramel Baby   **020 7589 7001**
291 Brompton Road, SW3

Children's Kingdom   **020 8682 2233**
209 Upper Tooting Road, SW19

Daisy & Tom   **020 7352 5000**
181 King's Road, SW3 5EB

Greater Tomorrow   **020 7737 5276**
80 Atlantic Road, SW9 8PX

Gucci   **020 7235 6707**
17-18 Sloane Street, SW1X 9NE

Iana   **020 8789 2022**
Putney Exchange, Putney High Street, SW15 1TW
www.iana.it

Iana   **020 7352 0060**
186 King's Road, SW3 5XP
www.iana.it
Italian designed clothes from 3mths - 14yrs.

Joanna's Tent   **020 7352 1151**
289b Kings Road, SW3 5EW

Kanga-roo   **020 7384 4518**
359 Fulham Palace Road, SW6

Kent & Carey
154 Wandsworth Bridge Rd, SW6   020 7736 5554
30 Bellevue Road, SW17   020 8682 2282

Little Willies   **020 7498 7899**
16 The Pavement, SW4

Lizzies   **020 7738 2973**
143 Northcote Road, SW11 6PX

Membery's   **020 8876 2910**
1 Church Road, SW13 9HE

Marie-Chantal   **020 7838 1111**
148 Walton Street, SW3 2JJ

Oilily   **020 7823 2505**
9 Sloane Street, SW1X 9LF

Pollyanna   **020 7731 0673**
811 Fulham Road, SW6 5HG

Patrizia Wigan Designs   **020 7823 7080**
19 Walton Street, SW3 2HX
www.patriziawigan.com
Refined gifts, babywear, christening, bridesmaid and pageboy outfits.

Quackers   **020 7978 4235**
155d Northcote Road, SW11 6QB

Rachel Riley   **020 7259 5969**
14 Pont Street, SW1X 9EN

Semmalina   **020 7730 9333**
225 Ebury Street, SW1

Tomboy Kids   **020 7223 8030**
176 Northcote Road, Battersea, SW11

Trotters   **020 7259 9620**
34 Kings Road, SW3 4UD

Young England   **020 7259 9003**
47 Elizabeth Street, SW1
www.youngengland.com
Traditional clothing for children from birth to eight years.(See advert on page 33)

CENTRAL & WEST LONDON

Bill Amberg Shop   **020 7727 3560**
10 Chepstow Road, W2 5BD

Bon Bleu
16 Hammersmith Mall, W6 — 020 8834 7205
Kendal Court, Kendal Avenue, W3 — 020 8992 5611

Bonpoint
17 Victoria Grove, W8 — 020 7584 5131
38 Old Bond Street, W1 — 020 7495 1680
197 Westbourne Grove, W11 — 020 7792 2515

Brora
66-68 Ledbury Road, W11 — 020 7229 1515
81 Marylebone High Street, W1 — 020 7224 5040

Buckle My Shoe — 020 7318 3548
within Selfridges, 400 Oxford Street, W1C 2BU

Burberry — 020 7839 5222
21-23 New Bond Street, W1S 2RE

The Cross — 020 7727 6760
141 Portland Road, W11 4LR

Catimini
52 South Molton Street, W1Y 1HF — 020 7629 8099
3 Paradise Road, TW9 — 020 8541 4635
38 High Street, Kingston — 020 8541 4635
75 Upper Thames Walk, Bluewater — 01322 624 765

Darch & Duff — 020 8840 0100
68 Northfield Avenue, W13

Jou Jou & Lucy — 020 7289 0866
32 Clifton Road, W9 1ST

Juniper — 020 8998 0144
88 Pitshanger Lane, W5 1QX

Pearlfisher — 020 7603 8666
12 Addison Avenue, W11 4QR

Paul Smith for Children — 020 7727 3553
122 Kensington Park Road, W11 2EP

Rachel Riley — 020 7935 7007
82 Marylebone High Street, W1U 4QW

Ralph Lauren — 020 7535 4888
143 New Bond Street, W1

Sasti — 020 8960 1125
8 Portobello Green Arcade, 281 Portobello Road, W10 5TY

Tartine et Chocolat — 020 7629 7233
66 South Molton Street, W1Y 1HH

Their Nibs — 020 7221 4263
214 Kensington Park Road, W11 1NR

Tots — 020 8995 0520
39 Turnham Green Terrace, W4 1RG

Tournicoti — 020 7229 3022
52 Lonsdale Road, W11 2DE
French boutique from 0-8yrs. Open 10-6pm and 2-6pm on Sun.

Trotters — 020 7937 9373
127 Kensington High Street, W8 6LE

HIGH STREET

Baby Baby — 020 8876 3153
193 Sheen Lane, East Sheen, SW14 8LE

BabyGap
223-245 Oxford Street, W1R 1AB — 020 7734 3312
122 King's Road, SW3 — 020 7823 7272
1-7 Shaftesbury Avenue, W1 — 020 7437 0138
Kew Retail Park, TW9 — 020 8876 8684
Brent Cross, NW4 — 020 8203 9696
99-101 Kensington High Street, W8 — 020 7368 2900
22-26 Chiswick High Road, W4 — 020 8995 3255
www.gap.co.uk

Breezy Stores — 020 8341 2020
142 Crouch Hill, N8 9DX

Bubblegum Childrenswear — 020 8807 5787
3-5 North Mall, Edmonton Green Shopping Centre, N9

Child — 020 7240 6060
49 Shelton Street, Covent Garden, WC2

Daphne & Mum — 020 8458 7095
7 Belmont Parade, 838 Finchley Road, NW11 6XP

E Sharp Minor — 020 8858 6648
6 Earlswood Street, SE10 9ES

French Connection Junior — 020 7225 3302
140-144 Kings Road, SW3

Gymboree
198 Regent's Street, W1 — 020 7494 1110
120 Centre Court Shopping
Centre, Wimbledon, SW19 — 020 8879 3001
www.gymboree.com

Jigsaw Junior
126-127 New Bond Street, W1 — 020 7491 4484
190 Westbourne Grove, W11 — 020 7229 8654
97 Fulham Road, SW3 — 020 7823 8915

Monsoon Baby — 020 7497 9325
25 The Market, WC2

YOUNG ENGLAND®

UPDATED CLASSICAL CHILDRENSWEAR FOR BOYS AND GIRLS

Available exclusively through our shop
Young England Limited, 47 Elizabeth Street, London SW1W 9PP.
Please telephone 020 7259 9003 or visit our website www.youngengland.com for information and mail order.

Petit Bateau
133 Northcote Road, SW11	020 7228 7233
73 Ledbury Road, W11	020 7243 6331
19 Hampstead High Street, NW3	020 7794 1731
106 King's Road, SW3	020 7838 0818
188 Chiswick High Road, W4	020 8987 0288
62 South Molton Street, W1	020 7491 4498
www.petit-bateau.fr	

Torkidz   020 7686 4057
27 Gladmuir Road, N19

Wearabouts
99 Sydenham Road, SE26	020 8659 9917
358 Norwood Rd, SE27	020 8244 7887

Wilson   020 8675 7775
51 Abbeville Road, SW4 9JX

CHEAP & CHEERFUL

Adams   020 7252 3208
Surrey Quays Centre, SE16
www.adams.co.uk

Asda   0113 243 5435
204 Lavender Hill, SW11	020 7223 0101
Edgware Road, NW9	020 8200 4833
31 Roehampton Vale, SW15	020 8780 2780
151 East Ferry Road, E14	020 7987 2614
www.asda.co uk	

Babies 'R' Us   020 7732 7322
Old Kent Road, SE15
www.babiesrus.co.uk

H&M   020 7368 3920
103 Kensington High Street, W8
www.hm.com

Matalan   020 8463 9830
Thurston Road, Loampit Lane, SE13 7SN

Peacocks   020 8852 0851
143-149 High Street, Lewisham, SE13 6AA

Primark   020 8748 7119
King's Mall, King Street, W6
www.primark.co.uk

OUTDOOR CLOTHING

Bush Baby   0161 474 7097
www.bush-baby.com

Muddy Puddles   0870 420 4943
www.muddypuddles.com

Raindrops   01730 810031
www.raindrops.co.uk

Snowdown   020 8992 2301
19 Tudor Court, Tudor Way, W3 9AQ
www.snowdown.co.uk
Complete range of outdoor clothing for toddlers, including ski wear, raincoats, hats, jackets, fleeces and splashsuits.

Togz (Hippychick)   01278 434 440
www.hippychick.com
The Togz range of outdoor clothing is 100% waterproof and made from Teflon coated, breathable nylon fabric.

CLOTHING: MAIL ORDER

Aztec   020 8877 9954
www.aztecstore.com

Baby Azure   020 8514 6700
www.babyazure.com

The Baby Closet   020 7924 4457
www.thebabycloset.co.uk
Simply laid out online store that's the work of an ex-fashion buyer and sells items from a selection of quality but lesser known ranges.

Baby Clothing   0113 394 4106
www.babyclothing.co.uk

Baby Planet   01225 470 314
www.baby-planet.co.uk

Bebe Amour   01494 819914
www.bebeamour.com

Cheeky B   020 8398 5595
www.cheekyb.co.uk

Clothes 4 Boys   01420 520 677
www.clothes4boys.co.uk

Children's Warehouse   020 8752 1166
www.childrens-warehouse.com

Cinnamon Kids   01243 573 674
www.cinnamonkids.com

Cotton Moon Ltd   020 8305 0012
www.cottonmoon.co.uk

Cyrillus   020 7734 6660
www.cyrillus.com

Dribble Factory   020 8758 2601
www.dribblefactory.com

Dynky   01675 436 165
www.dynky.com

Eat Yer Greens   020 8744 0330
www.eatyergreens.com
Fashionable, practical clothing for 0-4 year olds, combining fresh and imaginative design with a sense of humour.

Fat Face   0870 600 0090
www.fatface.co.uk

Greensleeves Clothing	020 8458 1559
www.greensleevesclothing.com	
Hansel and Gretel	01333 360219
www.hansel-and-gretel.co.uk	
JoJo Maman Bebe	**0870 241 0560**
www.jojomamanbebe.co.uk	
Adorable baby & children's clothes, nursery products & toys	
Kids Gear	01483 548552
www.kids-gear.co.uk	
Lacapucine	020 8664 6726
www.lacapucine.co.uk	
Lapin & Me	020 8473 5000
www.lapinandme.co.uk	
Clothes and accessories for girls and their mummies.	
Little Dye House	01737 555 394
www.littledyehouse.co.uk	
Lucky Me	**020 8944 8158**
www.luckyme-uk.com	
An adorable range of young childrens' clothing and knitwear.	
Mini Boden	0845 677 5000
www.boden.co.uk	
Mitty James	020 8693 501
www.mittyjames.com	
My Puku	**020 7585 0792**
www.mypuku.com	
Luxurious merino woollen baby blankets and clothing. Screenprinted designer muslins and stylish baby basics.	
Nappy Head	01582 573 630
www.nappyhead.co.uk	
Pelirocco	020 8802 6497
www.pelirocco.co.uk	
Pesky Kids Ltd	**020 8989 3276**
www.pesky-kids.co.uk	
Retro styles and cult labels for kids aged 0-10 years old.	
Planet Baby & Child	0800 074 1181
www.planetbaby.co.uk	
Schmidt Natural Clothing	01342 822169
www.naturalclothing.co.uk	
Tati	01749 323633
www.tati.co.uk	
VertBaudet	0500 012 345
www.vertbaudet.co.uk	
Wigglets	020 7738 5124
Mail order catalogue for children's nightwear.	
Zaki-do-Dah's	07808 159 211

department stores

Department stores are useful places, especially when it's bucketing outside. And with the recent changes at Selfridges, and refurbishment at Peter Jones, they're good for a quick nappy trip, major purchase or just a fun day out

Harrods   **020 7730 1234**
87-135 Brompton Road, SW1
www.harrods.com
A trip to Harrods wouldn't be complete without a visit to the ice-cream parlour, but for shopping head for the 4th floor where you will find the top of the range in nursery furniture, furnishings, fashion, toys, collectibles and a kids' hair-dressing salon. Pushchair access, nappy changing facilities and play area

John Lewis
278-306 Oxford Street, W1   020 7629 7711
Peter Jones, SW1   020 7730 3434
Brent Cross
Shopping Centre, NW4   020 8202 6535
www.johnlewis.com
Famed for its school uniform departments, the John Lewis stores offer a practical range of clothing and shoes, nursery equipment and toiletries. They also offer a good range of car seats, pushchairs, cots and highchairs. Pushchair access, nappy changing facility, play area.

Selfridges   **020 7629 7711**
400 Oxford Street, W1A 1EX
www.selfridges.com
Head for the 3rd floor Kids Universe to see fashion clothing, shoes and toys. As we went to press they had a special kids' yoga workshop week, so you might just be in for a surprise. Pushchair access, nappy changing facilities.

Debenhams   **020 7580 3000**
334-348 Oxford Street
www.debenhams.com
Open Mon-Sat 9.30am-8pm, Sun 12-6pm. VIP Baby Services in The Restaurant include: free baby food (Heinz & Organix), bottle warmers, highchairs, baby wipes and changing facilities. Clothes from the John Rocha and Jasper Conran collections start from size 3yrs+.

visit us at www.babydirectory.com

cribs, cots & first beds

All the following offer high-quality cots, cot-bed and first beds. For standard cots with adjustable bases we recommend visiting Lilliput, Mothercare or John Lewis, where many are on display

Alphabeds   **020 7636 6840**
92 Tottenham Court Road, W1P 9HE
www.alphabeds.co.uk
Wooden cot-beds made in England

Aspace   **01985 301 222**
The Old Silk Works, Beech Avenue, BA12 8LX
www.aspaceuk.com
Range of classic and contemporary beds, sleepover truckles and bedside cabinets. Good quality & affordable (see advert on page 53)

Bump   **020 7249 7000**
2 Dunston Street, E8 4EB
www.bumpstuff.com
Traditional Swedish cot-beds and beds (from £255 inc VAT)

Fun Beds   **01428 607 878**
www.funbeds.co.uk
Thomas the Tank Engine beds. Colour brochure available

Made to measure cot and crib mattresses, nursery furniture

Fleeces, blankets, bedding, duvets, bedclothes, gifts and so much more

Come to our new shop in Notting Hill or call for a mail order catalogue. Orders can be made online

The Natural Mat Company Ltd
99 Talbot Road, London W11 2AT
Tel: 020 7985 0474
www.naturalmat.com

Greer Beds   **020 7237 1062**
www.greerbeds.co.uk
Innovative and robust contemporary beds

Junior Living   **020 7376 5001**
293 Fulham Road, SW6
Over 25 bedroom designs displayed - great for getting ideas

Kerry Ward Antiques   **020 7350 1022**
19th century sleigh cot-beds and beds from the continent

Planet Little Kids   **020 8946 3320**
www.planetlittle.com

Simon Horn   **020 7731 1279**
117-121 Wandsworth Bridge Road, SW6 2TP
www.simonhorn.com
Hand-made wooden cots which transform into a bed then a sofa (see advert on page 55)

The Bunk Bed Company   **0870 774 6021**
www.bunkbedcompany.com
Bunk bed specialists

**The Children's
Furniture Company**   **020 7737 7303**
www.thechildrensfurniturecompany.com
Beautiful range of wood and painted furniture that evolves as children grow (see advert on page 56)

The Natural Mat Company   **020 7985 0474**
99 Talbot Road, W11 2AT
www.naturalmat.com
Stylish Moses baskets and cot-beds and the best made-to-measure cot and crib mattresses

Tots to Teens Furniture   **07957 870 043**
www.totstoteensfurniture.co.uk

MATTRESSES
(see also linens)

Greenfibres   **01803 868 001**
99 High Street, TQ9 5PF
www.greenfibres.com

The Natural Mat Company   **020 7985 0474**
99 Talbot Road, W11 2AT
www.naturalmat.com
The rull range of natual fibre mattresses in varying sizes or made to measure

Willey Winkle   **01432 268 018**
Offa House, Offa Street, HR1 2LH
www.willeywinkle.co.uk
Organic wool mattresses in all sizes, duvets and pillows

Hippychick Bed Protector   **01278 434 440**
www.hippychick.com
Two layers of brushed cotton sandwiching a waterproof polyurethane layer

dressing up

No nursery toybox would be complete without a few dressing - up clothes to extend the imagination and explore role play. Many of these suppliers manufacture in the UK and therefore you can be assured of good quality fabrics and well made accessories. Kits are also provided so when you are required to make something for the school play you won't be letting the side down

RETAIL

Cheeky Monkeys
202 Kensington Park Road, W11	020 7792 9022
24 Abbeville Road, SW4	020 8673 5251
1 Bellevue Road, SW12	020 8672 2025
4 Croxted Road, SE21	020 8655 7168
94 New King's Road, SW6	020 7731 3031
38 Cross Street, N12	020 7288 1948
34 High Street, W5	020 8840 2504

www.cheekymonkeys.com

Culture Vultures Ltd   020 8883 5525
200 High Road, East Finchley, N2 9AY

Escapade   020 7485 7384
150 Camden High Street, NW1
www.escapade.co.uk

Harlequin   020 8852 0193
254 Lee High Road, SE13

MAIL ORDER

Charlie Crow   01782 417133
www.charliecrow.co.uk

Frilly Lily   01666 510 055
www.frillylily.co.uk

Hopscotch Dressing   01483 813 728
Up Clothes
Summer Wood, Puttenham Heath Road, GU3 1DU
www.hopscotchdressingup.co.uk
Shop online for high quality children's fancy dress costumes & hats - delivered to your door.

J&M Toys   01274 599 314
www.jandmtoys.co.uk

Little Wings   020 7243 3840
www.littlewings.co.uk

Make Believe   01483 203 437
www.make-believe.co.uk

The Hill Toy Company   0870 607 1248
www.hilltoy.co.uk

food organic

Despite the expense, feeding your baby on organic baby food whether pre-prepared or by organising organic home delivery, you can be assured that the residual level of pesticides is minimised. These suppliers are the UK's top organic producers and suppliers.

The Soil Association   0117 929 0661
www.soilassociation.org
The main UK body which supervises the standard for UK organic produce and promotes organic farming.

Links Organic   020 7590 9272
www.linksorganic.com
An online directory of organic businesses, including home delivery services, retailers and organic farmers.

ORGANIC BABY FOOD BRANDS

Baby Organix   01202 479701
Knapp Hill, Mill Road, BH23 2LU
www.babyorganix.co.uk
Organic baby and toddler food

Babylicious   020 8998 4189
www.babylicious.co.uk

Babynat   0118 951 0518
www.organico.co.uk

Easy Freezy   01403 710 935
Organic frozen baby food and toddler meals

Fresh Daisy Organic Babyfood   0870 240 7028
www.daisyfoods.com

HIPP   01635 528 260
www.hipp.co.uk

MiniScoff   07798 526 090
www.miniscoff.co.uk

Pots for Tots   0845 450 0875
www.potsfortots.co.uk
Fresh organic home cooked baby and toddler meals.
National delivery. Non-dairy, non-gluten menus available

Simply Organic   0131 448 0440
www.simplyorganic.c.o.uk

Truuuly Scrumptious Organic   01761 239 300
www.bathorganicbabyfood.co.uk
Frozen organic baby and toddler food, home deliveries

HOME SHOPPING

Abel & Cole   020 7737 3648
www.abel-cole.co.uk
Box scheme deliveries across London

Farm-a-Round 020 7627 8066
www.farmaround.co.uk
Box scheme deliveries across London

Food Glorious Food 020 7582 9947
Emergency rescue packs for the first weeks of motherhood,
all freshly made to order and some suitable for freezing.

Portobello Food Company 020 8748 0505
Arch 215, Trussley Road, W6 7PS
www.portobellofood.com

Pure Meat Direct 01409 211 127
www.puremeatdirectonline.co.uk

Organic Delivery Co 020 7739 8181
www.organicdelivery.co.uk

The Real Meat Company 01985 840 562
www.realmeat.co.uk

Swaddles Green Farm 01460 234 387
www.swaddles.co.uk

West Country Organic Foods 01647 24724
www.westcountryorganics.co.uk

garden toys

With childhood being lost to hand-held gameboys
and television, these companies will provide
encourage a return to good old-fashioned
unsupervised fun. So if you're redeveloping your
garden this year, why not allocate some of your
budget towards imaginative and physical play

Advanced Play Systems 01793 485 200
www.advancedplay.co.uk
Ready built and DIY garden toys such as wendy houses.
Built to order and designed with "finger-friendly" doors.

Dunster House 01234 272 445
www.dhleisureandgarden.com
Outdoor playframes, playhouses, electric wheeled toys and
toy boxes.

Insect Lore 01908 563 338
www.insectlore-europe.com
Butterfly garden kits and other educational insect items.

Sarah Raven's Children's Seeds 0870 000 1057
www.crocus.co.uk
Sarah Raven's Children's Pack is a specially chosen selection
of flower seeds for children. It includes orange poppies,
marigolds, sweet peas

Social Climbers 01235 751 717
www.socialclimbers.com
Good range of New England outdoor playframes made from
cedar.

Super Tramp Trampolines 0800 197 1897
www.supertramp.co.uk
Comprehensive range of garden trampolines.

The Active Toy Company 01635 248 683
www.activetoy.co.uk
TP and Little Tikes outdoor equipment all on show for trial
and display. Wooden/steel climbing frames, swings and
slides, trampolines and paddling pools.

Toys for the Garden Ltd 0870 880 0246
www.toysforthegarden.co.uk
Selection of high quality outdoor toys which encourage
active, imaginative and physical play. Shop securely online.

TreeTops Play Equipment 01227 761 899
www.treetopsdirect.co.uk
Wooden modular designs including swings, climbing frames
and treehouses.

Playhouses & Tents

Just Playhouses 07768 727 016
www.justplayhouses.co.uk
Timber wendy houses

All Out Play 01458 832 920
www.alloutplay.co.uk
New company designing originally shaped wooden
playhouses

Toys FOR THE **Garden**

**The best for
your child in
outdoor play**

www.toysforthegarden.co.uk
Tel 0870 880 0246

Little Red House　01544 319 238
www.littleredhouse.co.uk
Contemporary wooden playhouse designs

**The Children's
Cottage Company**　01363 772 061
www.play-houses.com

The Win Green Company　01622 746 516
Reason Hill, Westerhill Road, Coxheath,
Kent, ME17 4BT
www.wingreen.co.uk

Honeypot Playhouses　0870 164 4002
www.waltons.co.uk
Choose from seven different cottage-style timber playhouses

gifts, personalised

Annie Haak Designs　01428 723 134
www.anniehaak.co.uk
A selection of handpainted, printed designs, documenting
name, date, place, weight and time of birth. Beautiful gifts for
births, christenings and birthdays.

Anne Taylor Designs　020 8748 9279
www.anne-taylor.co.uk

Bespoke Books　020 7359 9311
www.bespokebooks.com

Charlottes' Cot Blankets　01603 627 448
www.charlottecotblankets.com

Cute as a Button　01461 337 427
www.cuteasabutton.co.uk
Unique wooden heart birth announcements, the perfect
keepsake to celebrate the birth of your baby

Ends (UK) Ltd　01245 362 444
www.ends-uk.com
Colourful selection of personalised name-frames, jigsaws,
calendars, heightcharts

Happyhands　020 8671 2020
7 Brockwell Park Row, SW2 2YH
www.christeninggifts.co.uk
Hand and foot prints on personalised ceramic mugs.

Personal Presents Ltd　0870 7271 884
www.personalpresents.co.uk

Plate, Rattle and Bowl　01604 406320
www.babies-rattles.co.uk
Specialists in the craft of hand-made modern babies' rattles

RepeatRepeat　01782 845 870
www.repeatrepeat.co.uk
The Enfant Collection includes contemporary bone
china gifts, albums, christening spoons etc

Annie Haak Designs
Personalised Pictures

A selection of Hand
Painted and Printed designs,
Documenting name, day, date,
place, weight, time, etc.

A unique gift for Baby's Birth,
Christening, etc.

Telephone:　01428 723134
Website:　www.anniehaak.co.uk

gifts for newborns

Baby Gem　01932 863999
www.babygem.com
Classic newborn gift catalogue. Great for grandparents or
godparents looking for luxury and hard-to-find quality gifts.

Baby Treasuree　01481 610 101
www.babytreasures.co.uk
A large range of baby gifts from the traditional to modern
styles, including personalisation.

Babylist　020 7371 5145
www.babylist.co.uk
Beautiful range of contemporary and traditional gifts for
newborns.

happyhands™
A Special Gift

An easy to use inkless footprint kit is provided
Your own baby's foot prints on personalised mugs
Call us on **020 8671 2020**
www.happyhands.ws

Boxtot 01625 430 085
www.boxtot.com
Hand crafted keepsake boxes in three sizes filled with
delightful treats for mother and baby' all around the £25 price
range.

Brighter Babies Book Baskets 01933 275 275
www.brighterbabiesbookbaskets.co.uk
Bundles of books in a basket for newborns or christenings

Ede and Nia 020 7602 8229
www.edeandnia.co.uk
Luxurious and enchanting newborn felt shoes.

Hullabaloo Kids 020 8785 0415
www.hullabaloo-kids.co.uk
Stylish gifts for baby; satin backed comfort blankets fully
machine washable. Order online.

International Star Registry 020 7684 4444
www.starregistry.co.uk
Name a star to welcome your baby to the world.

Kit Heath 020 7379 6661
www.kitheath.com
Range of silver charm jewellery (alphabet, enamel) - bracelets,
necklaces and brooches.

Little Noggins 01673 878 110
www.littlenoggins.co.uk
Fine, unusual gifts for you and your little noggins: for birth,
christenings or just because…

Lucky Me 020 8944 8158
www.luckyme-uk.com
An adorable range of young children's clothing and knitwear.

Melting Hearts 020 7640 2794
Newborn gift box in ginham from £10-£125.

Petra Boase 020 7419 1061
www.petraboase.com
A range of newborn baby albums, notebooks and cards.

Seraphine Baby Gift Box 020 7937 3156
www.seraphine.co.uk
Stylish newborn gift box with pyjama outfit (100% cotton with
linen trimmings), 2 kimono style baby vests and 1 long-arm
teddy. Price £54.

Stork Express 01494 434 294
www.storkexpress.co.uk
Baby gifts and baby gift baskets sent nationwide

Stork News 01279 731 230
www.storknews.co.uk
The online birth announcement and baby website service.
Gift certificates and keepsake disks available.

Zaki-do dah's Hand Knits 07808 159 211
Beautiful handknits in lambswool and cashmere from
newborn to 8yrs. Brochure available

hairdressers

Angela Conway 01883 347 967
Home haircuts for adults and children in SW4

Cosmos 020 8995 9071
265 Chiswick High Road, W4 4PU

Daisy & Tom 020 7352 5000
181 King's Road, SW3

Hairloom 020 7736 5923
111 Munster Road, SW6
Children's haircuts for £6.50 during the week and £8.50 on
Saturdays.

Harrods 020 7730 1234
87-135 Brompton Road, SW3
Children's haircuts for £20.

Headmaster 020 8946 1855
32-34 Ridgeway, SW19
www.hmhair.co.uk
Children's cuts from £10.

Headways 020 8995 9107
7 Chiswick Terrace, Acton Lane, W4 5LY
Children's haircuts from £8.50.

Hopes & Dreams 020 7833 9388
339-341 City Road, EC1V 1LJ
www.hopesanddreams.co.uk

Little Nippers 020 8293 4444
Plaza Arcade, 135 Vanbrugh Hill, Greenwich, SE10

Little Willies 020 7498 7899
16 The Pavement, SW4

Mini Kin 020 8341 6898
22 Broadway Parade, Crouch End, N8 9DE
Children's cuts from £12.

Patricia 020 8747 3045
Have your children's hair cut at home by Patricia in W4

Pom D'Api 020 7431 9532
32 Rosslyn Hill, NW3 1NH

Snips 020 8840 0651
The Crypt, St John's Church, W13 9LA
Haircuts on Tues & Thurs 10-1pm during termtime.

SW4 020 8673 2221
41 Abbeville Road, SW4 9JX

Swallows & Amazons 020 8673 0275
91 Nightingale Lane, SW12 8NX

The Little Trading Co 020 8742 3152
7 Bedford Corner, The Avenue, W4 1LD

Trotters 020 7937 9373
127 Kensington High Street, W8 6LE

Trotters 020 7259 9620
34 King's Road, SW3 4UD

As soon as your baby can sit up comfortably for short periods (around 6-8mths old) you should consider buying a highchair. The highchairs we have selected evolve to suit the maturity and size of your child. A harness will ensure that your baby remains seated - and the foot rest is essential so that the strain is taken off the back. Highchairs range from £40 (lightweight metal and plastic) to around £300 for something utterly stylish.

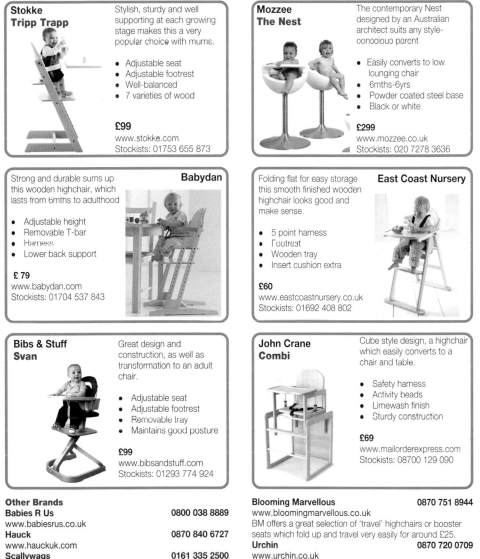

Stokke Tripp Trapp

Stylish, sturdy and well supporting at each growing stage makes this a very popular choice with mums.

- Adjustable seat
- Adjustable footrest
- Well-balanced
- 7 varieties of wood

£99
www.stokke.com
Stockists: 01753 655 873

Mozzee The Nest

The contemporary Nest designed by an Australian architect suits any style-conscious parent

- Easily converts to low lounging chair
- 6mths-6yrs
- Powder coated steel base
- Black or white

£299
www.mozzee.co.uk
Stockists: 020 7278 3636

Babydan

Strong and durable sums up this wooden highchair, which lasts from 6mths to adulthood

- Adjustable height
- Removable T-bar
- Harness
- Lower back support

£ 79
www.babydan.com
Stockists: 01704 537 843

East Coast Nursery

Folding flat for easy storage this smooth finished wooden highchair looks good and make sense.

- 5 point harness
- Footrest
- Wooden tray
- Insert cushion extra

£60
www.eastcoastnursery.co.uk
Stockists: 01692 408 802

Bibs & Stuff Svan

Great design and construction, as well as transformation to an adult chair.

- Adjustable seat
- Adjustable footrest
- Removable tray
- Maintains good posture

£99
www.bibsandstuff.com
Stockists: 01293 774 924

John Crane Combi

Cube style design, a highchair which easily converts to a chair and table.

- Safety harness
- Activity beads
- Limewash finish
- Sturdy construction

£69
www.mailorderexpress.com
Stockists: 08700 129 090

Other Brands

Babies R Us — 0800 038 8889
www.babiesrus.co.uk

Hauck — 0870 840 6727
www.hauckuk.com

Scallywags — 0161 335 2500
www.scallywagsbaby.com

Brevi — 01630 638 978
www.brevi.co.uk

Mamas & Papas — 01293 830 7700
www.mamasandpapas.co.uk

Blooming Marvellous — 0870 751 8944
www.bloomingmarvellous.co.uk
BM offers a great selection of 'travel' highchairs or booster seats which fold up and travel very easily for around £25.

Urchin — 0870 720 0709
www.urchin.co.uk

NCT Maternity Sales — 0870 112 1120
www.nctms.co.uk

JoJoMamanBebe — 0870 241 0560
www.jojomamanbebe.co.uk
Clip-on portable highchair which fixes easily to most tables and work surfaces.

linens & sleeping bags

Big Hugs Children's   **020 8343 0286**
Bed Linen
www.thebighugs.com
Cost-effective stylish bed linen and curtains, animal designs
on colourful fabrics in pure cotton.

Bonne Nuit   **020 8871 1472**
www.bonne-nuit.co.uk
Beautiful French baby sleeping bags, pyjamas and linen.

Boutique Descamps   **020 7235 6975**
197 Sloane Street, SW1X 9QX
www.descamps.com
Linen, towels and bathrobes in the Petit Descamps range,
also cot bumpers, sheets and pillowcases.

Comfort Blankets   **020 8302 6510**
www.comfortblankets.co.uk
Comfort blankets made from fleece and edged in satin and in
a range of funky designs.

Hippychick   **01278 434 440**
www.hippychick.com
100% natural cotton fleece baby blankets in a wonderful
array of colours

For stockists or a brochure call
020 8871 1472 or order online at
www.bonne-nuit.co.uk

Cuski International   **0845 166 2906**
www.cuski.co.uk
A natural cotton blanket comforter

Damask   **020 7731 3553**
www.damask.co.uk
Luxury range of linens and traditional embroidered nightwear.

Fig   **020 7884 1312**
www.figchildrensnightwear.co.uk
Children's classic nightwear from 12mths to teenagers

Grobag   **0870 606 0276**
www.grobag.com
The UK's best selling baby sleeping bags. For your nearest
stockist and details on their full range visit their website

Ideal Cottons   **0131 553 4191**
www.idealcottons.com
Linens, bed covers, washbags and nightwear

Libella Bedwear   **0065 985 758 10**
www.libellabedwear.com
Fine 100% cotton pyjamas for children and adults (matching
sets available).

The Linen Merchant   **020 7584 3654**
11 Montpelier Street, SW7 1EX
www.thelinenmerchant.com
An irresistible collection of bedlinen, towels and bath robes
for children; and clothing and accessories for the newborn.

The White Company   **020 7881 0783**
261 Pavilion Road, SW3
www.thewhiteco.com
Classic range of white nursery linens, plaid blankets and
accessories

The Nursery Company   **020 8878 5167**
www.nurserycompany.co.uk
Baby sleeping bags, covered coat hangers, quilts, bumpers,
blankets and nightwear.

The Volga Linen Company   **01728 635 020**
www.volgalinen.co.uk
A beautiful collection of 100% linen sheet sets, duvet sets,
bedcovers and pyjamas.

Three Bags Full   **0115 875 3683**
www.threebags.co.uk
Gorgeous, practical and unique all-in-one wraps - cosy
fleece, fluffy towelling and cotton for sun safety.

The
Linen
Merchant

lotions & potions (natural)

If you are looking for something a little more special than the supermarket standards, all these suppliers offer an organic, additive- and SLS- free alternative

Barefoot Botanicals   **0870 220 2273**
282 St Paul's Road, London, N1 2LH
www.barefootuk.com
Good quality natural skincare including an SOS Skin Rescue Bath Oil with Lavender, Neroli and Chamomile

Bodywise (UK) Ltd -   **01275 371 764**
Natracare
www.natracare.com
Organic and natural baby toiletries and feminine hygiene products.

E45 Junior
Available from all leading supermarkets and pharmacies,
www.e45.com
Dermatologist and paediatrician approved. Developed for children with dry, sensitive skin or eczema

Farmacia   **020 7404 8808**
www.farmacia123.com
Central London health clinic, pharmacy and shop. Pregnancy safe nail varnish, aromatherapy oils and many more additive - free remedies.

Green Baby   **020 7359 7037**
345 Upper Stree, N1 0PD
www.greenbabyco.com
Natural baby toiletries and baby massage oils

Green People   **0870 240 1444**
www.greenpeople.co.uk
Organic range of products developed for children with sensitive skins.

Little Miracles   **020 7431 6153**
www.littlemiracles.co.uk
Flower remedies.

The Organic Pharmacy   **020 7351 2232**
396 King's Road, SW3
www.theorganicpharmacy.com
Baby massage oils, bath oil, nappy balm

Neil's Yard Remedies
32 Blackheath Village, SE3	020 8318 6655
6 Northcote Road, SW11	020 7627 1949
15 Neal's Yard, Covent Garden	020 7379 7222
9 Elgin Crescent, W11	020 7727 3998
Chelsea Farmers Market, SW3	020 7351 6380
68 Chalk Farm Road, NW1	020 7284 2039
Aromatherapy, homeopathy and herbal remedies plus a natural beauty range

Smilechild   **01242 269 635**
www.smilechild.co.uk
Earth Friendly Baby, Badger, Faith in Nature brands offered as well as natural toothbrushes and sponges (includes natural lice products)

Verde
15 Flask Walk, NW3	020 7431 3314
75 Northcote Road, SW11	020 7924 4379
www.verde.co.uk
Mother and baby range. 16 products including Extra Rich Stretch Mark Oil, Chamomile Baby Body Balm, Bizzy Kids Bathtime Soother, Lice Repel Lotion

Well-care. Well-being.   **020 7354 2083**
Well-ness
48 Upper Handa Walk, N1 2RG
Care products free of carcinogens, contaminants and potentially harmful ingredients

maternity wear

RETAIL SHOPS

9 London   **020 7352 7600**
8 Hollywood Road, SW10 9HY
www.9london.co.uk
Well established and friendly boutique in SW10 specialising in fashionable, designer maternity wear.

Blooming Marvellous   **020 7371 0500**
725 Fulham Road, SW6 3LE
www.bloomingmarvellous.co.uk
Stylish maternity wear as well as baby clothing and nursery products.(see advert on page 45)

Blossom Mother & Child   **020 7589 7500**
164 Walton St, SW3 2JL

Carla C   **020 7243 3950**
302 Westbourne Grove, London, W11 2PS
www.carla-c.com
Swedish designer maternity shop. Mon-Sat 11am-6pm.

Formes
28 Henrietta Street, WC2 8NA	020 7240 4777
313 Brompton Road, SW3 2DY	020 7584 3337
33 Brook Street, W1K 4HJ	020 7493 2783
66 Rosslyn Hill, Richford Street, NW3	020 7431 7770

Great Expectations   **020 7581 4886**
78 Fulham Road, SW3 6HH

H&M Mama
103-111 Kensington High Street, W8	020 7368 3920
481 Oxford Street, W1	020 7493 8557
Whiteleys Shopping Centre, W2	020 7313 7500
7-8 Brent Cross, NW5	020 8202 5440

JoJo Maman Bébé   020 8731 8961
3 Ashbourne Parade, 1259 Finchley Road, NW11
www.jojomamanbebe.co.uk
Also baby and children's clothing.(See advert on page 46)

La Conception   020 7228 7498
46 Webbs Road, SW11 6SF
Maternity wear that speaks for itself. Also children's wear 0-4yrs. Gifts for christenings, births and new mums.

The Maternity Co.   020 8995 4455
42 Chiswick Lane, W4 2JQ
www.thematernityco.com
A refreshing look at maternity fashion! The search for fashionable maternity wear stop here. See advert on page 47)

Maternus   020 7359 5791
54 Cross Street, N1 2BA
www.maternus.co.uk
(See advert on page 46)

Mums 2 Be   020 8332 6506
3 Mortlake Terrace, Mortlake Road, Kew, TW9
157 Lower Richmond Road, , SW15   020 8789 0329
119 Revelstoke Road, SW15   020 8879 3467
www.mums-2-be.co.uk
For all your fashion needs during pregnancy. (See advert on page 46)

PUSH Maternity   020 7359 2003
9 Theberton Street, Islington, N1 0QY
www.pushmaternity.com

Seraphine   020 7937 3156
28 Kensington Church Street, W8
www.seraphine.co.uk
Designer maternity wear and everything to set up your baby's nursery, including a wide range of sophisticated and original birth gifts. (See advert on page 47)

MAIL ORDER

Arabella B   020 7408 1688
www.arabellaB.com
Contemporary maternity wear for all occasions. Look great, feel confident.

Broody Hens   07787 502 175
www.broodyhens.co.uk

Bumps Maternity   0191 565 3232
www.bumpsmaternity.com
Classic collection of maternity wear including underwear and swimwear.

Business Bump   0870 240 5476
www.businessbump.co.uk
Stylish maternity wear for the professional woman.

Cache-Mere   020 8874 2031
www.cache-mere.co.uk
New mail order company specialising in cashmere maternity clothes

Funky Mama   020 7622 7564
www.funkymama.co.uk
Contemporary range of maternity t-shirts with "Don't Push - That's my Job" as well as other captions

Isabella Oliver   0870 240 7612
www.IsabellaOliver.com
A stylish collection of maternity essentials, loungewear and sleepwear made from stretchy, soft, easy-care jersey fabric. With Ulrika Jonsson and Trinny Woodall buying the whole collection - need we say more?

Harry Duley   020 7377 0181
www.harryduley.co.uk
Good range of comfortable maternity wear, baby clothes and children's collection.

i Maternity
www.imaternity.com
US maternity online store. Good range of separates, sundresses and clothes for the workplace. We liked their range of camisoles and other undergarments. For shipping to the UK add $40

Joy Maternity   0845 226 4825
www.joymaternity.com
Our personal shopping advise and consultancy service helps you choose your ideal maternity wardrobe

Long Tall Sally   020 8649 9009
www.longtallsally.com
Maternity jeans for the long-legged

Mamas & Papas   0870 830 7700
www.mamasandpapas.co.uk
Stylish collection of maternity clothes and maternity underwear (white/black and grey marl) as well as black hosiery

NCT Maternity Sales   0141 636 0600
www.nctms.co.uk
The direct mail order catalogue from the NCT.

Next Maternity   0845 6100 500
www.next.co.uk

Tiffany Rose Maternity
www.tiffanyrosematernity.com
For fun and glamorous maternity fashion

maternity bra specialists

Body Comfort   020 8459 2910
www.maternitybras.co.uk
Mail order company supplying a good range of maternity and nursing bras

Bravado   020 7738 9121
www.bravadodesigns.com

Bravissimo
28 High Street, W5   020 8579 6866
20 Tavistock Street, WC2   0845 408 1907
www.bravissimo.com
Offering lingerie for D-JJ cup sizes, swimwear and nursing
bras. Also a mail order catalogue.

Bresona   **01624 670 380**
www.9monthsplus.com
Bresona manufacture the largest selection of
maternity/breast-feeding clothes on the Internet and have a
policy of manufacturing primarily in natural fibres.

Emma-Jane   **020 8599 3004**
www.emma-jane.com
Bras and underwear manufacturer of the zip and drop-cup
style. Highly recommended by the Royal College of
Midwives. Also swimwear and supportive hosiery.

Figleaves   **0800 279 2557**
www.figleaves.com
Possibly the best online and mail order catalogue for lingerie
shopping. All brands, all sizes stocked and delivered within
24hrs – with free returns if they don't fit

Mothernature   **0161 485 7359**
www.mothernaturebras.co.uk
Comfortable pregnancy and breastfeeding bras

ISABELLA OLIVER

WWW.ISABELLAOLIVER.COM 0870 2407612

Blooming Marvellous

BABY ON BOARD

Call us for a FREE 92 page catalogue and quote code BD4M.

0870 751 8977
www.bloomingmarvellous.co.uk/bd

Visit our shop in Fulham: 725 Fulham Road,
London, SW6 5UL. (Tel: 020 7371 0500)

Maternity • Baby • Nursery

JoJo Maman Bébé

Call for a 144 page catalogue, quoting BD42

0870 241 0451

www.jojomamanbebe.co.uk

Retail shops:
1259 Finchley Rd, London NW11
68 Northcote Road, London SW11   Allders of Croydon
House of Fraser Birmingham   Newport (sale shop)

54 Cross Street Islington London N1 2BA
020 7359 5791
Includes baby wear department
from birth to 4 years

Also at House of Fraser Guildford and
House of Fraser Birmingham

Head Office 020 8670 1144
www.maternus.co.uk

maternus&baby

**MATERNITY FASHION SO GOOD THAT
NINE MONTHS JUST ISNT ENOUGH**

**ITALIAN & SPANISH COLLECTIONS
LEADING BRANDS INCLUDING NOPPIES
BRA FITTING BY TRAINED STAFF
ALTERATION SERVICE AVAILABLE**

**COME AND VISIT
THE FRIENDLY TEAM
IN OUR BRANCHES ACROSS
SOUTH WEST LONDON**

3 Mortlake Terrace
KEW
Richmond Surrey TW9 3DT
0208 332 6506

157 Lower Richmond Road
PUTNEY
London SW15 1HH
0208 789 0329

119 Revelstoke Road
WIMBLEDON
London SW18 5NN
0208 879 3467

www.mums-2-be.co.uk

The baby of your dreams is on its way...

... the maternity and nursery store is already here

Chic maternity & baby wear and everything to set up the nursery in style.

SÉRAPHINE
CELEBRATING BIRTH

www.seraphine.com
Mail order: 020 7937 74 19

The
Maternity
Co.

A refreshing look at maternity fashion!

The search for good quality maternity wear stops here!

A large range of european brands catering for all occasions, including the famous "Noppies" label.

42 Chiswick Lane, London W4 2JQ
Tel: 020 8995 4455
www.thematernityco.com

Open: Mon-Sat 10am-5.30pm

magazines

Angels & Urchins   020 7603 13666
www.angelsandurchins.co.uk
London-based family lifestyle magazine published quarterly.

Baby & Toddler Gear   0870 262 6900
www.babyandtoddlergear.co.uk
Bi-annual specialising in in-depth product reviews, price comparisons and detailed fabric swatches

BBC Parenting   020 7733 4955
Monthly parenting magazine for pre-school children.

Bumps & Babies (NCT)   0870 444 8707
www.nctpregnancyandbabycare.com
A free publication given out to new members of the NCT and at some antenatal checks at 20 weeks

Families Magazine   020 8696 9680
www.familiesmagazine.co.uk
Free monthly magazine covering London (South West, South East, East etc and the Thames Valley) (See advert on page 48)

Flying Start   01772 499 014
www.flyingstartmagazine.co.uk
Free to parents and carers of 0-6yrs in the North West and more recently across the UK

I'm Pregnant   0800 318 846
www.impregnantmagazine.co.uk

Junior Magazine   01858 438 874
www.juniormagazine.co.uk
Monthly glossy aimed at high income, highly fashion conscious parents (also Junior Pregnancy & Baby)

London's Child   01242 519 936
www.childmagazines.co.uk
Quarterly magazine for parents with young children

Mother & Baby Magazine   01733 555 161
Best selling monthly magazine with good advice, product reviews and reader experiences

Parents Directory Publications   01243 527 605
Produced quarterly and distributed throughout London (editions are South West London, North West London and Central London

Practical Parenting   01444 475 675
From pregnancy to early childhood.

Pregnancy & Birth   020 7347 1800
www.pregnancyandbirth.co.uk

Prima Baby   01858 438 838
www.primababy.co.uk

Right Start   020 7878 2336
Produced in association with Tumble Tots for parents with children aged 6mths-7yrs. Comes out 6 times a year

The Lady   020 7379 4717
www.lady.co.uk

Twins & Supertwins   01843 845 885
www.twinsmag.com

A monitor is a must-have as soon as you decide to move the baby out of your own bedroom, and would like the comfort of seeing and hearing your baby when you are not in the room. The new sound and movement monitors are surprisingly inexpensive and the new baby camera monitors are a feat of technical innovation. We particularly like the new Board Bug which evolves from being a baby monitor worn as a wrist watch, to a toddler monitor keeping your little adventurer within reach.

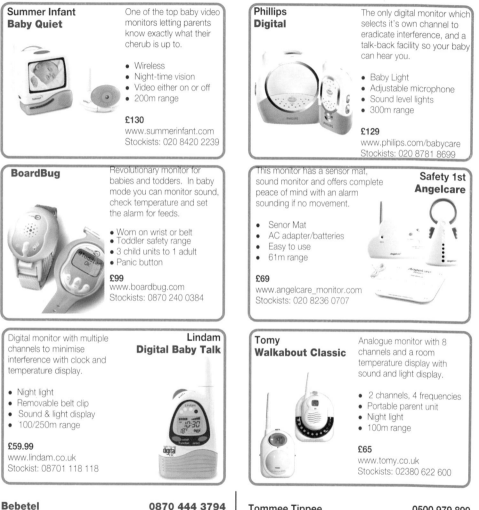

Summer Infant Baby Quiet

One of the top baby video monitors letting parents know exactly what their cherub is up to.

- Wireless
- Night-time vision
- Video either on or off
- 200m range

£130
www.summerinfant.com
Stockists: 020 8420 2239

Phillips Digital

The only digital monitor which selects it's own channel to eradicate interference, and a talk-back facility so your baby can hear you.

- Baby Light
- Adjustable microphone
- Sound level lights
- 300m range

£129
www.philips.com/babycare
Stockists: 020 8781 8699

BoardBug

Revolutionary monitor for babies and todders. In baby mode you can monitor sound, check temperature and set the alarm for feeds.

- Worn on wrist or belt
- Toddler safety range
- 3 child units to 1 adult
- Panic button

£99
www.boardbug.com
Stockists: 0870 240 0384

Safety 1st Angelcare

This monitor has a sensor mat, sound monitor and offers complete peace of mind with an alarm sounding if no movement.

- Senor Mat
- AC adapter/batteries
- Easy to use
- 61m range

£69
www.angelcare_monitor.com
Stockists: 020 8236 0707

Lindam Digital Baby Talk

Digital monitor with multiple channels to minimise interference with clock and temperature display.

- Night light
- Removable belt clip
- Sound & light display
- 100/250m range

£59.99
www.lindam.co.uk
Stockist: 08701 118 118

Tomy Walkabout Classic

Analogue monitor with 8 channels and a room temperature display with sound and light display.

- 2 channels, 4 frequencies
- Portable parent unit
- Night light
- 100m range

£65
www.tomy.co.uk
Stockists: 02380 622 600

Bebetel   0870 444 3794
www.bestworld.co.uk
Bebetel listening device. At last! Relax on holiday. Bebetel will turn your mobile phone into a baby monitor. Zero interference and unlimited range.

Baby View Cam   0870 744 2298
www.babyviewcam.co.uk
BabyViewCam offers the largest range of great value, high quality video, audio and breathing monitors.

Tommee Tippee   0500 979 899
www.tommeetippee.com

Why Cry Analyser   01903 889 520
www.why-cry.co.uk
The WhyCry is a baby monitor for first time parents, to assist with the process of learning to interpret a baby's crying during the first 12 months. The device analyses the pitch of a baby's cries and gives the user a clear indication of why. The baby's cry is digitally analysed and transmitted to one of 5 simple 'expressions': Hunger; Boredom, Annoyed, Sleepy and Stressed.

London's favourite parenting magazine!

London's Child
The quarterly parenting magazine with a difference.
Pick a copy up Free at your local nursery or school.

child
MAGAZINE

The Croft, 9 Croft Street,
Cheltenham, GL53 0ED
T: +44 (0)1242 519936
F: +44 (0) 12142 243229
E: info@childmagazines.co.uk

Subscribe to London's Child for only £8
www.childmagazines.co.uk

angels&urchins

London's only family lifestyle magazine

targeting	parents with children ages 0-10 and expectant mums
published	four times a year
how to get a copy	by subscription (£10 for 4 issues) or free through schools, clubs, shops, doctors and crèches

To subscribe call 020 7603 1366 or email subs@angelsandurchins.co.uk
To advertise call 020 7603 1366 or email advertising@angelsandurchins.co.uk

Families® Magazines

Free useful local magazines for parents with young children and a brilliant website…

www.familiesmagazine.co.uk

FREE sample issue for your area **020 8696 9680**
editor@familiesmagazine.co.uk

Bespoke Mural Designs by

ELJ Design

For **exclusive** mural design including decoration of new and old nursery furniture and specialist paint effects

Simply call

Emma van Klaveren

07958 646 113

emma@eljdesign.co.uk

www.eljdesign.co.uk

murals

Cow Jumped over the Moon 020 8883 0888
www.thecowjumpedoverthemoon.com
Beautiful children's murals, paintings to order and hand-painted furniture

ELJ Design   07958 646 113
www.eljdesign.co.uk
Bespoke mural design and painting of old & new nursery furniture

Transformations   020 7737 4276
www.transformations.decor.org.uk
Beautiful murals - original or traditional designs, hand-painted furniture, paint effects and paintings to order.

name tapes

Don't think that this pursuit actually needs to include a needle and thread. Iron on, stick on and peel & press are all the rage. These suppliers still do the traditional embroidered name tapes as well as shoe stickers, bag tags and tapes that go on plastic (and in the dishwasher) so that you will no longer be left with six lids and only three beakers

Easy 2 Name   01635 298326
www.easy2name.com
Suppliers of dishwasher - proof stickers and iron-on tapes. We like the white transfer nametapes which are perfect for dark coloured socks

Stuck on You   0845 456 0014
www.stuckonyou.biz
We like the 0-5yrs nursery pack which includes 50 name labels (including telephone number), 20 shoe labels, 2 bag tags and 50 bottle/beaker stickers

Cash's (UK) Ltd   02476 466466
www.jjcash.co.uk
Traditional woven nametapes (maximum 30 characters). Also available from department stores

OFF TO NURSERY?
Use Easy2name

- Dishwasher & steriliser proof stickers
- Iron-on nametapes

For samples & & order form
Tel: 01635 298326 or
visit www.easy2name.com

nappies, cloth

ECO-DISPOSABLES

Eco-friendly disposables (around £35 for a box of 232 newborn size) are just beginning to take a hold in the UK market although they are still not generally stocked. Eco-friendly nappy sacks are due to be joining the range from Smilechild soon. Other brands include Tushies and Weenees

REUSABLE

You need around 15 cloth nappies to keep you fully stocked. There are a few to consider: traditional Terries, All-in-ones (cotton and integral waterproof outer); Two-Piece (fitted cotton terry with separate outer), Waterproof Pads (fitted into shaped pants) and Wraparounds (fitted cotton with ties). The suppliers below will help you figure out which system to use to suit your budget and lifestyle

Bambino Mio Ltd   **01604 883 777**
www.bambino.co.uk

Bumkins
www.bumkins.com
Reusable nappies from the USA available from Blooming Marvellous.

Cotton Bottoms   **0870 777 8899**
www.cottonbottoms.co.uk
Cutting edge design; high quality, modern cotton nappies laundered and delivered to your door.

Eco Babes   **01366 387 851**
www.eco-babes.co.uk
Online and mail order service specialising in reusable nappies and eco friendly baby clothing.

Eezy Peezy Cotton Nappy Hire   **01959 534207**
SE/SW London

Green Baby Company   **020 7226 9244**
www.greenbaby.co.uk

Kushies   **0870 120 2018**
www.thebabycatalogue.com
Washable nappies and a 100 page catalogue for all your baby's needs.

Little Green Earthlets   **01825 873301**
www.earthlets.co.uk

Lollipop Cloth Nappies   **07971 270 949**
www.teamlollipop.co.uk

Modern Baby   **0800 093 1500**
www.modernbaby.co.uk

Naturally Nappies   **0845 1664716**
www.naturallynappies.com
They stock all major brands except those they don't consider up to scratch. You can try before you buy which is the key to getting the right fit for your baby.

Plush Pants Cloth Nappies   **0161 485 4430**
www.plushpants.co.uk
Nappies, wraps, accessories, baby clothes and treats for mum too

Real Nappy Association   **020 8299 4519**
www.realnappy.com
Information on all nappy-related issues

Sam-I-Am   **01522 778 926**
www.sam-I-am.co.uk
Cloth nappies, covers and accessories; also facts and advice about real nappies.

Schmidt Natural Clothing   **01342 822169**
www.naturalclothing.co.uk

Smilechild   **0800 195 6982**
www.smilechild.co.uk
Biodegradable disposables, Moltex, Tushies, Motherease, natural wipes and creams

Snuggle Bums Nappies   **020 8361 9087**
www.snugglebumsnappies.co.uk

Spirit of Nature Ltd   **0845 200 6745**
www.spiritofnature.co.uk

The Buzzness   **01280 841 262**
www.thebuzzness.co.uk
Online retailer of a good range of washable nappies

The Nice Nappy Company   **01424 756839**
www.nicenappy.co.uk

Twinkle on the Web   **0118 934 2120**
www.twinkleontheweb.co.uk
Free advice on choosing washable nappies, and a huge range in stock

nappy laundry

Cotton Bottoms   **0870 777 8899**
www.cottonbottoms.co.uk
Offering a laundry service, collecting the dirties and supplying fresh ones weekly

Nappycare   **020 8998 8799**
www.nappycare.co.uk

Nappy Express   **020 8361 4040**
www.nappyexpress.co.uk

Number 1 for Nappies   **01992 713 665**
www.numberonefornappies.co.uk

nearly new

Baby London   07947 143 667
www.baby-london.com
Nearly new baby equipment found, sold and bought including carriage prams, buggies, cots, furniture and garden toys.

Baby Things   01453 885594
www.baby-things.com
Online service for second hand baby goods.

Boomerang   020 7610 5232
69 Blythe Road, , W14 0HP
www.boomerangonline.co.uk

Bunnys   020 8875 1228
201 Replingham Road, SW18

Chocolate Crocodile   020 8985 3330
39 Morpeth Road, E9

eBay   www.ebay.co.uk
Pick up some amazing bargains via this online auction website.

Little Trading Company   020 8742 3152
7 Bedford Corner, The Avenue, W4

Merry-Go-Round   020 8985 6308
22 Clarence Road, E5

Mum & Me   020 8255 0073
61 High Street, TW11

Pixies   020 8995 1568
14 Fauconberg Road, W4 3JY
www.pixiesonline.co.uk

Rainbow   020 8340 8003
249 & 253 Archway Road, N6

Rocking Horse   020 8542 4666
600 Kingston Road, SW20

Simply Outgrown   020 8801 0568
360 Lordship Lane, N17

Swallows and Amazons   020 8673 0275
91 Nightingale Lane, Clapham, SW12

The Rocking Horse   020 8542 4666
600 Kingston Road, SW20

Yummy Tots   020 8891 4678
6 Crown Road, St Margarets, TW1
www.yummytots.com

nursery furniture

Ark Rugs   01273 770 877
www.arkrugs.co.uk

Aspace   01985 301 222
The Old Silk Works, Beech Avenue, BA12 8LX
www.aspaceuk.com
A full range of beautiful beds, wardrobes, chests of drawers, etc, with bedding to match.

Baby Flair   0870 246 1875
www.babyflair.co.uk
Unique furniture and linens including cots, bumpers, rockers and fleece sleeping bags in natural colours. Also stocks good swimwear

Billie Bond Designs   01245 360 164
Warners Farm, Howe Street, CM3 1BL
www.billiebond.co.uk
Specialists in children's hand-painted beds, cots, toy boxes. Also offers personalised gifts such as hairbrushes, stools and door plaques.

The Children's   020 7737 7303
Furniture Company
PO Box 31681, SW2 5ZE
www.thechildrensfurniturecompany.com
Exclusive range of children's furniture in hardwoods or painted finishes

Dutailier   020 8810 8818
www.dutailier.co.uk
Manufacturers of the Glider rocking chair and foot rest. In four wood finishes and a good range of different fabrics

Global Nursery Products   01244 348 869
www.globalnurseryproducts.com
Manufacturer of the original Bedside Cot (which align with your own bed). Also pushchairs, highchairs, cribs and changing bags

It's Childsplay   01637 830 896
www.itschildsplay.co.uk
Makers of children's wooden furniture

Joshua Jones   01258 858 470
www.joshua-jones.co.uk
Beautiful hand-painted nursery furniture tailor-made to recreate favourite scenes from children's story and verse

Kantara Furniture   01594 860 328
Mail order shelving including a bi-plane and tri-plane

To the Manor Barn   01672 811713
www.tothemanorbarn.co.uk

lionwitchwardrobe   020 8318 2070
www.lionwitchwardrobe.co.uk
Hand-crafted contemporary furniture for style-conscious parents, including a bespoke design service

ASPACE

REAL FURNITURE - FOR KIDS

ASPACE designs & builds furniture for children from their early years to mid-teens. Our catalogue is bursting with beds, bookcases, cupboards, desks, chairs, trolleys & sleepover truckles.

Ordering is simple, we deliver promptly, everything is easily assembled, and if you're not entirely happy, we'll be happy to take it back!

Get your free ASPACE catalogue today call 01985 301222 or visit :

www.aspaceuk.com

Please quote ref: LB4F

RETAIL SHOPS

E18
Tom Thumb Fantasy Designs   020 8504 8334
227a High Road, E18 2PB

N8
Mini Kin   020 8341 6898
22 Broadway Parade, Crouch End, N8

N22
Infantasia   020 8889 1494
103 Wood Green Shopping Centre, N22

NW3
Humla   020 7794 7877
13 Flask Walk, NW3

NW2
Ikea   020 8208 5600
Brent Park, NW2

NW4
Baybiz   020 8203 3377
www.baybiz.co.uk
Take the stress out of nursery shopping. Let Baybiz co-ordinate your complete baby shop in one personal consultation

NW7
The Children's Room   020 8959 2978
Sequora House, 4 Uphill Drive, NW7 4RR

NW8
St John's Wood Interiors   020 7722 9204
27 St John's Wood High Street, NW8 7NH
A range of hand-painted nursery furniture including cots and beds, toy chests etc

Mark Wilkinson   020 7586 9579
41 St John's Wood High Street, NW8 7NJ

NW11
JoJo Maman Bebe   020 8731 8961
3 Ashbourne Parade, 1259 Finchley Road, NW11
www.JoJoMamanBebe.co.uk
Furniture and accessories for the kitchen, bedroom, bathroom, playroom and garden

SW3
Daisy & Tom   020 7352 5000
181 King's Road, SW3
www.daisyandtom.com

Dragons of Walton Street   020 7589 3795
23 Walton Street, SW3 2HX
www.dragonsofwaltonstreet.com
For the finest handpainted children's furniture, fabrics and interior design

Nursery Window   020 7581 3358
83 Walton Street, SW3 2HP
www.nurserywindow.co.uk
Exclusive accessories, fabrics, wallpapers, bedding and furniture

SW6
Babylist   020 7371 5145
50 Sullivan Road, SW6 3DX
www.babylist.co.uk
Beautiful range of nursery furniture including handmade oak cots and cot beds as well as bespoke mural designs.

Blue Lemon   020 7610 9464
160 Munster Road, SW6 5RA

Simon Horn   0207 736 1754
117-121 Wandsworth Bridge Road, SW6 2TP
www.simonhorn.com
Superb quality furniture for children that will last for generations

SW8
Lilliput   020 7720 5554
255-259 Queenstown Road, SW8 3NP
www.lilliput.com

SW10
Junior Living   020 7376 5001
293 Fulham Road, SW10 9PZ
www.juniorliving.co.uk

SW13
Tobias and the Angel   020 8296 0058
66-68 White Hart Lane, SW13 0PZ

SW15
Chic Shack   020 8785 7777
77 Lower Richmond Road, SW15 1ET
www.chicshack.net

SW19
Lilliput   020 8542 3542
100 Haydons Road, SW19
www.lilliput.com

W4
Red Studio   020 8994 7770
12a Spring Grove, W4 3NH

W11
Mark Wilkinson   020 7727 5814
126 Holland Park Avenue, W11

Natural Mat   020 7985 0474
99 Talbot Road, W11
www.naturalmat.com (see advert on page x)

The Nursery Window

www.nurserywindow.co.uk

Come to the Nursery Window to create your dream nursery from the little details - layette baskets, embroidered babygrows, to the big essentials - a solid oak cot bed and Moses baskets.

Choose from our range of fabrics, floor rugs, Cashmere and Lambswool blankets to wrap your baby in luxury.

To order a catalogue please call 01394460040 Otherwise come and vist us at:
Nursery Window
83 Walton Street
London
SW3 2HP
Tel:02075813358

THE SIMON HORN NURSERY COLLECTION

The Simon Horn Nursery Collection is an inspirational collection of 'metamorphic' furniture designed to change as your child grows up... from tiny baby to teenager and beyond. Handmade from hardwoods, these pieces will become family heirlooms. For a sixteen page brochure detailing the complete Nursery Collection, including furniture, bedlinens and accessories, please telephone 020 7736 1754 or fax 020 7736 3522 www.simonhorn.com

THE CHILDREN'S FURNITURE COMPANY

"FUN FURNITURE FROM CHILDHOOD AND BEYOND"

Telephone: 020 7737 7303
www.thechildrensfurniturecompany.com

Maternity Baby Nursery

JoJo Maman Bébé

Call for a 144 page catalogue, quoting BE42

0870 241 0451
www.jojomamanbebe.co.uk

Retail shops:
1259 Finchley Rd, London NW11
68 Northcote Road, London SW11   Allders of Croydon
House of Fraser Birmingham   Newport (sale shop)

THE FINEST HAND-PAINTED **CHILDRENS** FURNITURE & FABRICS

Did you know that in your garden, in every wood, meadow and hedgerow hundreds of Flower Fairies work and play, caring for flowers and trees.

Visit the enchanted world of Dragons of Walton Street where you can invent your own fairies.

DRAGONS
of Walton Street

Online www.dragonsofwaltonstreet.com / **London Showroom** 23 Walton Street, London SW3 2HX 0207 589 3795 /
Outlet Store & Customer Service The Dragons Studios, Henfield Road, Small Dole, West Sussex BN5 9XH 01903 816916

Flower Fairies © The Estate of Cicely Mary Barker 2001. Licensed by Copyrights Group - By Dragons of Walton Street

Tel: 020 7371 5145   www.babylist.co.uk

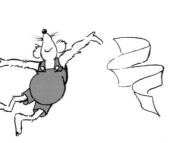

You deliver the baby, we'll deliver the rest.

Babylist is the U.K.'s premier advisory and supply service which helps you, the mother-to-be, select and source the right equipment for your newborn baby.

During one private consultation in our London showroom, our consultants will provide you with expert, independent advice tailored to your personal needs.

Babylist provides a one-stop service where you can buy everything you need for your new arrival; bespoke and exclusive products as well as everyday items.

Babylist then delivers anywhere in the world, right to your door!

No pressure, no stress, just a professional and thoughtful solution to suit increasingly busy lives.

nursery goods

NURSERY ADVISORY SERVICES

You can choose to shop without actually having to set foot on a pavement. These three companies advise you on the products that you will actually use, recommend the best brands and have all the goods shipped to your door closer to your due date. All by appointment only

Baby Concierge   **020 8202 4060**
3 Hollyview Close, NW4 3SZ
www.babyconcierge.co.uk
Personal baby shopping at high street prices. Expert advice and guidance. All major brands and many more exclusive.

Babylist   **020 7371 5145**
50 Sullivan Road, SW6 3DX
www.babylist.co.uk
Unique advisory and supply service for all your baby's needs.

Baybiz   **020 8203 3377**
www.baybiz.co.uk
Take the stress out of nursery shopping. Let Baybiz co-ordinate your complete baby shop in one personal consultation.

RETAIL

(see end for the John Lewis and Mothercare branches across London)

EAST LONDON

Sensations   020 7247 6361
33-35 Commercial Road, E1

Jelly Tots   020 8374 5212
97 Middlesex Street, E1

Potty People   020 7729 2217
316 Bethnal Green Road, E2

Khalsa   020 7729 3286
388 Bethnal Green Road, E2

Kiddi Centre   020 8809 4251
147 Clapton Common, E5

Freedman at Salters   020 8472 2892
17-19 Barking Road, East Ham, E6

E.Gibbons   020 8985 3129
7-17 Amhurst Road, E8

Family Care   020 7254 8720
90-94 Kingsland High Street, E8

London Prams   020 7537 4117
175-179 East India Dock Road, Poplar, E14

Mothercare   020 85345714
33-34 The Mall, Stratford, E15

Baby This 'N' Baby That   020 8527 4002
359 Forest Road, E17

NORTH LONDON

Baby Munchkins   020 7684 5994
186 Hoxton Street, N1
www.babymunchkins.com

Green Baby Company   020 7226 4345
345 Upper Street, N1 0PD
www.greenbabyco.com
Baby equipment, linens, furniture, eco-friendly clothing,
reusable nappies and gifts.

Cuddlepie   020 8455 6991
4 Rowan Walk, N2

Rub A Dub Dub   020 8342 9898
15 Park Road, Crouch End, N8
Also stocks linens, shoes, clothes and reusable nappies.

Mini Kin   020 8341 6898
22 Broadway Parade, N8
Stockists of a range of baby equipment from pushchairs to
potties.

All Seasons Nursery Shop   **020 8445 6314**
654-656 High Road, Tally Ho Corner, N12

Totland   020 8808 3466
4 Bruce Grove, N17
Baby equipment stockist including cots, prams, pushchairs
and general baby goods

Cheeky Kids   020 8807 5898
175 Fore Street, N18
Stockists of baby equipment and inexpensive baby clothes.

London Nursery Supplies   020 8889 3003
Hardy Passage, Berners Road, N22

Infantasia   020 8889 1494
103 Wood Green Shopping Centre, N22
www.infantasia.co.uk
Stockists of a wide range of baby equipment including cots,
pushchairs (and pushchair repairs)

NORTH WEST LONDON

Babies R Us   020 8209 0019
Tilling Road, NW2

Just Babies   020 7916 8762
38-46 Malden Road, Kentish Town, NW5

Baby Munchkins   020 7684 5994
91 Kentish Town Road, NW5
www.babymunchkins.com

Bush Babes   020 8203 2111
Fiveways Corner, Watford Way, NW7

Yummy Kids   020 8201 8871
1-2 Russel Parade, Golders Green Road, NW11

SOUTH EAST LONDON

G. Swaddling Ltd   020 8697 2992
21-23 Rushey Green, SE6

Babies R Us   020 7732 7322
760 Old Kent Road, SE15

Wear & Cheer   020 7635 9252
160-162 Rye Lane, SE15
Baby equipment, clothing and nursery furnishings.

Goldilocks   020 7231 8550
214 Jamaica Road, SE16

Kindercare   020 7703 0488
207 Walworth Road, SE17

SOUTH WEST LONDON

Conran Shop   020 7589 7401
81 Fulham Road, SW3

Daisy & Tom   020 7349 5810
181-183 King's Road, SW3 5EB

The White House   020 7629 3521
102 Waterford Road, SW6 2HA
www.the-white-house.com
Also baby clothing and nightwear.

Babyworld   020 7386 1904
239 Munster Road, SW6
www.babyworldlondon.co.uk

Lilliput   020 7720 5554
255-259 Queenstown Road, SW8
www.lilliput.com

Greater Tomorrow   020 7737 5276
80 Atlantic Road, SW9

Babies Product Centre   020 8333 9067
76 Balham High Road, SW12

Bebeworld   020 8675 8871
191 Balham High Road, SW12

Lilliput   020 8542 3542
100-106 Haydons Road, SW19
www.lilliput.com

WEST LONDON

Young Smarties   020 7723 6519
64 Edgware Road, W2

W J Daniel   020 8567 6789
96-122 Uxbridge Road, W13

Mothercare

115 High Street North, E6	020 8472 4948
33-34 The Mall, E15	020 8534 5714
448 Holloway Road, N7	020 7607 0915
38-40 High Road, N22	020 8888 6920
Brent Cross Shopping Centre, NW4	020 8202 5377
146 High Street, SE9	020 8859 7957
41 Riverdale High Street, SE13	020 8852 2167
2 Aylesham Centre, SE15	020 7358 0093
Surrey Quays, SE16	020 7237 2025
62 Powis Street, SE18	020 8854 3540
316 North End Road, SW6	020 7381 6387
416 Brixton Road, SW9	020 7733 1494
71 St John's Road, SW11	020 7228 0391
14-16 High Street, SW17	020 8862 3947
461 Oxford Street, W1	020 7629 6621
1-8 The Broadway, W5	020 8579 6181
26 Kings Mall Shopping, W6	020 8741 0514
64 The Broadway, W13	020 8567 7067
www.mothercare.com	

John Lewis

279-306 Oxford Street	020 7629 7711
Peter Jones, Sloane Square	020 7730 3434
Brent Cross Shopping Centre	020 8202 6535
www.johnlewis.com	

nursery goods: mail order

Babyamaze   **01452 741155**
www.babyamaze.co.uk
Baby and toddler goods

Baby Goods Direct   **01795 666 625**
www.babygoodsdirect

Babyneeds Superstore   **02380 454 544**
www.baby-needs.co.uk
Massive range of prams, buggies, cots, furniture, bedding,
carseats, toys, etc

Babyou   **01494 868 383**
www.babyou.com
Online retailer of nursery furniture, wooden toys, arts and craft
projects and carriers.

Babys Mart   **0870 787 8978**
www.babys-mart.co.uk

Bump to 3   **0970 6060 276**
www.bumpto3.com
From the makers of Grobag, this Bump to 3 catalogue
includes all of Grobag's sleeping bag range and additional
products through to pre-school

interior design - high chairs - storage solutions - potty training - bath toys - safety essentials - swimming aids

Over 1000 products designed to make your life as a parent easier

Phone **0870 850 6000** for your copy of our FREE catalogue

www.gltc.co.uk   Please quote ref GBAB4

The **Great Little Trading** Co.

Practical products for
parents and kids

travel essentials - mealtime accessories - personalised gifts - furniture - books - educational play - arts&crafts

Cheeky Rascals   0870 873 2600
www.cheekyrascals.co.uk
Mail order company with a good selection of products for babies and children (such as the BuggyBoard).

Cradle And All   01767 600 601
www.cradleandall.co.uk
Comprehensive online store offering nursery goods from well-known brands.

Great Little Trading Company   0870 2414081
www.gltc.co.uk
Hundreds of practical products designed to make your life as a parent a little bit easier (mail order and online)

Hoppa Board Ltd   020 8809 4097
www.hoppaboard.co.uk

Huggababy   01874 711 629
www.huggababy.co.uk
Pregnancy bras, baby slings, natural lambskins and soft leather shoes.

Just Kidding   0121 622 3100
www.just-kidding.com
Comprehensive range of baby equipment and nursery furniture

Little Green Earthlets   01825 873301
www.earthlets.co.uk

Littlebugs   01934 710 340
www.littlebugs.co.uk
Hard -to -find nursery goods online.

Nurserygoods   01858 469162
www.nursurygoods.com

Perfectly Happy People (PHP)   0870 120 2018
www.thebabycatalogue.com

Sleepy Bunnies   01865 300310
Extendable sleeping bags suitable from 3mths to 3yrs

Smilechild   0800 1956 982
www.smilechild.co.uk

The Nursery Emporium   01380 859171
www.nursery-emporium.com

Two Left Feet   01234 857 777
www.twoleftfeet.co.uk
The UK's largest baby goods website and showroom in Bedford. Search by product or manufacturer

Urchin   01672 518 645
www.urchin.co.uk
They supply the best, brightest, most innovative, useful and good-looking products for 0-8yrs. Furniture, nursery goods, travel items, toys, kitchen and bathroom products - all delivered hassle-free. Free catalogue by phone or online

nursery interior design

Dragons of Walton Street   020 7589 3795
23 Walton Street, SW3
www.dragonsofwaltonstreet.com
For the finest handpainted children's furniture, fabrics and interior design

Pom Pom   020 7244 9296
22 Astwood Mews, SW7 4DE

The Nesting Company   020 7371 2717
www.thenestingcompany.com
Interior design service creating and installing stylish and contemporary nurseries that fit perfectly into your home.

The Uncommon Touch   020 7228 1487
184 Northcote Road, SW11 6RE
Full design service for children's rooms including fabrics, wallpapers and furnishings. Good place to get your ideas formalised.

Uglows   020 8529 0011
28-30 Station Road, E4 7BE
Comprehensive range of nursery fabrics and furnishings, linens, duvet covers. Full make-up services also available

ORGANIC PAINTS

Auro Organic Paint Supplies   01799 543 077
www.auroorganic.co.uk
Environmentally friendly paints

Charter Design   01924 413 813
Lead-free paints for wood and plaster

Ecos Organic Paints   01524 852 371
Odourless, solvent-free organic paints and interior/exterior woodstains

visit www.babydirectory.com

Pom Pom

Bringing children's imagination to life

nurseries - playrooms - bedrooms - bathrooms
We do it all: from sourcing a single cushion to creating a complete room

Call Daisy or Suzannah to arrange a free initial consultation
T: 020 73419321   E: imagination@pom-pom.net
W: www.pom-pom.net

photographers & portraits

Carolyn Cowan 020 7701 3845
www.mooncycles.co.uk
Ordinary people, extraordinary photographs

Carolyn Weller 020 7272 5545
25 yrs experience photographing babies and children in their
homes (North London only)

Diana Vowles 020 8452 0715
www.dianavowles.co.uk
Black and white photographs taken at home or on location

Family Portraits 020 8693 3925
www.familyportraits.uk.com
Exceptional black and white hand-printed photographs of
children.

Haydn Photography 0800 781 0877
www.hphoto.co.uk

Jo Newman 020 8776 7698
www.jonewman.co.uk

Julia Laderman: 07803 121 923
Body Painter for pregnant women
www.embody.org.uk
Become a canvas for the day and remember your pregnancy
forever.

Kate Magson/Kiddipics 07941 688 012
www.kiddipics.com
Natural pictures of your babies and children at home, studio
or location

Little Darlings Photography 07775 686 505
www.littledarlingsphotography.com

Miche Gray-Newton 02073 769 649
Enchanting individual and family portraits in oil or
watercolours

Nicola Hippisley 020 7690 1957
Fun and funky child/family photography in studio or park.
Specialist in NCT group shots

Pamela Lloyd-Jones 0208 993 5697
www.pamelalloydjones.com

RebeccaLouise 020 7702 9280
Photographics
www.rebeccalouise.com
Rebecca Portsmouth captures your child just the way they
are, in your own home or close by using natural light

Robin Farquhar-Thomson 020 7622 3630
www.robinft.co.uk
Wonderful pictures of children

Family Portraits

David and Pia Randall-Goddard
www.familyportraits.uk.com

East Dulwich 020 8693 3925

CAROLYN
COWAN
portrait
photography
020 7701 3845
www.mooncycles.co.uk

Sara Langdon Photography 020 8964 1786
www.langdonphotography.com

Stacey Mutkin 020 7221 0503
www.mutkinphoto.com
Black & white portrait photography at home or on location

Tia May 020 7731 4988
www.tiamay.com
Natural and happy photographs of children

Vibeke Dahl Photography 020 8876 8113
www.dahlphotography.com

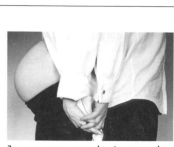

Jo newman photography
020 8776 7698
www.jonewman.co.uk

TIA MAY
Natural & happy photographs
of children
020 7731 4988

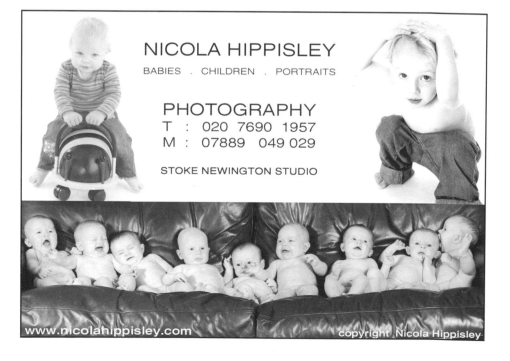

NICOLA HIPPISLEY

BABIES . CHILDREN . PORTRAITS

PHOTOGRAPHY
T : 020 7690 1957
M : 07889 049 029

STOKE NEWINGTON STUDIO

www.nicolahippisley.com

copyright Nicola Hippisley

CAROLYN WELLER • Photographer

Beautiful informal timeless b/w & colour photographs.

Taken in the comfort of your home with no obligation to buy.

25 years experience photographing babies children & families.

Carolyn is based in London N6. For details or to book, call her on

020 7272 5545

or to view

www.carolynweller.com

CAROLYN COWAN

portrait photography

020 7701 3845

www.mooncycles.co.uk

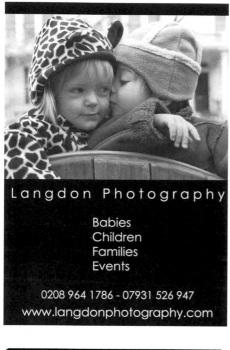

Langdon Photography

Babies
Children
Families
Events

0208 964 1786 - 07931 526 947
www.langdonphotography.com

Kate Magson
photography

natural portraits of
your babies & children
tel: 07941 688 012

www.kiddipics.com
enquiries@kiddipics.com

MOBILE BABY
PHOTOGRAPHY

0800 781 0877

Haydn & Co.
BABY PHOTOGRAPHY

Gallery and
online booking

www.
hphoto
.co.uk

Fine Art Portraits
of Babies and
Children.

www.
dahlphotography.
com

0208 876 8113

ROBIN FARQUHAR-THOMSON
Wonderful pictures of children. 020 7622 3630
www.robinft.co.uk

RebeccaLouise
Photographics

Capturing your
child just the way
they are

www.rebeccalouise.com
t 020 7702 9280

PORTRAIT
Drawings and Paintings

Pamela Lloyd-Jones
020 8993 5697
website: www.pamelalloydjones.com

s t a c e y   m u t k i n
ARPS LBIPP

black & white portrait photography

sessions at home or on location

t: 020 7221 0503

m: 07976 431 630

www.mutkinphoto.com

Diana Vowles
Images of childhood

Naturalistic black and white photographs
of children at home or on location, printed
and framed to fine art archival standards.

email info@dianavowles.co.uk
website www.dianavowles.co.uk

020 8452 0715

pram & buggy repairs

Barnes Buggy Repair Centre   020 8543 0505
278 Upper Richmond Road, SW15

Bebeworld   020 8675 8871
191 Balham High Road, SW12

Beryl Gerwood   01732 847 790
Restores and sells traditional coach prams

Infantasia   020 8889 1494
103 Wood Green Shopping Centre, N22

London Nursery Supplies   020 8889 3003
Hardy Passage, Berners Road, N22

Mamas & Papas Repairs   01604 597 700

Nanny's Prams Restoration   01953 884 164
30 Swaffam Road, Watton, IP25 6LA
Traditional coach built pram repairs

Soup Dragon   020 8348 0224
N8 & SE22

WJ Daniel & Co   020 8567 6789
96-122 Uxbridge Road, W13

Although many London houses and flats cannot accommodate the classic carriage pram, they do offer parents a supremely elegant and old-fashioned appeal. Otherwise you can opt the lightweight pushchair frame with a carrycot that can be swapped for a pushchair seat or car seat (a 3-in-1). Or a pushchair with a reclining seat (a 2-in-1).

SilverCross Balmoral

This classic hand-made pram will give your baby the most luxurious childhood experience. And will no doubt maintain or double its value over the years.

- Rigid steel body
- Hand sprung chassis
- Leather suspension
- Chrome shopping tray
- Mattress & changing bag

£850
www.silvercross.co.uk
Stockists: 0870 840 6727

Quinny Freestyle

This has the contemporary feel of an all-terrain pushchair with the elegance of a traditional carrycot. It is easy to fold and has removable wheels.

- 3-in-1
- Reversible seat
- Air tyres
- Mesh shopping basket

£250
www.quinny.com
Stockists: 020 8236 0707

Hauck Mini Star M360

This has a carrycot, and a car seat/pushchair frame to complete the travel system. Mid-size swivel wheels makes for easy manoeuvring around town.

- 3-in-1
- Pneumatic tyres
- Multi-position seat
- Large shopping basket

£225
www.hauckuk.com
Stockists: 0870 840 6727

Chicco Cortina

This carrycot, car seat and pushchair fit together very easy with one click, and with twist handles which rotate to 8 different positions' it's very comfortable to push

- 3-in-1
- Adjustable handle
- Large pneumatic tyres
- Thermo regulation system

£380
www.chicco.co.uk
Stockists: 01623 750 870

Maclaren Global

In pram mode this pram reclines fully and has a cosy and enclosed feel with luxuriously padded seat and side wings. Accommodates the Britax 0+ car seat.

- 2-in-1
- 5 position backrest
- Washable fabric
- Lockable swivel wheels

£190
www.maclarenbaby.com
Stockists: 020 7385 5338

Graco Quattro Tour TS

This spacious travel system has a bigger than usual (and easy to access) shopping basket and folds down simply and easily. One click to add their AutoBaby car seat.

- 2-in-1
- 5 position backrest
- Washable fabric
- Fits Britax 0+ car seat

£199
www.graco.co.uk
Stockists: 0870 909 0501

Other brands

Britax
www.britax.co.uk
01264 386 034

Bebecar
www.bebecar.co.uk
020 8201 0505

Cosatto
www.cosatto.com
0870 050 5900

Emmaljunga
www.emmaljunga.co.uk
0800 652 8007

Johnston Prams
www.johnstonprams.co.uk
02890 770 779

Mamas & Papas
www.mamasandpapas.co.uk
0870 830 7700

For London stockists please see nursery goods on page 57)

Top Online Stockists:

www.babygoodsdirect.co.uk
www.babymunchkins.com
www.pushchairs.co.uk
www.londonprams.co.uk
www.practicalpushchairs.co.uk
www.pramsdirect.co.uk
www.twoleftfeet.co.uk
www.vanblanken.co.uk

This may well be your biggest purchase, and the choice is large. Many lifestyles will dictate two (city pushchair that fits easily into the back of a car or bus and an all-terrain for wet weekends in the countryside). Below are our favourites based on style, practicality and value. Most of these models come as prams and evolve into pushchairs as your baby matures.

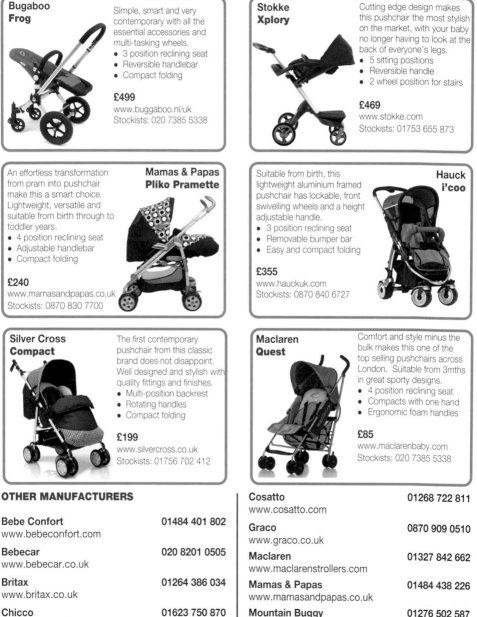

Bugaboo Frog

Simple, smart and very contemporary with all the essential accessories and multi-tasking wheels.
- 3 position reclining seat
- Reversible handlebar
- Compact folding

£499
www.buggaboo.nl/uk
Stockists: 020 7385 5338

Stokke Xplory

Cutting edge design makes this pushchair the most stylish on the market, with your baby no longer having to look at the back of everyone's legs.
- 5 sitting positions
- Reversible handle
- 2 wheel position for stairs

£469
www.stokke.com
Stockists: 01753 655 873

Mamas & Papas Pliko Pramette

An effortless transformation from pram into pushchair make this a smart choice. Lightweight, versatile and suitable from birth through to toddler years.
- 4 position reclining seat
- Adjustable handlebar
- Compact folding

£240
www.mamasandpapas.co.uk
Stockists: 0870 830 7700

Hauck i'coo

Suitable from birth, this lightweight aluminium framed pushchair has lockable, front swivelling wheels and a height adjustable handle.
- 3 position reclining seat
- Removable bumper bar
- Easy and compact folding

£355
www.hauckuk.com
Stockists: 0870 840 6727

Silver Cross Compact

The first contemporary pushchair from this classic brand does not disappoint. Well designed and stylish with quality fittings and finishes.
- Multi-position backrest
- Rotating handles
- Compact folding

£199
www.silvercross.co.uk
Stockists: 01756 702 412

Maclaren Quest

Comfort and style minus the bulk makes this one of the top selling pushchairs across London. Suitable from 3mths in great sporty designs.
- 4 position reclining seat
- Compacts with one hand
- Ergonomic foam handles

£85
www.maclarenbaby.com
Stockists: 020 7385 5338

OTHER MANUFACTURERS

Bebe Confort www.bebeconfort.com	01484 401 802
Bebecar www.bebecar.co.uk	020 8201 0505
Britax www.britax.co.uk	01264 386 034
Chicco www.chicco.com	01623 750 870

Cosatto www.cosatto.com	01268 722 811
Graco www.graco.co.uk	0870 909 0510
Maclaren www.maclarenstrollers.com	01327 842 662
Mamas & Papas www.mamasandpapas.co.uk	01484 438 226
Mountain Buggy www.mountainbuggy.com	01276 502 587

The appeal of the all-terrains has grown enormously in recent years. They not only cope well with the wet and muddy UK climate, but are surprisingly versatile across London's parks and pavements. They are heavier, bulkier and take up more boot space than lightweight pushchairs – so if you've got a small car do experiment first.

Mountain Buggy Breeze

Suitable from birth, this lightweight aluminium framed 3-wheeler folds easily, quickly and compactly with no need to remove the wheels.

- 3 position reclining seat
- No puncture tyres
- Very lightweight
- Fits into small cars
- Available in 4 colours
- **£355**

www.mountainbuggy.com
Stockists: 0870 840 6727

Graco Expedition

Suitable from birth, this lightweight aluminium framed 3-wheeler folds easily, quickly and compactly with no need to remove the wheels.

- 2 position reclining seat
- Soft-grip handlebar
- Handbrake and tether
- Large shopping basket
- Soft seat pad
- **£120**

www.graco.co.uk
Stockists: 0870 909 0501

Quinny Formula

We like this rugged design and the innovative automatically tilting steering wheel which can be locked. Also has a hand and foot brake.

- Aluminium wheels
- Adjustable handlebar
- Smooth suspension
- Integrated folding mechanism
- **£240**

www.quinny.com
Stockists: 020 8236 0707

Urban Detour Glacier

Suitable from birth this 3-wheeler comes with quick release wheels for easy transportation and storage. Also fits with car seat for 3in1versatility.

- Multi-seat positioning
- Covered bumper bar
- Pneumatic tyres/pump
- Viewing window in hood
- Newborn head support
- **£160**

www.mothercare.com
Stockists: 0845 330 4030

Maclaren MAC 3

This award winning stroller folds down to the smallest size and is fine even for small cars.

- 2 position reclining seat
- Lightweight chassis
- Adjustable hand brake
- Quick release wheels
- Storage in hood
- Coordinated accessories
- **£199**

www.maclarenbaby.com
Stockists: 020 7385 5338

Red Castle Shop n' Jogg

This light aluminium framed 3-wheeler with a lockable front swivel wheel has a 3 position seat and disc brakes.

- Removable cushion pad
- Integral rain cover
- Zip storage pocket
- Wheel covers
- **£299**

www.bettacare.co.uk

Stockists: 01293 851 896

Other Brands

Phil and Teds
www.philandteds.com

Baby Jogger   01455 550 600
www.babyjogger.co.uk

Babies R Us   0800 038 8899
www.babiesrus.co.uk

Babystyle   01509 816 444
www.babystyle.co.uk

Accessories

Abstract   01273 693 737
www.abstractuk.com
Fleecy blankets

Baby Direct   01273 693 737
www.baby-direct.com
Wide range of 3 wheelers for sale including correctly fitting accessories

Buggysnuggle Co   01869 340 694
www.buggysnuggle.com
Funky fleeces and fake fur buggysnuggles to keep your child warm and snug

rocking horses

Dreamland Rocking Horses 07976 739535
Winterhill House, Rocky Lane, RH16 4RN
Also games tables, chess sets etc

Quality Rocking Horses 01326 231 053
www.qualityrockinghorses.co.uk
We like their Western saddle, or removable tack with
coloured numnah. Prices from £825

GyGy 01630 638 978
www.gygy.co.uk
French brand of rocking horses. Small models from £60.

The Kensington Rocking 08704 464 687
Horse Company
www.kensington-rocking-horses.co.uk
Best selection of handmade rocking horses in UK.

Robert Mullis 01793 813583
www.rockinghorsesmaker.com
Robert Mullis is a craftsman producing traditional rocking
horses. In addition to the dappled greys made from
hardwoods you can also choose Muffin the Mule, a duck,
tortoise or The Loch Ness Monster

Rocking Horse Works 01952 811 266
www.rockinghorseworks.co.uk
Choose from dappled greys, Black Beauty or commission
your own

Stevenson Brothers 0808 108 6120
www.stevensonbros.com
Take your pick from the Golden Jubilee dappled grey
complete with the Queen's racing colours, or a limited edition
of the Serengeti Zebra. Prices start from £700. Website also
includes antique rocking horse sales

The Ringinglow Rocking 0800 0746104
Horse Company
www.dapplegrey.co.uk
Beautiful horses in polished hardwoods or rocking sheep
from £145

shoes & shoe shops

Birkenstock 0800 132 194
www.birkenstock.co.uk

Bobux 07002 466 466
www.bobux.com

Clarks 0990 785 886
www.clarks.com

Daisy Roots 01604 880 066
www.daisy-roots.com
Soft leather pull-on shoes in a great selection of colours and
designs.

Hippychick **01278 434 440**
www.hippychick.com
Their Shoo Shoos are imaginative and refreshingly different,
soft leather baby shoes (0-24 months)

Inch Blue 02920 865 863
www.inch-blue.com

Jester Boots 01243 790 009
www.jesterboots.co.uk
Have fun designing your own "stay-on" fleecy slipper shoes

Papillon Shoes 020 7834 1504
www.papillon4children.com
Ballerinas, moccasins, Jack Rogers flip flops and canvas
mules

Pom D'Api 020 7431 9532
www.pomdapi.fr

Start-rite 0800 783 2138
www.start-rite.co.uk

Shoozies 01726 851 755
www.shoozies.com
Hand -knitted baby booties in a great selection of colours

Starchild Shoes **01509 817 600**
www.starchildshoes.co.uk
Handmade soft leather shoes that stay on. Wonderful
designs for boys and girls (0-4yrs)

Timberland 020 7495 2133
www.timberland.com

Welligogs 01785 662 277
www.welligogs.com

SHOE SHOPS
EAST LONDON

Clarks Shoes 020 8534 7118
6 The Mall, E15
www.clarks.com

Starchild
Magic shoes for happy feet

Call for free brochure 01509 817 600
www.starchildshoes.co.uk

NORTH LONDON

Kiddie Shoes   020 8809 5059
8 Amhurst Parade, N16 5AA

Shoe & Fashion Boutique   020 8806 5581
28 Stamford Hill, N16 6XZ

NORTH WEST LONDON

Instep   020 8458 3911
117 Golders Green Road, NW11
www.instepshoes.co.uk

Brians Children's Shoes   020 8455 7001
2 Hallswelle Parade, Finchley Road, NW11 0DL

Look Who's Walking   020 7433 3855
78 Heath Street, NW3 1DN

Pom d'Api   020 7431 9532
33 Rosslyn Hill, NW3 1NH
www.pomdapi.fr

Clarks Shoes   020 8202 6423
Brent Cross, NW4 4FH
www.clarks.com

Sole Mates   020 8959 3649
42B The Broadway, Mill Hill, NW7 3LH

Instep   020 7722 7634
45 St John's Wood High Street, NW8 7NJ

SOUTH EAST LONDON

Merlin Shoes   020 8771 5194
44 Westow Street, SE19 3AH

David Thomas   020 8670 8100
8 Croxted Road, SE21 8SW
Uniform stockist for local Dulwich schools as well as Start-rite
and Dr Martens shoes.

Pares Footwear   020 8297 0785
24 Tranquil Vale, Blackheath, SE3 0AX

SOUTH WEST LONDON

Instep   020 8741 4114
80 Church Road, SW13 0DQ

One Small Step,   **020 8487 1288**
One Giant Leap
409 Upper Richmond Rd West, East Sheen, SW14
www.onesmallsteponegiantleap.com

Pied Piper   020 8788 1635
234 Upper Richmond Road, SW15 6TG

one small step one giant leap

Winner Best Children's Footwear Retailer 2004

5-6 Cheap Street
Bath BA1 1NE
☎ 01225 445345

409 Upper Richmond
Road West, East Sheen
London SW14 7NX
☎ 020 8487 1288

3 Blenheim Crescent
Notting Hill
London W11 2EE
☎ 020 7243 0535

Footwear
for the next
generation

www.onesmallsteponegiantleap.com

Clarks Shoes   020 8769 4308
170 High Road, Streatham, SW16 1BJ
www.clarks.com

Instep   020 8767 3395
11 Bellevue Road, SW17

Footsies   020 8947 3677
15 High Street, Wimbledon, SW19

Elys of Wimbledon   020 8946 9191
16 St George's Road, SW19 4DP
Stocks Clarks shoes and toys.

Start-rite   020 8946 9735
47 High Street, Wimbledon, SW19 5AX
www.start-rite.co.uk

Little Willies   020 7498 7899
16 The Pavement, Clapham, SW4 0HY

Gillingham & Co   020 7736 5757
365 Fulham Palace Road, SW6
www.gillinghamshoes.com

Pollyanna   020 7731 0673
811 Fulham Road, SW6 5HG

French Sole   020 7736 4780
184 Munster Road, SW6 6AU

Footsies   020 7589 4787
27 Bute Street, SW7 3EY

The Shoe Station   020 8940 9905
3 Station Approach, Kew Gardens, TW9 3PS
www.theshoestation.co.uk

CENTRAL & WEST LONDON

Clarks Shoes   020 7629 9609
476 Oxford Street, W1
www.clarks.com

Buckle My Shoe   020 7935 5589
19 St Christopher's Place, W1M 5HD

Pieton Shoes   020 7792 0707
9 Westbourne Grove, W2

Chiswick Shoes   020 8987 0525
1 Devonshire Road, W4 2EU

Stepping Out   020 8810 6141
106 Pitshanger Lane, W5 1QX

Millie Claude   020 7313 4634
202 Kensington Park Road, W11 1NR

One Small Step,   020 7243 0535
One Giant Leap
3 Blenheim Crescent, Notting Hill, W11 2EE
www.onesmallsteponegiantleap.com

swimwear & sun stuff

Baby Banz   01460 281 229
www.babybanz.co.uk
UV protective clothing and sunglasses.

Incy Wincy   0118 377 3581
www.incywincy.org
Comprehensive catalogue and website selling buoyancy aids
and swimming accessories.

Kidsafe Lifejacket
www.hellyhansen.com
A revolutionary lifejacket for babies and kids. A must-have for
all boating parents with small children.

Kool Sun   01483 417 753
www.koolsun.com
Sun protective clothing & accessories for children 6mths-
12yrs

P20
www.p20.co.uk
The once- a- day application sun cream for children who are
constantly in and out of water – recommended by many
mums

Sunhatters   01235 521 783
Mail order range of sun-protective clothing and Legionnaire-
style hats.

Sunsuits   01798 865 189
Offering a wide range of quality sun protective clothing that
allows children to enjoy time in the sun. Baby and toddler all-
in -one sunsuits and legionnaire hat.

Wilf Nicholson   01539 432 235
www.outdoorfamily.co.uk
Polyotter buoyancy suits and swim shoes

toy shops

NORTH LONDON

Cheeky Monkeys   020 7288 1948
38 Cross Street, N1 2BG
www.cheekymonkeys.com
Unusual & traditional children's toys and gifts, furniture, china,
dressing-up, etc

Soup Dragon   020 8348 0224
27 Topsfield Parade, Tottenham Lane, N8 8TT
www.soup-dragon.co.uk

Word Play   020 8347 6700
1 Broadway Parade, Crouch End, N8 9TN

Fagin's Toys   020 8444 0282
84 Fortis Green Road, N10 3HN

Never Never Land   020 8883 3997
3 Midhurst Parade, Fortis Green, N10 3JE

Route 73 Kids   020 7923 7873
92 Stoke Newington Church Street, N16 0AP

NORTH WEST LONDON

Harvey Johns   020 7485 1718
16-20 Parkway, NW1 7AA

Toys 'R' Us   020 8209 0019
Tilling Road, NW2
Branches in Croydon, Enfield, Hayes Road

Happy Returns   020 7435 2431
36 Rosslyn Hill, NW3 1NH

Kristin Baybars   020 7267 0934
7 Mansfield Road, NW3 2JD

Toy Wonderland (Toymaster)   020 7722 9821
10-11 Northways Parade, Finchley Road, NW3 5EP

Early Learning Centre 020 8202 6948|
Brent Cross Shopping Centre, NW4 9FE
www.elc.co.uk
The well-known specialist retailer of toys for pre-school children.

J.J.Toys 020 7722 4855
138 St John's Wood High Street, NW8 7SE

SOUTH EAST LONDON

2nd Impressions Ltd 020 8852 6192
10 Montpellier Vale, Blackheath, SE3

Early Learning Centre 020 8294 1057
7 St Mary's Place, High Street, SE9 1DO

Early Learning Centre 020 8318 3930
110 High Street, SE13 4TJ

Art, Stationers & Toyshop 020 8693 5938
31 Dulwich Village, SE21 7BN

Cheeky Monkeys **020 8655 7168**
4 Croxted Road, SE21 8SW
www.cheekymonkeys.com
Unusual & traditional children's toys and gifts, furniture, china, dressing-up, etc

Soup Dragon 020 8693 5575
106 Lordship Lane, SE22 8HF
www.soup-dragon.co.uk

Artemidorus 020 7737 7747
27b Half Moon Lane, SE24 9JU

SOUTH WEST LONDON

Worldly Goods 020 7259 0295
43 Elizabeth Street, SW1

Traditional Toys 020 7352 1718
53 Godfrey Street, SW3 3SX

Early Learning Centre 020 7581 5764
36 King's Road, SW3 4HD

Daisy & Tom 020 7352 5000
181 King's Road, SW3 5EB

Cheeky Monkeys **020 8673 5215**
24 Abbeville Road, SW4 9NH
www.cheekymonkeys.com
Unusual & traditional children's toys and gifts, furniture, china, dressing-up, etc

Cheeky Monkeys

Cheeky Monkeys toy shops are renowned across London for their fabulous array of children's gift items. Now, the company has launched a stylish new website:

www.cheekymonkeys.com

There's also the **Birthday Book** - a groundbreaking service which reminds you when important birthdays are coming up and recommends appropriate gifts.

Notting Hill	020 7792 9022
Clapham	020 8673 5251
Wandsworth	020 8672 2025
West Dulwich	020 8655 7168
Parsons Green	020 7731 3031
Islington	020 7288 1948

Cheeky Monkeys　　　**020 7731 3031**
94 New King's Road, SW6 4UL
www.cheekymonkeys.com
Unusual & traditional children's toys and gifts, furniture, china,
dressing-up, etc

Patrick's Toys & Games　　**020 7385 9864**
107-111 Lillie Road, SW6 7SX
www.patrickstoys.co.uk

Tridias　　　**020 7584 2330**
25 Bute Street, SW7 3EY
www.tridias.co.uk

Q.T.Toys　　　**020 7223 8637**
90 Northcote Road, SW11 6QN
Games, toys and educational products for most age groups.

Bug Circus　　　**020 8741 4244|**
153 Church Road, SW13 9HR

The Farmyard　　　**020 8332 0038**
63 Barnes High Street, SW13 9LF

Toystop　　　**020 8876 5229**
377 Upper Richmond Road West, SW14 7NX

Tiny Set Toys　　　**020 8788 0392**
54 Lower Richmond Road, SW15

Domat Designs　　　**020 8788 5715**
3 Lacy Road, Putney, SW15 1NH
www.domat.co.uk

Early Learning Centre　　**020 8780 1074**
8 Putney Exchange Centre, SW15 1TN

Havanas Toy Box　　　**020 8780 3722**
Ground floor, Putney Exchange Centre, SW15 1TW
Baby clothes, shoes and toys.

Cheeky Monkeys　　　**020 8672 2025**
1 Bellevue Road, SW17 7EG
www.cheekymonkeys.com
Unusual & traditional children's toys and gifts, furniture, china,
dressing-up, etc

Early Learning Centre　　**020 8944 0355**
111 Centre Court Shopping Centre, 4 Queen's
Road, SW19 1YE

Little Wonders　　　**020 8255 6114**
3 York Street, Twickenham, TW1 3JZ

CENTRAL & WEST LONDON

The Disney Store　　　**020 7491 9136**
360-366 Oxford Street, W1N 9HA
www.disney.co.uk
Apart from Disney toys the Disney Stores also include:
newborn clothing, boys & girls clothing & accessories, videos,
DVDs, books, stationery and costumes. Stores also at: 22a
& 26 The Broadway Shopping Centre, Hammersmith, W6
(020 8748 8886) and 91 The Piazza, London, WC2 (020
7836 5037)

Peter Rabbit and Friends　**020 7497 1777**
Unit 42, The Market, Covent Garden, WC2 8RS
www.charactergifts.com

Hamleys　　　**0870 333 2455**
188-196 Regent Street, W1R 6BT
www.hamleys.com
Also branches in Covent Garden and Heathrow Airport

The School Shop　　　**020 7402 3406**
31 Connaught Street, W2 2AY

Snap Dragon　　　**020 8995 6618**
56 Turnham Green Terrace, W4 1QP

The Bay Tree　　　**020 8994 1914**
10 Devonshire Road, W4 2HD

Early Learning Centre　　**020 8567 7076**
8 The Broadway Centre, W5 2NP

Cheeky Monkeys　　　**020 8840 2504**
34 High Street, Ealing, W5 5DB
www.cheekymonkeys.com

Early Learning Centre　　**020 8741 2469**
7 Kings Mall, Kings Street, W6 0TZ

Barnett Novelty House　　**020 7727 7164**
17 Kensington Park Road, W11

Cheeky Monkeys　　　**020 7792 9022**
202 Kensington Park Road, W11 1NR
www.cheekymonkeys.com
Unusual & traditional children's toys and gifts, furniture, china,
dressing-up, etc

Barnetts Toys　　　**020 7727 7164**
14 Elgin Crescent, Notting Hill, W11 2HX

mail order : toys

American Toys　　　**01952 281905**
www.americantoys.co.uk

Applepie Toys Ltd　　　**020 8807 9777**
www.spottydogtoys.com

Bright Minds　　　**0870 442 2144**
www.brightminds.co.uk
Educational toys for young children.

Brio   01509 231 874
www.brio.co.uk

Cheeky Monkeys   020 7792 9022
www.cheekymonkeys.com
Unusual & traditional children's toys and gifts, furniture, china,
dressing-up, etc

Clementine Toys   02380 556 352
www.clementinetoys.com
Clementine Toys offers a wide range of colourful, entertaining
and educational traditional and wooden toys.

Cuddle Pie Baby Products   020 8455 6991
www.cuddlepie.co.uk
A range of teddy bears, soft toys and much more.

Eduzone   0845 644 5556
www.eduzone.co.uk
Education toys for toddlers and pre-schoolers.

Emma Jefferson   01536 772 074
www.emmajefferson.co.uk
Also nursery furniture such as soldier lamps and shades, wall
hooks, shelves, wooden animal height charts.

e-niko   01768 210 121
www.e-niko.co.uk
Extraordinarily imaginative toys in unusual designs.

Fisher Price Nursery Products   01327 842 662
www.fisher-price.com

Hawkin's Bazaar   0870 429 4000
www.hawkin.co.uk
Best selection of stocking fillers, tricks, educational and
science based toys from £1 up.

Holz Toys Ltd   0845 130 8697
www.holz-toys.co.uk
Traditional wooden toys handmade in Germany

In 2 Play   01304 375 788
www.in2play.com
Well priced, quality wooden toys

Insect Lore   01908 563 338
www.insectlore.co.uk
Butterfly kits and other scientific toys

Jigsaw Tree   01527 545 545
www.jigsawtree.co.uk
Mail order wooden jigsaws.

Lapin & Me   020 8473 5000
www.lapinandme.co.uk
Original toys for little girls and their mummies.

Letterbox   0870 600 7878
www.letterbox.co.uk

Midnight Mushroom   020 7724 7311
www.midnightmushroom.co.uk
Mushroom and Lighthouse nightlights.

Miriam Stoppard   020 7630 1400
www.miriamstoppard.com
Educational range of baby toys.

Mulberry Bush   01403 754 400
www.mulberrybush.co.uk
Traditional wooden and soft toys, gifts and games. Phone for
free catalogue or visit website.

Perfect Puzzles   01634 351 262
Personalised puzzles available by mail order. Make great
gifts

The Little Experience   0870 241 8464
www.the-little-experience.com

The Ragged Rascal   0845 166 8604
www.theraggedrascal.co.uk

The Tintin Shop   020 7836 1131
www.thetintinshops.uk.com
Tintin heaven.

Toys Direct to your Door   01642 714 882|
www.directtoyourdoor.co.uk
Complete and comprehensive range of wooden trains and
sets, also dolls houses and other character toys.

Tridias   0870 240 2104
www.tridias.co.uk
Definitive christmas stocking and birthday catalogue.
Includes pre-school wooden classics, puppets, dressing up,
board games and outdoor fun

Vtech Electronics   01235 546 810
www.vtechuk.com
Brightly coloured electronic toys which make noises, play
tunes and are very interactive. The IQ Builders have an
English accent, quite a welcome relief from the US accent

travelcots

Samsonite Pop-Up   01746 769 676
Travel Cot
www.baby-travel.com
From 0-6mths this pop up travel cot is perfect for weekends
or when dining with friends. It's very lightweight and folds
away into its own hand carry bag

Travelling with Children   01684 594 831
www.travellingwithchildren.co.uk
The lightest full size travel cots with own UV protection,
mosquito net and carry sack – up to 3yrs. Price £124.99

Baby Dux   01925 817 892
www.babydux.com
Approved as hand luggage, this lightweight cot stands above
ground and has a machine wash lining. Price £64.99

Chicco   01623 750 870
www.chicco.co.uk
Their Caddy Line travel cot is a no-frills design at low cost.
Price £50. The Lullaby Bed has a little changing station
attachment and wheels for easy travelling. Price £80.

Cheeky Rascals   0870 873 2600
www.cheekyrascals.co.uk
Their Candide carry cot is totally soft and can fold neatly into
a suitcase. Price £55

au pair agencies

The majority of "au pairs" are aged between 17-25, and are admitted from non-EC countries, and work for around 6 months. Due to the recent changes in EC member countries, there has been a change in the composition of nationalities applying to be au pairs so ensure you are aware of the qualifying countries. Expect to pay between £35-£45 per week, in exchange for around 25hrs work of light housework, childcare and babysitting. They are not suitable for sole care of babies and young children. Set clear guidelines about telephones, internet access, boyfriends, dismissal procedures and your expectations of what "housework" entails to ensure an optimum relationship. The agencies below will do a lot of the hard work for you in terms of selecting suitable and reliable candidates and verifying all their details

ABC Au Pairs   020 8299 3052
www.abc-aupairs.co.uk

Adria Recruitment   023 802 54287
www.adriarecruitment.com

Anderson Au Pairs & Nannies   01303 260 971
www.childcare-europe.com

A-One Au-Pairs & Nannies   0800 068 7011

Au Pair International   **020 7370 3798**
118 Cromwell Road, London SW7 4ET
www.apni.co.uk

Aupairs4London.co.uk   020 8350 0284

Friends Au Pair Agency   020 8847 0920
www.friendsaupairs.com

Jolaine Agency   020 8449 1334
www.jolaine.com

Jobs In Demand Childcare   01932 855 327
www.globalaupairs.com

Just Help   **01460 30775**
www.just-help.co.uk
Voted 'Best agency for personal service,' Evening Standard.
Au pairs from Germany, Austria, Holland and Eastern Europe

Mar's Au Pair Agency   **020 8995 6594**
marsaupairagency@btconnect.com
Small and personal West London au pair agency

Park Avenue Aupair Agency   020 8904 0340
www.parkagency.co.uk

**Richmond & Twickenham
Au Pairs and Nannies**   01283 716611
www.aupairsnationwide.co.uk

The Au-pair Agency   020 8958 5261
www.aupairagency.com

MAR's *Au Pair Agency*

Dutch, English, French & Spanish Speaking Au Pair Agent.
Caring Service
Help with school and social contracts.
Marianne Walsh-van Elburg
16 Spencer Road, Chiswick London W4 3SN
Tel/Fax: 020 8995 6594
E-mail: marsaupairagency@btconnect.com

AU PAIR NETWORK INTERNATIONAL

Established 1992

Great selection of qualified and experienced international
AU PAIRS
MOTHER'S HELP/ NANNIES
Available for immediate start.
Professional service.
No registration fee.

020 7370 3798
(Emp.Ag)

I A P A

118 Cromwell Road,
London SW7 4ET
E-mail: admin@apni.co.uk

*Our Au Pairs are chosen for
their love of children*

babysitters

The agencies below offer a comprehensive service with fully qualified nannies, nurses and nursery school teachers, all of whom will have had the appropriate police checks and are trained in first aid. The recommended suggestion is that you develop between 3-4 babysitting contacts so that you can go out when a last-minute invitation arrives or when spontaneity strikes. For peace of mind you should check candidate references yourself to ensure that you are satisfied. Current rates are around £5-£7 per hr + taxi home after midnight

Babysitters Childminders　　**020 7935 3000**
6 Nottingham Street, London W1U 5EJ
www.babysitter.co.uk
London's leading babysitting service since 1967. Local sitters - all areas

In Trust　　**020 8395 0796**
Serving Southwest London, In Trust provides kind, reliable, vetted babysitters, most of whom are mothers

Babysitters Unlimited　　**01296 437 245**
Serving West London only

Hopes and Dreams　　**020 7833 9388**
Nanny & Babysitting Agency
www.hopesanddreams.co.uk
Providing first-class, fully screened nannies, maternity nurses and babysitters (see advert on page 83)

Kasimira for Children　　**020 7581 5383**
29 South Terrace, London SW7
www.kasimira.com

Sitters　　**0800 389 00 38**
www.sitters.co.uk

Special People　　**020 7686 0253**
Specialising in special needs

childminders

Usually offering childcare between 7.30am–7pm a childminder may be your best option, offering a family environment and the socialising benefits of a nursery. Your local council (see Councils) will have the most up-to-date lists of vacancies in your area. Some of the top childminders will advertise in local family magazines

National Childminding
Association (NCMA)　　**0800 169 4486**
Promoting qualified registered childminders, giving advice on negotiating terms and conditions

Childminders
London's Leading Babysitting Service   Established 1967

Locally based nurses, teachers, nannies, etc. throughout London. All sitters interviewed and referenced.

020 7935 3000

www.babysitter.co.uk

6 Nottingham Street
London W1U 5EJ

LICENSED AGENCY · ESTABLISHED 1967 · REC MEMBER

Simply Childcare   020 7701 6111
16 Bushey Hill Road, SE5
Weekly listings of childminders looking for new children, and
parents looking for a childminder

doulas

Doulas, usually mothers themselves, have trained
to help a mother before and after birth particularly
with getting breastfeeding off to a good start as
well as running the house and keeping things
together generally. Like having your Mum but
without the "in my day"...

British Doula Association   020 7244 6053
Flat 2, 49 Harrington Gardens, SW7 4JU
www.britishdoulas.co.uk
Provides a code of practice and training to British doulas

Heather Guerrini   020 7352 0245
30 Redesdale Street, SW3 4BJ
Trained doula who works through the NCT

Top Notch Doulas   020 7244 6053
49 Harrington Gardens, SW7 4JU
www.britishdoulas.co.uk

DOULAS FOR NEW MUMS

Doulas cosset and cherish new
mums. Our fully-trained and
experienced doulas will support
you emotionally and
physically during the birth
and the weeks following.

CALL: **020 7244 6053**

.....and we will send you the
best doula to meet your needs.

www.britishdoulas.co.uk
ANOTHER TOP NOTCH SERVICE

maternity nannies & nurses

Specialising in the care of newborns, a maternity
nurse will look after your baby on return from
hospital, allowing you to rest. Normally, they are on
call 24hrs a day with one day off per week

Eden Nannies   020 7569 6771
118 Piccadilly, Mayfair, London W1J 7NW
www.eden-nannies.co.uk
The best maternity service in London (see advert on p g 84)

Elite Nannies   020 7801 0061
22 Rowena Crescent, London SW11 2PT
www.elitenannies.co.uk
An excellent agency - highly recommended by clients,
nannies and maternity nurses (see advert on pg 85)

Maternity Connections   0870 242 0614
Alison Evans, private maternity nurse (see advert on page 79)

Maternally Yours   020 7795 6299
17 Radley Mews, London W8 6JP
www.maternallyyours.co.uk
(see advert on page 80)

Nannies Incorporated   020 7593 5898
Suite 7, 2 Caxton Street, London SW1H 0QE
www.nanniesinc.com
Specialists in maternity care (see advert on page 79)

**Occasional & Permanent
Nannies**   020 7225 1555
2 Cromwell Place, London SW7 2JE
www.nannyworld.co.uk
Specialist in the recruitment of Maternity Nurses to
care for newborns (see advert on page 91)

Platinum Nanny Services   020 8673 5771
65 Thurleigh Road, SW12
www.platinumnannyservices.co.uk
Run by mothers for mothers. Efficient professional service.
English-speaking and reference-checked
(see advert on page 79)

The Nanny Service   020 7935 3515
6 Nottingham Street, London W1U 5EJ
www.nannyservice.co.uk
Specialists in maternity nurses and maternity nannies since
1975 (see advert on page 79)

Tinies Childcare   020 7384 0322
Unit 14, 126-128 New Kings Road, London SW6
www.tinieschildcare.co.uk
Most progressive agency with more nannies, maternity
nurses, part-time & emergency carers (see advert on pg 92)

NANNIES INCORPORATED

Nannies Incorporated was established in 1989. We provide Maternity Nurses in London and overseas. We have a long and successful record of fulfilling our client's expectations. We achieve this through:

- *In depth interviewing of each candidate.*
- *Careful matching of clients and candidate's profiles*
- *Thorough reference checks, including checks carried out by the Criminal Record Bureau.*
- *Providing a generous refund policy with 8 weeks of engagement.*

MATERNITY NURSES

Our maternity nurses are trained or experienced nurses/nannies, registered nurses or midwives who specialise in the care of the newborn, including multiple births.

A maternity nurse will advise you in all aspects of feeding (breast/bottle), care and hygiene and assists you in establishing a suitable routine. She is on call 24 hours a day, 6/5 days a week or on a nightly/daily basis. Advance bookings available.

Nannies Incorporated Suite 7, 2 Caxton Street, London, SW1H 0QE
TEL: 020 7593 5898   FAX: 020 7593 5899
email: nanniesinc@aol.com   www.nanniesinc.com

PLATINUM
NANNY SERVICES

Platinum Offer the New Flexible Maternity Option.

We place Maternity Nannies either on a live-in basis or on a daily basis, or a mixture of the two.

We will also place follow on daily nannies for our maternity clients.

Platinum is owned and run by mothers and nannies and offers a personal and professional service.

We verbally reference check all our applicants and supply a written reference report to all families

Tel: 020 8673 5771
Fax: 020 8673 5769

Email: info@platinumnannyservices.co.uk
As recommended by www.bestbear.co.uk

The Nanny Service
www.nannyservice.co.uk   EST 1975

MATERNITY NURSES

We have a substantial base of high quality maternity nurses available for full-time, part-time and overnight placements. We always put a premium on the right combination of experience, personality and flexibility and all are personally interviewed and reference checked.

Call Liz Watson: 07734 059353 or 020 7935 3515
8 Nottingham Street W1U 5EJ

Maternity Connections

Alison Evans SEN MNP. Maternity Nurse, Parental Advisor, Baby Care Consultant, Trainer and Mentor

Offering solutions, advice, support and reasssurance to parents, through telephone consultations and/or home visits.
Baby care lessons during and after pregnancy.
Specific problem solving on any baby related issue.
Help to establish a 'reality based' routine.
Set-up visits when you and baby come home from hospital.
Specialist advice on the care of multiples
0870 242 0614 / 07879 840003

CONGRATULATIONS...

A new baby on the way!

Make those first weeks happy and memorable by booking your very own MATERNITY NURSE from...

Maternally Yours
Specialists in maternity care

Established in 1996, we are London's leading MATERNITY NURSE AGENCY. We satisfy the needs of over 500 families a year, most of whom have approached us through recommendation.

All our MATERNITY NURSES are personally interviewed, are of the highest calibre, with verified references. They will ensure you have plenty of rest, 'show you the ropes', settle your baby into that all important routine and leave you feeling confident for the future.

Whether you are a first-time mother, have a sibling on the way or are expecting twins, please call one of our experienced consultants to discuss your particular needs.

TELEPHONE: +44(0)20 7795 6299 FAX: +44(0)20 7937 8100
OR VISIT OUR WEBSITE AT: www.maternally-yours.com

MATERNALLY YOURS, 17 RADLEY MEWS, KENSINGTON, LONDON W8 6JP

midwives: independent

Independent midwives care for women during pregnancy, labour and for about six weeks after the birth. They either work independently or in a practice and can provide telephone support as necessary

**Independent
Midwives Association**　　**01483 821 104**
www.independentmidwives.org.uk
Independent Midwives are fully qualified midwives who, in order to practise the midwife's role to its fullest extent, have chosen to work outside the NHS in a self-employed capacity, although they support its aims and ideals

Ali Herron　　**020 8309 8561**
16 Hasting Street, The Royal Arsenal, Woolwich, SE18

Alison Evans　　**07879 840 003**
Covering the whole of London (see advert on page 79)

Birth Rites Midwifery Practice　　**020 8771 7143**
94 Auckland Road, Upper Norwood, SE19 2DB

Private Postnatal Services　　**07950 848 666**
29 Otley Road, Victoria Dock, E16 3JT

South London Independent Midwives
Tina Perridge　　020 8874 6624
Annie Francis　　020 8875 1582

The Birth Centre　　**020 7498 2322**
34 Elm Quay Court, Nine Elms Lane, Vauxhall, SW8 5DE
www.birthcentre.com
Give birth at home, in hospital or in their purpose-designed Birth Centre (see advert on page 5)

West London Midwifery Practice　　**020 8994 0284**
Hogarth Clinic, Airedale Road, W4 2NW

L&R Midwifery　　**01895 635 111**
50 Swakeleys Road, UB10

nanny agencies

Abbeville Nannies　　**020 7627 3352**
18a Franconia Road, SW4
www.abbevillenannies.co.uk
A selection of the best nannies, mothers' helps and maternity nurses across London (see advert on page 83)

Babes in the Wood　　**020 7722 9047**
St John's Wood, NW8
jacbabesinthewood@btinternet.com
A professional, caring, personal and understanding service that you can rely on

Eden Nannies　　**020 7569 6771**
118 Piccadilly, Mayfair, W1
www.eden-nannies.co.uk
The complete childcare solution (see advert on page 83)

Elite Nannies　　**020 7801 0061**
22 Rowena Crescent, SW11
www.elitenannies.co.uk
An excellent agency - highly recommended by clients, nannies and maternity nurses (see advert on page 86)

Greatcare.co.uk　　**020 7924 6660**
99-100 Lavender Hill, SW11
www.greatcare.co.uk
The essential website for childcare jobs (see advert on pg 89)

Greycoat Placements　　**020 7233 9950**
Grosvenor Gardens House, 35-37 Grosvenor Gardens, SW1
www.greycoatplacements.co.uk
The professional service for all permanent and temporary nanny requirements (see advert on page 86)

**Hopes and Dreams Nanny
and Babysitting Agency**　　**020 7833 9388**
339 -341 City Road, Islington, EC1
www.hopesanddreams.co.uk
Providing first-class, fully screened, nannies, aternity nurses and babysitters (see advert on page 84)

Hyde Park International　　**020 7730 0112**
Belmont House, The Dean,　　**01962 733 466**
Alresford SO24 9BQ
www.hydeparkint.com
One of UK's leading agencies, est. 1983. Friendly, professional, thorough and efficient (see advert on page 89)

Ideal Nannies　　**020 8994 5888**
4 Stilehall Parade, Chiswick High Road, W4
www.idealnannies.com
(see advert on page 87)

Imperial Nannies　　**020 7795 6220**
17 Radley Mews, Kensington, W8
www.imperialnannies.co.uk
Providing the very best for your children all over London and throughout the UK (see advert on page 85)

Just Help   **01460 30775**
www.just-help.co.uk
Voted 'Best agency for personal service,' Evening Standard
(see advert on page 88)

Kensington Nannies   **020 7937 2333/3299**
3 Hornton Place, Kensington High Street, W8
www.kensington-nannies.com
Nanny agency who knows about childcare needs from good
experience (see advert on page 92)

KiwiOz Nannies   **020 8740 6695**
1 Richmond Way, W12
www.kiwioznannies.com
Specialists in the placement of qualified, experienced
Australian and New Zealand nannies (see advert on page 88)

Knightsbridge Nannies   **020 7610 9232**
London House, 100 New Kings Road, SW6
www.knightsbridgenannies.com
Providing a personal childcare service in the UK and overseas
for professionals looking for high calibre nannies (see advert
on page 90)

London Nanny Company   **020 7838 0033**
Collier House, 163-169 Brompton Road,SW3
www.LondonNannyCompany.co.uk
Agency offering nannies, maternity nurses, governesses,
baby sitters and jobs overseas (see advert on page 90)

Nannies Incorporated   **020 7593 5898**
Suite 7, 2 Caxton Street, SW1
www.nanniesinc.com
(see advert on page 89)

Nannies of St James   **0870 300 0824**
100 New King's Road, SW6
www.nanniesofstjames.com
The professional agency providing professional nannies and
maternity nurses (see advert on page 86)

Nannies One   **020 7801 1461**
31 Battersea Bridge Road, SW11
www.nanniesone.co.uk
The fiendly agency offering nannies, mother's Hhlps and
maternity nurses and home visits

Nanny Match   **0845 490 0254**
100 St George's Avenue, N7
www.nanny-match.co.uk
Listening to parents and nannies to make the best match
(see advert on page 90)

Nanny Search   **020 8348 4111**
7 Broadbent Close, 22-25 Highgate High Street, N6
www.nanny-search.co.uk

Nanny Service   **020 7935 3515**
6 Nottingham Street, W1
www.nannyservice.co.uk
Temporary, permanent, daily, residential & part-time. Est
1975 (see advert on page 91)

Night Nannies   **020 7731 6168**
3 Kempson Road, SW6
www.night-nannies.com
Get yourself a good night's sleep, call their team of night
nannies (see advert on page 91)

Occasional & Permanent
Nannies   **020 7225 1555**
2 Cromwell Place, SW7
www.nannyworld.co.uk
(see advert on page 91)

Park Nanny Agency   **020 7604 4000**
36 Winchester Avenue, NW6
www.parknannies.co.uk
As recommended by Bestbear, they specialize in live in/live
out nannies, maternity nannies and mother's helps across
London

Riverside Childcare   **020 7374 6363**
29 Milligan Street, Limehouse, E14
riversidechild@btconnect.com
Experienced team of childcare professionals interview all
applicants personally, introducing families to nannies,
babysitters, maternity nurses and mother's helps (see advert
on page 88)

South of the River   **020 7228 5086**
128c Northcote Road, SW11
www.southoftheriver.co.uk
South London's leading nanny and babysitting agency
established 1976

Swansons   **020 8994 5275**
4 Brackley Road, W4
www.swansonsnannies.co.uk
West London agency supplying nannies, mother's helps,
shares & part-timers (see advert on page 92)

The Nanny Agency   **020 8883 3162**
29 Cranbourne Road, Muswell Hill, N10
www.thenannyagency.co.uk
(see advert on page 88)

Tinies International
Childcare   **020 7384 0322**
Unit 14 Block A, 126-128 New Kings Road, SW6
www.tinieschildcare.co.uk
Most progressive agency with nannies, maternity nurses,
part-time & emergency carers (see advert on page 92)

eden nannies
complete childcare solutions

Eden Nannies specialises in offering a wide range of childcare options to suit our client's individual needs. Our experienced consultants will listen to your requirements and offer professional advice and tailor made solutions. All of our candidates are personally interviewed by one of our consultants. We thoroughly vet and check all references and qualifications prior to registering any candidates.

Daily Nannies
Full time, Part time, Permanent, Temporary
In London and throughout the UK

Live-In Nannies
Full time, Part time, Permanent, Temporary
In London and throughout the UK

Mother's Help
Full time, Part time, Permanent, Temporary
In London and throughout the UK

Overseas Nannies
Experienced Nannies looking for opportunities
to work in worldwide locations

Maternity Nurses
Full time, Nightly, Daily Temporary Care
In London and throughout the UK

Maternity Nannies
Full time, Nightly, Daily Temporary Care
In London and throughout the UK

Nursery Placements
In London and surrounding counties

Why not visit our web site for more details or call...

0845 1284279

118 Piccadilly, Mayfair,
London W1J 7NW
Tel: 0845 1284279
Fax: 0845 1284281
Email: info@eden-nannies.co.uk
www.eden-nannies.co.uk
Nearest Tube Station:
Green Park Tube UNDERGROUND

Tinies North London	**020 7544 8620**
Tinies South London	**020 7720 2045**
Tinies South West London	**020 8876 4391**
Tinies South East London	**0845 600 3590**

Top Notch Nannies   **020 7259 2626**
49 Harrington Gardens, SW7
www.topnotchnannies.com
Top Notch Nannies is a Kensington based nanny agency
offering a high quality recruitment service to families
(see advert on page 88)

Walleroo Nannies   **020 7736 2331**
123 Munster Road, SW6
www.walleroonannies.com
(see advert on page 91)

www.bestbear.co.uk   **020 7352 5852**
www.bestbear.co.uk
Bestbear.co.uk offers childcare listings, information and
searches for parents/childcarers

Need a Nanny? Childminder? Nannyshare?
Au Pair? Mother's Help? Don't know where to
look? Don't know what to do? Then try

Simply Childcare

the childcare listings magazine

It has lots of people offering childcare & lots
of parents looking for childcare: part-time,
full-time, temporary, occasional. Read Simply
Childcare & solve your problem. For details call

020 7701 6111

website: www.simplychildcare.com
email: info@simplychildcare.com

PLUS if you need unbiased, up-to-date, practical
information on all aspects of finding and handling
childcare e.g. different kinds of childcare, their
merits & drawbacks, costs, tax/NIC, interviewing,
contracts, police checks, etc then send a cheque
for our Childcare Information Pack (£9.95) to
Simply Childcare, 16 Bushey Hill Road, London SE5 8QJ

As recommended in local & national press

Hopes and Dreams...   NANNY AND
BABYSITTING AGENCY

Professional Nannies,
Maternity Nurses and Babysitters

All of our staff are personally
interviewed by us and extensively checked and
vetted for your total peace of mind

Hopes and Dreams Nanny and Babysitting Agency Ltd
339 - 341 City Road, Islington, London EC1V 1LJ
T: 020 7833 9388   F: 020 7837 5517
E: office@hopesanddreams.co.uk   www.hopesanddreams.co.uk

The Hopes and Dreams Nanny and Babysitting Agency is a
subsidiary company of Hopes and Dreams Montessori Nursery
School, the first Quality Counts Accredited Nursery in London

abbeville
NANNIES

Permanent, temporary & part time

- ## Nannies
- ## Mother's helps
- ## Housekeepers
- ## Maternity

accredited by
bestbear.co.uk

020 7627 3352

email us at info@abbevillenannies.co.uk
www.abbevillenannies.co.uk

IMPERIAL NANNIES

Providing the very best for your children

We specialise in placing qualified and experienced childcarers with families in London, the country and overseas. We aim to ease the difficult process of nanny selection by providing an individual, tailor-made service for your particular needs. All our nannies are fully reference checked, with at least two years private household experience and are personally interviewed by our dedicated consultants.

We provide an excellent selection of:

DAILY NANNIES
Four to five days per week. Candidates are available with years of excellent service.

LIVE-IN NANNIES
Flexible childcare based in the privacy of your own home.

OVERSEAS NANNIES
Experienced nannies looking for an exciting challenge.

NANNY/GOVERNESSES
Working towards developing the mind and skills of your children.

NANNY/HOUSEKEEPERS
Combining the abilities of childcare and domestic chores in the home.

AU PAIRS & MOTHERS HELPS
Young people to help with childcare and housekeeping duties whilst improving their English.

17 RADLEY MEWS, KENSINGTON, LONDON W8 6JP
TELEPHONE: +44(0)20 7795 6220 FACSIMILE: +44(0)20 7937 2251
www.imperialnannies.com

THE PROFESSIONAL AGENCY WHICH CARES

Elite Nannies

22 Rowena Crescent
London
SW11 2PT

**PERMANENT AND TEMPORARY NANNIES
EXPERIENCED MATERNITY NURSES**

For a friendly and personal service,
call Kim on:

020 7801 0061

Fax: 020 7801 0063

Email: elite.nannies@virgin.net

www.elitenannies.co.uk

GREYCOAT
PLACEMENTS

DAILY · LIVE IN · TEMPORARY · PERMANENT

**Nannies
Maternity Nurses
Mother s Helps**

IN LONDON, THE UK & INTERNATIONALLY

020 7233 9950

www.greycoatplacements.co.uk

35-37 GROSVENOR GARDENS
LONDON SW1W 0BS

REC   Part of the
Empresaria Group

ST JAMES

*Specialists in Recruitment
Nannies -- Maternity Nursers*

We provide a professional and personal childcare consultancy for clients in
the UK and Overseas looking for top notch nannies.

Tel: +44 (0) 20 7348 6100
      +44 (0) 1483 557220 *(perms)*   +44 (0) 1483 557221 *(temps)*
Fax. +44 (0) 1483 557235
E-mail: nanniesstjames@aol.com   *Website:*www.nanniesofstjames.com

ideal **nannies**

- All staff personally interviewed

- References thoroughly checked

- Nannies, Mothers Helps & Maternity Nurses

- Live in & Live out

- Full time & Part time

- Permanent & temporary

- Babysitting Service available

- First Aid courses

Karen Murphy of Ideal Nannies has been running this flourishing agency since 1988. It is manned by sensible, careful staff who are easy to talk to and have practical experience in the childcare world

Tel: 020 8994 5888
www.idealnannies.com
info@idealnannies.com
4 Stilehall Parade Chiswick High Road London W4 3AG

JUST HELP

agency with a difference...

Do you need help for a week, a month, a year, or for life?

If so please give us a ring as we have
- **temporary and permanent nannies** •
- **housekeepers** • **mothers' helps** • **au pairs** •

Voted "Best agency for personal service"
Evening Standard

Phone Suze on 01460 30775
www.just-help.co.uk

---

kiwioznannies
london

- Specialists in placing Australian and NZ nannies in the UK & Abroad

- Ask about our 1 year guarantee

Temporary - Permanent - Nannies - Mothers Helps - Maternity Nurses

Ph: 020 8740 6695
www.kiwioznannies.co.uk

Riverside Childcare
Established 1989

We suppply nursery staff, nannies, mother's helps, and babysitters.

7.30 AM Early Morning Emergency Desk to support any unexpected childcare needs you may have

Do you take on freelance projects? We have developed the perfect system to support your childcare needs, used by many parents working in the media and arts

020 7374 6363/4   020 7536 9566
riversidechild@btconnect.com
A Criminal Record Bureau Registered Agency

---

the Nanny agency

the Nanny agency

We ....

- meet you and all our nannies personally

- check our nannies' references and qualifications

- offer you advice and guidance

North London

020 8883 3162

www.thenannyagency.co.uk
email:nlondon@thenannyagency.co.uk

TOP NOTCH NANNIES
OF KENSINGTON

Trustworthy and reliable nannies to support you and your family

Experienced, qualified nannies, mother's helps, maternity nurses, doulas and housekeepers with excellent references. Don't delay, contact us today!

CALL: 020 7259 2626
www.topnotchnannies.com

49 Harrington Gardens, London SW7

NANNIES INCORPORATED

Nannies Incorporated was established in 1989. We provide Nannies in London and overseas. We have a long and successful record of fulfilling our client's expectations. We achieve this through:

- *In depth interviewing of each candidate.*
- *Careful matching of clients and candidate's profiles.*
- *Thorough reference checks, including checks carried out by the Criminal Record Bureau.*
- *Providing a generous refund policy with 8 weeks of engagement.*

**LIVE IN AND DAILY NANNIES
PERMANENT AND TEMPORARY**

Nannies Incorporated believe that creating a loving and stimulating environment for your children can only be achieved by adopting a professional interview and selection procedure.

We always seek to provide for the different needs and individual circumstances of our families.

Our nannies will either hold the NVQ, BTEC or similar qualification, will be privately trained or will have considerable experience.

Nannies Incorporated Suite 7, 2 Caxton Street, London, SW1H 0QE
TEL: 020 7393 3898   FAX: 020 7593 5899
email: nanniesinc@aol.com   www.nanniesinc.com

greatcare.co.uk

the essential website for childcare jobs

Looking for childcare?
- Post jobs on our user friendly site
- Get details of local agencies
- Contact agencies directly

Looking for your next job?
- Search for jobs, apply directly
- Find and register with agencies
- Receive jobs by email

nannies • au pairs
maternity nurses • mothers' helps
babysitters • nursery staff

www.greatcare.co.uk

"Definitely worth a look if you are either looking for a childcare job, or are seeking childcare staff." - The Good Web Guide

HYDE PARK
INTERNATIONAL LTD.

ESTABLISHED 1983
•Nannies • Maternity Nurses •
•Couples • Housekeepers • Dailies •
• Cooks/Chefs • Butlers/Valets •
•Gardeners • Chauffeurs •

Permanent and temporary.
Call our friendly experienced
consultants for a personal service.

020 7730 0112 or 01962 733466

Fax: 01962 735700
Email: info@hyde-park-int.co.uk
www.hydeparkint.com

Recruitment &
Employment
Confederation

K**nightsbridge** **N**annies

Established since 1962

Specialist in Recruitment of

Nannies
Maternity Nurses
Mothers Helps

We provide a personal childcare service in the UK and overseas for professionals looking for high calibre nannies.
All staff interviewed and thoroughly checked.

Tel: +44 020 7610 9232
Fax: +44 020 7610 6409

Email: knbridgenannies@aol.com
www.knightsbridgenannies.com

nannymatch

matching nannies with families

London's friendly, professional and personalised agency that matches the best Nannies, Maternity Nurses & Mother's Helps with the best families in London.

All applicants personally interviewed and police checked.

0845 4900254
www.nanny-match.co.uk

THE LONDON NANNY COMPANY

PERMANENT AND TEMPORARY NANNIES
(LIVE IN AND DAILY)
MATERNITY NURSES
UK AND OVERSEAS
BABYSITTING SERVICE

FROM FULLY QUALIFIED BRITISH NANNIES TO "ROLL UP YOUR SLEEVES AND GET STUCK IN" AUSTRALIAN/NEW ZEALANDERS

WE CAN COVER ALL YOUR CHILDCARE REQUIREMENTS

WE INTERVIEW ALL OUR STAFF AND TAKE UP REFERENCES
A FRIENDLY PROFESSIONAL SERVICE RUN BY EX-NANNIES

020 7838 0033
COLLIER HOUSE, 163-169 BROMPTON ROAD, LONDON SW3 1PY
www.londonnannycompany.co.uk

The Nanny Service

SPECIALISTS IN NANNIES FOR LONDON SINCE 1975

www.nannyservice.co.uk

LIVE IN NANNIES	020 7935 3515
LIVE OUT NANNIES	020 7935 3515
TEMPORARY NANNIES	020 7935 6976
MATERNITY NANNIES	07734 059 353
NIGHT-TIME NANNIES	020 7935 2049
SKI SEASON NANNIES	07734 059 353
PART-TIME NANNIES	020 7935 8247
AU PAIRS	020 7935 8247

Email: nannyserv@aol.com
Corrina Slater-Simmons – Manager

6 Nottingham Street, London W1U 5EJ

REC
Recruitment &
Employment
Confederation

Night Nannies®

**Nominated for the 2003 Orange
"Small business of the Year award"**
Daily Telegraph says *"for this relief, much thanks"*
Having a Baby Magazine *"Giving tired parents a break"*

* Are you completely exhausted?
* Does your baby need settling at night?
* Do you need help with sleep training?

For £85 per night you can
"Get yourself a good night's sleep"
and call on our team of experienced Night Nannies

Tel: 020 7731 6168
www.nightnannies.com

OCCASIONAL & PERMANENT NANNIES

2 Cromwell Place, London SW7 2JE
Tel: 020 7225 1555 Fax: 020 7589 4966
e-mail: all@nannyworld.co.uk
www.nannyworld.co.uk

WE OFFER A SUPERB SELECTION OF
NANNIES
MATERNITY NURSES, GOVERNESSES
and all
DOMESTIC STAFF
for temporary and permanent positions
in the UK and OVERSEAS

• We interview all our applicants in person
• References and qualifications are checked
• Help and advice given

• Est 50 years • REC member

020 7225 1555

Walleroo Nannies

Established 1992

**Nannies, Maternity Nurses/Nannies, Night
Nannies, Babysitters & Housekeepers**

If you need not just good - but
excellent, fully vetted,
reference checked childcare,
we are here to help you.

Support & advice for all periods of placement.
Contact us: **020 7736 2331**

walleroonannies@btconnect.com
www.walleroonannies.com
123 Munster Rd, Fulham, London, SW6 6DH

SWANSONS
NANNY AGENCY

Nannies, Mothers Helps, Nanny Shares
and Part-Time Arrangements
in the West London Area

Contact Anne Babb
020-8994-5275

4 Brackley Road, Chiswick,
London W4 2HN
fax: 020-8994-9280
email: anne@swansonsnannies.co.uk
www.swansonsnannies.co.uk

Tinies

Recruitment &
Employment
Confederation

Childcare for the modern world

*Over 25 years experience, with more branches
and more childcarers than anyone else*

- **Nannies**
- **Maternity Nannies**
- **Mothers Helps**
- **Emergency /
  Temporary Childcare**

Tel: 0800 783 6070
www.tinies.co.uk

Unit 14, 126-128 New Kings Rd, London SW6 4LZ

kensington nannies

London's Longest Established Nanny Agents

3 Hornton Place,
Kensington High Street, London W8 4LZ

UK & Overseas (ex-USA)
Temporary & Permanent
Appointments needed for nannies to register
020 7937 2333 or 3299
Overseas Jobs **020 7938 3525**

Fax: 020 7937 1027
E-mail: nannies@easynet.co.uk
www.kensington-nannies.com
REC Member

Nanny Finder Service

If you are at a loss to know where to find quality childcare then our online Nanny Finder may be a useful tool to help you get started.

Simply enter your requirements and we will forward them to a selection of 6 agencies, who will contact you at your convenience with their company details and a selection of suitable candidates. You will only be contacted by the agencies who have specialist areas of expertise for the type of childcare you require.

Log on to **www.babydirectory.com** and select Nanny Finder from main headings:

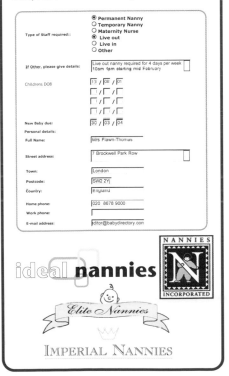

nanny share

To find a suitable nanny share you can look for or post an ad locally on a noticeboard (the appropriately named "Wailing Wall" a cornershop in Ravenscourt Road, W6 or one of the Cheeky Monkey sores), subscribe to Simply Childcare (see advert opposite) or network like mad around your nearest sand-pit. Some nanny agencies also run nanny share lists so its worth enquiring with them as well. Also consider posting a small ad in one of the Families Magazines.

We have also developed the Baby Directory Nanny Finder (see opposite), which enables you to enter your details once and be called by the agencies that specialise in the type of childcare you require.

This has been found to be particularly useful if you have had a last minute cancellation, cannot make the time to ring round the agencies and explain the same details again, or require something fairly specialist. Also good for families who are based overseas with the intention of coming to London.

nanny payroll services

If you've never seen the small binder that encompasses the PAYE tax tables then we do recommend you value your time highly and delegate all responsibility for calculating tax to one of the services below. Sanity could at least be your upside

Nanny Tax   **0845 226 2203**
PO Box 988, Brighton BN2 1BY
www.nannytax.co.uk
Nannytax is the UK's leading payroll service for parents employing a nanny.

Payroll Café   **01844 351 061**
www.payrollcafe.co.uk
A timesaving, comprehensive payroll service, entirely online, make you eligible for a £250 Inland Revenue rebate.

Taxing Nannies   **020 8882 6847**
28 Minchenden Crescent, N14 7EL
www.taxingnannies.co.uk
London's leading payroll agency for employers of nannies

The service that costs you nothing...

nannytax⁺

Payroll **plus** for parents & nannies

- The UK's leading payroll support service

- All Nannytax subscribers automatically receive £250 in Inland Revenue incentive payments in the summer of 2005

- We transform the hassle of domestic employment into peace of mind

- We lead the market but follow the customer

0845 226 2203 www.nannytax.co.uk

Use our first class payroll service (and get the taxman to pay for it!)

Taxing Nannies is a specialist payroll service which has helped thousands of parents through the minefield of battling through forms and calculations, dealing with the taxman etc. We will take care of everything related to your nanny's tax including opening a PAYE scheme, calculating tax and national insurance and providing regular payslips, advising on Sick and Maternity pay, and handling all dealings with the Inland Revenue.

But here's the best bit. We have systems in place to submit your Employer's annual return electronically to the Inland Revenue and this means that at the end of the tax year you'll receive a refund from the taxman of £250, which is more than the cost of a year's service from Taxing Nannies. (You could receive total refunds of £825 if still an employer in 2009).

Taxing Nannies is the very best nanny payroll service, because we have a very high ratio of staff to clients. The service is highly personal, responsive and efficient – and in effect, it costs you nothing.

Call: 020 8882 6847 for a brochure or for more information.
Alternatively, email: post@taxingnannies.co.uk
or visit our website: www:taxingnannies.co.uk

Taxing Nannies, 28 Minchenden Crescent London N14 7EL

taxing
nannies

hotels & holidays

The following offer special facilities for children and babies, ranging from crèches to child listening, playgrounds, pools, etc

Centerparcs Ltd	0990 200 200

Avon
The Bath Spa Hotel 01225 444424
Sydney Road, Bath

Channel Islands
Stocks Island Hotel 01481 832001
Manor Valley, Sark

Co.Durham
Redworth Hall Hotel 01388 772442
Hedworth, Nr Newton Aycliffe

Cornwall
Cornwall Beach House **01460 30609**
www.beachhouse-cornwall.co.uk
(see advert below)

Fowey Hotel **01726 833866**
Hanson Drive, Fowey
www.luxuryfamilyhotels.com

Bedruthan Steps Hotel 01637 860555
Mawgan Porth

Carlyon Bay Hotel 01726 812304
Sea Road, St Austell

Cawsand Bay Hotel 01752 822425
Cawsand, Torpoint

Coombe Mill 01208 850344
St. Breward

Long Cross Hotel 01208 880243
Trelights, Port Isaac

Penmere Manor Hotel 01326 211411
Mongleath Road, Falmouth

Polurrian 01326 240421
Mullion

Sands Family Resort 01637 872864
Watergate Road, Porth

Tredethy House Country Hotel 01208 841262
Helland Bridge, Bodmin

Watergate Bay Hotel 01637 860543
Watergate Bay, Newquay

Whipsiderry Hotel 01637 874777
Trevelgue Road, Porth, Newquay

Wringford Down Hotel 01752 822287
Cawsand

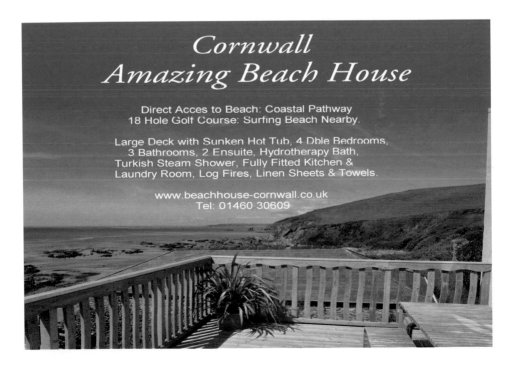

Cornwall
Amazing Beach House

Direct Acces to Beach: Coastal Pathway
18 Hole Golf Course: Surfing Beach Nearby.

Large Deck with Sunken Hot Tub, 4 Dble Bedrooms,
3 Bathrooms, 2 Ensuite, Hydrotherapy Bath,
Turkish Steam Shower, Fully Fitted Kitchen &
Laundry Room, Log Fires, Linen Sheets & Towels.

www.beachhouse-cornwall.co.uk
Tel: 01460 30609

A peaceful oasis of traditional style
with a wonderful atmosphere
~
Easy access to three miles of golden beach
Outdoor pool (level deck), golf and tennis
Health Spa with plunge pool and sauna
~
Family suites of connecting rooms
Separate young children's restaurant
Playroom and fabulous safe Adventure Playground
~
Daily half board terms from £92
Children much less, by age
Excellent low season offers for young families:
£848 five nights full board, parents and two children
~
Open Easter - end October. Dogs also welcome

STUDLAND BAY
DORSET

BH19 3AX
TEL 01929 · 450450 FAX 01929 · 450423
Email: info@knollhouse.co.uk
Website: www.knollhouse.co.uk

ONLY 2 HOURS FROM HEATHROW

Cumbria
Allerdale Court Hotel — 01900 823654
Market Place, Cockermouth

Armathwaite Hall Hotel — 01768 776551
Nr. Keswick

Castle Inn Hotel — 01768 776401
Bassenthwaite, Keswick

Hilton Keswick Lodore — 01768 777285
Borrowdale Road, Keswick

Devon
Langstone Cliff Hotel — 01626 868000
Mount Pleasant Road, Dawlish Warren, Dawlish
www.langstone-hotel.co.uk
19 acres of woodland, children's suppers, indoor and
outdoor pools, tennis, therapy rooms, go-karts

Boswell Farm — 01395 514162
Sidford

The Bulstone Hotel — 01297 680446
Higher Bulstone, Branscombe, Sidmouth

Radfords County Hotel — 01626 863322
Dawlish

Thurlestone Hotel — 01548 560382
Thurlestone

Dorset
The Knoll House — **01929 450450**
Studland Bay
www.knollhouse.co.uk
Gardens, pools, tennis, golf, health spa, playroom, children's
restaurant, adventure playground (see advert on page x)

Moonfleet Manor — **01305 786948**
Moonfleet, Nr Weymouth
www.luxuryfamilyhotels.com
Play area, crèche, extensive leisure facilities including indoor
pool (see special offer voucher)

Chine Hotel — 01202 396234
25 Boscombe Spa Road, Bournemouth

Fairfields Hotel — 01929 450224
Studland Bay

Hotel Buena Vista — 01297 442494
Pound Street, Lyme Regis

Sandbanks Hotel — 01202 707377
15 Banks Road, Sandbanks, Poole

Dyfed
Hotel Penrallt — 01239 810227
Aberporth, Cardigan

East Lothian
Maitlandfield House Hotel — 01620 826513
24 Sidegate, Haddington

Essex
Churchgate Manor Hotel — 01279 420246
Churchgate Street, Old Harlow

Flintshire
St. David's Park Hotel — 01244 520800
Ewloe

Gloucestershire — 01666 890391
Calcot Manor
Tetbury

Gwynedd
Trefeddian Hotel — 01654 767213
Aberdyfy

Hampshire
Watersplash Hotel — 01590 622344
The Rise, Brockenhurst

Hertfordshire
Marriott Hanbury Manor — 01920 487722
nr Sandridge, Ware

Inverness
Polmaily House Hotel — 01456 450343
Drumnadrochit, Loch Ness

Isle of Wight
The Clarendon Hotel -
The Wight Mouse Inn — 01983 730431
Chale

Priory Bay Hotel — 01983 613146
Eddington Road, St. Helens

Isles of Scilly
St Martin's on the Isle — 01720 422092
Lower Town, St Martin's

Kent
The Hythe Imperial — 01303 267441
Hythe

Kinross-shire
The Green Hotel — 01577 863467
2 The Muirs, Kinross

Lancashire
St Ives Hotel — 01253 720011
St Anne's on Sea

Leicestershire
Field Head Hotel — 01530 245454
Markfield Lane, Markfield

London
Chiaroscuro at Townhouse — 020 7636 2731
24 Coptic Street, WC1

Days Inn Hotel — 020 7922 1331
54 Kennington Road, SE1

London County Hall
Travel Inn Capital — 0870 238 3300
Belvedere Road, SE1

myhotel — 020 7667 6040
11-13 Bayley Street, Bedford Square, WC1

Norfolk
White Acres   **01485 518 822**
Marsh Side, Brancaster, King's Lynn
Family holiday house, sleeps eight, additional cots &
highchairs available

Heath Farm House B & B   01986 788417
Homersfield, Harleston

North Devon
Saunton Sands Hotel   01271 890212
nr Braunton

Northumberland
Granary Hotel   01665 710872
Links Road, Amble

Ryecroft Hotel   01668 281459
Ryecroft Way, Wooler

Perthshire
Gleneagles Hotel   0800 328 4010
Auchterarder
Playground, crèche

Stronvar House
Scottish Vacations   01877 384688
Balquhidder

Shropshire
Redfern Hotel   01299 270395
Cleobury Mortimer

South Devon
Gara Rock   01548 842342
East Portlemouth, nr Salcombe

Suffolk
Ickworth Hotel   **01284 735 350**
Nr Bury St Edmonds
www.luxuryfamilyhotels.com
East wing of Ickworth House, within 1,800 acre National Trust
estate. Indoor pool and crèche (see special offer voucher)

Sussex
Family-Friendly Bed & Breakfast   01273 477388
Coombe Barn, Lewes

Warwickshire
Lea Marston Hotel   01675 470468
Haunch Lane, Lea Marston

Wiltshire
Woolley Grange Hotel   **01225 864705**
Woolley Green, Bradford on Avon
www.luxuryfamilyhotels.com
Play area, crèche, outdoor pool, bicycles

Old Bell   01666 822344
Abbey Row, Malmesbury

Worcestershire
Evesham Hotel   01386 765566
Coopers Lane, Off Waterside, Evesham

Worcs
Holdfast Cottage Hotel   01684 310288
Welland, Nr Malvern

overseas travel

Holidays which the kids want do not necessarily
match the holiday that their parents need. And it all
comes down to the type of childcare you want and
can afford. It ranges from taking your own nanny,
relying on childcare provided by a tour operator
(crèche or kid's clubs) or simply baby listening in
order to have a civilised dinner in your hotel.
Babies do require their own passport to travel
overseas and application forms have to be
submitted with the birth certificate and
photographs. The fastrack service for an additional
£30 takes around 7 days. The companies we have
selected below have a special interest in ensuring
that families get the holiday they expect and can
offer advice (and special offers) throughout the
year.

Babygoes2.com   **01273 230669**
www.babygoes2.com
Essential travel website for families with young children

Family Travel   **020 7272 7441**
www.family-travel.co.uk
Subscription website recommending good family holidays
abroad. A wide ranging database of destinations and types
of holiday

Quo Vadis? Family Travel   **01279 639 600**
www.quovadistravel.co.uk
Overseas family holiday experts - free, objective advice and
hassle-free booking service.

Travelling with Children   **01684 594 831**
30a Old Street, Upton-upon-Severn, WR8 0HW
www.travellingwithchildren.co.uk
The one stop shop for all your family holiday and day to day
travel needs

camping

Alan Rogers Travel Services   **01580 214014**
www.markhammerton.com
Camping, walking and cyling holiday specialist.

Canvas Holidays   **08709 022 022**
www.canvas.co.uk
An independent family camping holiday company with 39
years' experience of providing self-drive camping and mobile
home holidays in France and the rest of Europe, including
Spain, Italy, Luxembourg, Germany, Austria, Switzerland and
Holland.

Cornish Tipi Holidays   **01208 880 781**
www.cornish-tipi-holidays.co.uk
Family based holidays with an authentic flavour of camping.
The accommodation consists of medium and large tipis fully
equipped for 3 or 6 people. Large freshwater lake offers
swimming, boating and fishing with great beaches of Rock,
Polzeath and Port Isaac a few minutes' drive away.

Eurocamp   **0870 366 7558**
www.eurocamp.co.uk
Eurocamp is the market-leader in self-catering holidays to
Europe. Holidays cater for families (including babies) on 167
superbly equipped holiday parcs in 9 European countries.

Haven Europe   **0870 242 7777**
www.haveneurope.com
With 8 Haven Europe parcs in France and an additional 23 across France, Spain and Italy, these family orientated holidays offer specific children's activities between May and September. PAWs for the 1-4yr olds and the Tiger Club for the 5-12yrs olds. Babysitting from £3 per hour.

Keycamp Holidays   **0870 700 0123**
www.keycamp.co.uk
Stay in a fully equipped tent with 4 bedrooms or a luxury mobile home with shower and toilet. Camping sites are across France, Spain, Italy, Luxembourg, Austria, Switzerland and Holland.

homeswaps

National Childbirth Trust   **0870 444 8707**
The NCT Homeswaps register has been active for over 25 years, but welcomes non NCT members. Mainly UK properties with London homes being the most popular

Home Base Holidays   **020 8886 8752**
www.homebase-hols.com
International home holiday swaps.

Homelink International   **01344 842 642**
www.homelink.org.uk
With over 12,000 members in 50 countries.

Intervac Intl Home Exchange   **01225 892 208**
www.intervac.co.uk
One of the most well-known homeswap companies.

Latitudes Home Exchange   **01273 581 793**
www.home-swap.com

family villages & resorts

Club Med   **020 7581 1161**
Kennedy House, 115 Hammersmith Road, W14
www.clubmed.com
All- inclusive holiday villages located all over the world. A number of them offer childcare facilities for babies and young children during the day with good family discount packages.

Mark Warner   **08708 480 482**
10 Old Court Place, Kensington Church Street, W8
www.markwarner.co.uk
Winter ski and summer sun for children from 4mths+ with no additional childcare costs from 2-7yrs. Locations are Turkey, Greece and Corsica.

Sunsail   **023 9222 2300**
The Port House, Port Solent, PO6 4TH
www.sunsail.com
Family resorts in Antigua, Turkey and Greece. Many parents have recommended the Sunsail winter holiday in Antigua, but always lament that taking a toddler on such a long- haul flight almost ruined it. Childcare additional.

family ski companies

Chilly Powder   **020 7289 6958**
www.chillypowder.com
The Chilly Powder chalet is situated in Morzine on the French/Swiss border. Their in-house nanny can look after babies (2mths+), with bottle warming, sterilizer and baby-listening service also available. A crèche in Morzine (1-4yrs) provides all-day entertainment for toddlers and from 4yrs+ ski school is provided by the Ecole de Ski.

Meriski   **01451 843100**
If you have your heart set on Meribel, then Meriski provides either in-chalet nannies or crèche facilities (maximum of 8 places) from 9am-5pm Mon-Sat. Cots and highchairs are provided in the chalets, as well as kids' meals cooked separately by your chef. From 3yrs+ children can ski with Les Petits Loups, a ski school run by École de Ski Francais, accompanied by an English-speaking nanny.

Simply Ski   **020 8541 2207**
Simply Ski organise holidays to France, Austria, Switzerland and the USA (Aspen, Beaver Creek, Sundance). Their childcare is currently orientated around Europe where they provide their own crèches and ski schools as well as private nannies, ensuring that you and your children have great early experiences of family skiing holidays.

Ski Beat   **01243 780405**
Ski Beat offer holidays with childcare in 4 French resorts (La Plagne, Les Arcs, La Tania and Val d'Isere). Your options are crèches, nannies and afternoon care. Care is provided between 8.45am-5pm and include lunch and facilities for sleeping as well as toys, games and art & craft materials. If you are taking a whole chalet you may want to go for the private chalet nanny.

Ski Esprit   **01252 618300**
Ski Esprit have holidays in France, Italy and Austria. Their Classic Childcare options cater for children from 4mths-3yrs in a nursery setting, and the Spritolote Ski School from 3yrs-5yrs (max 6 in a class). A Snow Club in the afternoon keeps the non-skiing 3-5yr olds well entertained. The nannies are all English-speaking and care is available 6 days per week from 8.30am-5pm.

Ski Famille   **01223 363777**
www.skifamille.com
Ski Famille don't charge extra for childcare. They provide fully qualified nannies to your chalet where playrooms are equipped with toys, games and arts/craft materials. When the weather allows they encourage them to play outside. For older children they ensure they are at ski school on time and pick them up afterwards. Childcare is available between 9am-4.30pm except on Saturday or Wednesday. They have children's ski clothes for hire, sell nappies at cost and provide baby bottles, sterilizers, high chairs, cots and bedding.

Ski Scott Dunn   **020 8767 0202**
Ski Scott Dunn provide private nannies, children's clubs and the famous Scott Dunn Ski Schools to get even the youngest snowbears off to a good start. Chalets are well equipped with cots, highchairs etc including Pampers to enable you to travel lightly. Children are also not expected to share their parents' bedroom (for no additional cost).

parties

1st birthday parties are a baptism by fire for most first-time parents. The key is to provide lots of Champagne and food for the adults, and then things flow very well. Most babies find the wrapping paper the most interesting part of the present, and many young children are just too excited to eat. Once you are on the 3rd party, things do need to be well organised in order that there are no tears before cutting the cake, and your house isn't destroyed.

We have given some suggestions for choosing the right type of party for the age group with tips from the experts. Luckily for you there is an entire industry dedicated to making this a special day, so take your pick of our favourites.

First Birthdays

Usually held at home with family and a few friends (and not necessarily any other babies) – an excuse for them to shower your angel or urchin with gorgeous baby gifts (see personalised gifts).

Second and Third Birthdays

A tea party at home with small tables and chairs (see party equipment) will ensure that the catering aspect of the party contains itself to one room and not your carpet. A ball pond or a few tunnels will provide plenty of excitement for 2yr olds – but remember to put away toys that you don't want to be played with (especially the favourites or new presents). Party games like "pass the parcel" don't really work at 2yrs – so you can leave that one for another year.

At 3yrs we think the musical party is a must. The companies who offer music can orientate song selection around your child's favourites – or themed to the time of year. Many songs are acted out with a few props/costumes, making the whole event come alive.

You must plan to cater for parents as well – and make it clear whether siblings can come. We recommend that you just invite children from your child's age-group otherwise you will find you have older children getting bored and running riot

Fourth and Fifth Birthdays

If your child attends a nursery or playgroup, then you will find that this becomes a whole class event.

Parents are not expected to stay and you can let them know what time to pick the children up afterwards. You also need space if you want to hold the party at home – so many opt for an indoor activity centre (see toddler activities), or a party venue that has a party programme pre-prepared (see party venues). Themed parties with dressing up are very popular. You can also play traditional party games or try making things (see arts and crafts or cooking).

Party entertainers are in their element with the 4-5yr olds. Magic, silly songs, puppets, balloon modelling, bubble machines, face painting, white rabbits, doves, snakes – all delight and entrance; and such is their popularity you need to book around 6 weeks ahead, particularly during festive seasons such as Christmas. Entertainers normally attend for around 2 hrs with a 45 minute session whilst you are getting the food ready, then another 45 minutes after the meal. What makes a good entertainer? Getting all the children to remain seated, fully engaged and responsive for the whole session – and they're worth every penny.

Tips from the Experts

• Book your entertainer well ahead. If you haven't found a venue locally then many party organisers, such as Twizzle, have a whole range at their fingertips for every postcode. Let them know how many children they are entertaining and what the age range will be.

• Try and orientate parties around your child's natural mealtimes so that everyone has a good appetite. For 2-3yrs they recommend 11-1pm or 12-2pm rather than afternoons, and for 3-5yrs 12.30-2.30pm or 3.30-5.30pm.

• Liaise with other parents if children's birthdays in the same class clash across one weekend.

• Make sure the sweet things aren't on the table before the savoury – and decide whether to put the cake in the party bag or serve it at the table. Ask parents to mention allergies before the day so you can cater accordingly.

• Party bags are becoming ever more sophisticated, but stick to your budget and you'll be surprised how much you can find that delight the under 5s. (see party bag companies later).

For additional entertainers in other areas of the UK check the **www.babydirectory.com** website for our recommendations.

party food

Amato's Patiserie   020 7734 5733
14 Old Compton Street, W1
www.amato.co.uk
Seriously delicious cakes in all ranges (sponge, chocolate, fruit) in classic or themed styles

Annie Fry Catering Ltd   020 7351 4333
134 Lots Road, SW10 0RJ

Cake Dreams   **020 8889 2376**
61 Palace Gate Road, N22
www.cakedreams.co.uk
Delicious hand crafted fantasy cakes (see advert below)

Cake Artistry Centre   020 8567 1081
109 Midhurst Road, W13

Canapes Gastronomiques   **020 7794 2017**
34 Cholmley Gardens, Aldred Road, NW6
Catering for children's parties specialising in mini decorated cakes

Choccywoccydoodah   020 7724 5465
47 Harrowby Street, W1
www.choccywoccydoodah.com
Chocolate cakes that can be layered with fresh Belgian truffles for a really indulgent mouthful

Cake Dreams

come to life –
as a delicious
home-made cake!

Birthdays, Christenings,
all special occasions – adults too

Tracey Bush 020 8889 2376

www.cakedreams.co.uk

Extraordinary Cakes   020 8674 3570

Jane Asher Party Cakes   020 7584 6177
22-24 Cale Street, SW3
Select an off-the-shelf design, buy a cake kit and DIY, or design your own

La Cuisiniere   020 7223 4487
81-83, Northcote Road, SW11
Hire cake tins, birthday cakes, etc. Children's cutlery

Mallard Catering   020 7642 5495
84 Bellenden Road, SE15 4RQ

Nikki Brown Catering   020 8336 0395

Sweet Sensation   020 8838 1047
39 Goodhall Street, NW10

The Cake Store   0800 052 0058
www.thecakestore.com
Highly recommended online cake store with delivery to all London postcodes

party ideas

ARTS & CRAFTS

**Amazing Magical
Parties with NETTI**   01298 872 752
www.magicalnetti.co.uk

Art 4 Fun
212 Fortis Green Road, N10   020 8444 4333
172 West End Lane, NW6   020 7794 0800
444 Chiswick High Road, W4   020 8994 4100
196 Kensington Park Road, W11   020 7792 4567
www.Art4Fun.com
Make, design and decorate ceramics, wood, glass, mosaic. Great for parties

Brush Strokes   **020 8346 1486**
St Peter Le Poer Church Hall, Muswell Hill, N10
Art birthday parties. 18mths – 4yrs

Paint your own ceramics, wood, mosaics and fabric. Daily studio fee £4.95 and items from just £2.50. Ask about our parties

Chiswick, West Hampstead, Muswell Hill, Notting Hill
www.Art4Fun.com
020 8449 6500

The Clay Café   020 8905 5353
8-10 Monkville Parade, Finchley Road, NW11
www.theclaycafe.co.uk
Party fun at this ceramic cafe

Creative Wiz Kids   020 7794 6797
Fun and stimulating art parties with music, dancing, face
painting, parachutes and much more!

Crafty Parties   020 8992 3767
Have fun with clay, making jewellery and creative cards at an
arty party

Ink Tank Parties   020 7639 5611

Messy Play Parties   020 8959 9045
From 2yrs+ experiment with finger art, collage, playdough,
decorating biscuits, painting, water-play, stampers, glass
painting and beadwork for 5yrs+

Nellie's Art Parties   020 7428 7600
Kids spend 1 hr painting and decorating a giant collage
followed by games, food & drinks. Can be themed to the
child's favourite idea

Party Creations   020 7738 8495
Create an all in one party and going home present - how
smart is that? Paint your own apron, photo frame or
decorate a flower pot. From 2-8yrs

Petit Artisan   020 8931 3687
www.petitartisan.com
Creative and fun craft activities for children

Pottery Café   020 7736 2157
735 Fulham Road, SW6
www.pottery-café.com
Includes invitations, clay items & paints, sandwiches and drinks

COOKERY

Cookie Crumbles   020 8876 9912
www.cookiecrumbles.net
Arrange a cookery party for up to 15 kid.

Gill's Cookery Workshop   020 8458 2608
7 North Square, NW11
Saturday cookery parties at this location

Little Chefs   07989 771 379
Hands-on children's cooking parties and workshops.

FACE PAINTING

Fantastic Faces   020 8677 4193
Call Caragh for face painting parties and other occasions

Mini Makeovers   020 8398 0107
www.minimakeovers.com
Witness the metamorphis of your child into a glittering,
sparkling fairy

Creative Faces   07885 966 336
www.creativefaces.co.uk
A company supplying face painters to entertainers and direct
to parents. Over 10 years experience

David Jackson   020 7723 2913

Face Painting by Lynn   020 8749 0067

Fancy Faces   020 7372 1045

Magic Mirror   020 8764 8986

Sandra Wiseman   020 7794 8032

MUSIC

Amanda's Action Kids   020 8578 0234
W3/W4/W5
www.amandasactionkids.co.uk

Blueberry Playsongs   020 8677 6871
Clapham, Putney, Chelsea, Hammersmith
www.blueberry.clara.co.uk

Gymboree Play and Music   0800 092 0911
Bayswater, Islington, Putney, Swiss Cottage,
Wimbledon
www.gymboreeplayuk.com

Monkey Music   01582 766 464
www.monkeymusic.co.uk

Whippersnappers   020 7738 6633
Brockwell Lido, Dulwich Road, SE24
Including tables, chairs, helium balloons as well as songs,
puppets, disco, bubble machine

Vicky's Pop Star Parties   020 8446 7641
Makeover, dance routine, rehearsal and performance. Their
dreams come true

Story Fun   020 8444 0244
Specialising in birthdays for under 6s, acting out stories with
percussion instruments, drums and music.

SPORT

Active Kids   020 7281 2604
Unique, high energy, health-promoting parties. Tailor-made
to incorporate your child's favourite sport or activity. Call the
number above or 07939 277 943

Alexandra Palace Ice Rink   020 8365 2121
www.alexandrapalace.com
Includes 15 minutes of tuition before a free skating session,
drinks and a standard hot meal. Weekends only

Goals Wembley   020 8997 4040
www.goalsfootball.co.uk
You have 1hr on the all-weather five-a-side pitch with a
trophy given to the birthday boy/girl. Hot dogs, drinks and a
chocolate bar to fill up afterwards

In the Zone Jnr   07931 160 580
www.inthezonesports.co.uk
Tennis birthday party specialists

The Little Gym   **020 8874 6567**
Compass house, Riverside West, SW18
www.thelittlegym.co.uk
Fully supervised private party with music, games and obstacle courses that kids love. And they can take care of everything from invitations to clean-up. Parties are held on Saturday and Sunday afternoons

party entertainers

Action Station   020 7263 8468
www.theactionstation.co.uk
Interactive storytelling parties for 4-7 yrs. Fairies, mermaids, wizards, witches, spacemen, action heroes, pirates, cowboys

Albert & Friends Instant Circus   020 8741 5471
Albert the Clown does 2 styles of parties. For the 2-5yr age group he does games, magic, silly songs, balloons. For the 6yrs+ he does special circus workshops

Anna Bananna   020 8889 2695
Magic, puppets, balloons, music and dancing

Clarity The Clown   020 8690 4453
Puppets, silly songs, games, balloons, magic and bubbles

Clown Violly & Fairies   020 7281 2366
www.enchantingparties.com
Magic, music, puppets, balloons

Clozo The Clown   020 8907 3790
Mime, magic, music and dance with balloons, games and silly tricks. Circus-trained clown who gets up to lots of tricks

Diane's Puppets   020 7820 9466
1yr+. Gentle puppet parties for the very young

Fairy Jane   020 8877 0703
Fairyland parties for girls and boys under 5. 1-2hrs of treasure hunt, traditional party games, shake the parachute, music, cat and mouse games. Also little dances with fairies, mice and other small animals. All over London

Fizzie Lizzie   020 7723 3877

Happy Puzzle Company   0800 376 3727
www.happypuzzle.co.uk
For 5yrs+. Children will not just be sitting watching someone - this is a hands-on experience. The children are divided into teams and each team will do the same puzzle, moving on to the next challenge as they finish the previous one. It's all about puzzles!

Impeyan Productions   01992 446211
www.impeyan.co.uk
Have you thought about having a chinchilla, barn owl or Chilean rose spider to your party? Well if you have a young naturist in the family, then this is the perfect entertainment

Jenty the Gentle Clown   020 8207 0437
Singing, balloon modelling, puppets, face painting and dancing

Jolly Roger   020 8546 7985
From 4yrs+ join pirate Jolly Roger and his ship the Dirty Rat for a hilarious afternoon of entertainment

Julie's Gymjive Parties   020 8932 4123
For 1-4yrs. Parties with music and dance, bubbles, finger puppets, tunnels and climbing equipment

Jugglers etc   0870 777 2425
www.jugglingjohn.com
From 3yrs+ one of the artists from this agency will delight children with storytelling, juggling, comedy jokes

Katie Kickers Dance Parties   020 8803 2465
Dance parties with bubble machines, activity crafts, songs, parachute and games

Katie Rainbow   020 8675 3380
Fantastic storytelling with puppets (enormous giant puppets "it's behind you" pantomine style). Exotic magic, games and dancing. Delightful rainbow costume

Larry Parker   020 8788 4831
Experienced children's entertainer who will travel anywhere. Puppet show, balloon modelling, traditional games

Laurie Temple   **020 8840 5293**
The Party Wizard
www.thepartywizard.co.uk
Highly recommended. Fun filled parties for all ages plus themed parties and organising services (see advert on page 104)

Little Actors Drama Company   020 7231 6083
From 3yrs+. Themed parties, including request of your favourite cartoon character. A pool of professional actors (Equity members) ensures a great afternoon of entertainment

Lydie's Parties   020 7622 2540
Magical storytelling for Peter Pans, Batmans or in fairyland. Lydie has 10yrs experience as a dancer and jazz musician

Marvellous Productions   020 0679 0917
www.marvellousproductions.co.uk
Mrs Marvel will take you on a magic carpet ride with singing, dancing and music, and then make a puppet or mask in the theme of the event. See their website for lots of ideas

Mr Boo Boo   020 7727 3817
www.mr-booboo.co.uk
Music, games, puppets, silly songs, juggling, balloon modelling, bubble machines and much more (high recommended).

Mr Squash   020 8808 1415
Mr Squash puppets, magic and fun for 2-6 year olds

Mr Toots   020 8366 6051
Comedy magic, glove puppets, balloon modelling, games, mini discos. Performed at the Queen's Jubilee

Mrs Roundabout   01474 350 712
Specialising in parties for the under 7s

Mystical Fairies   020 7431 1888
Specialising in unique parties featuring fairies, princesses, Wizmo the Wizard, Peter Pan and many more magical characters

Partyplay   020 7737 6817
Drama leader for children's games and activities based around a theme (eg princes and princesses, Toy Story). Role play, physcial theatre, make-believe - very interactive and action packed. Suitable for 6-9yr olds

Patchy Peter & Snowy   01442 261 767
Magic, balloons, ventrilloquism, puppets and a live rabbit

Pekko's Puppets   020 8579 7651
www.pekkospuppets.co.uk
Excellent with the under-5s; wonderful puppets; imaginative, gentle, funny

Pippin Puppets   020 8348 4055
Choose from one of 12 popular puppet shows with magic and games from 2-8yrs

Pop Group Dance Parties   07778 122277
Disco, lights and atmospheric "smoke", teaching pop moves for the under 8s

Potters Parties   07779 271655
Games, drama, dancing and magic for children aged 3-8yrs

Pukka Parties   020 8677 6025
4yrs+

Sandy Sparkle   020 8747 3358
Puppets, face painting, magic, balloons, treasure hunts, party games keeping everyone fully engaged and enjoying every minute.

Seahorse Parties   020 8997 3355
Hundreds of fancy dress costumes for princes/princesses, medieval knights, animals and witches/wizards

Silly Milly the Clown   020 7823 8329
Funny magic shoes, puppets, party games, silly songs and balloon animals

Splodge   020 7350 1477
www.planetsplodge.com
Themed parties at Battersea Zoo or Holland Park Ecology centre for children aged 2-12yrs. Puppets and interactive treasure hunts are all part of the show

Tony Macaroni   020 8442 0122
Magic, puppet shows, games, storytelling from 3-13yrs

Vicky's Pop Star Parties   020 8446 7641
Makeover, dance routine, rehearsal and performance. Their dreams come true

Laurie Temple & The Party Wizard Company

Comedy magic, juggling, puppets, guitar & song, mini-disco, balloons,prizes, storytelling and games.

"Laurie is a regular favourite with all our nurseries" - A. Cook, Director Happy Child Nurseries Ltd.

"Highly Recommended" Time Out

Tel: 020 8840 5293
www.thepartywizzard.co.uk

Walligog The Wizard   0118 973 0737
Games, magic and animal fun with live rabbits and doves

Yogabananas   020 8874 3858
www.yogabananas.com
An inspiring, original and fun approach to a party that will introduce your child to the many benefits of yoga

YogaBugs   020 8772 1800
www.yogabugs.com
Yoga parties for the under 5s.

Zozo the Clown   020 7924 4649

party equipment

B Bounced   01895 905949
www.bbounced.co.uk

Bouncing Kics   020 8998 1008
www.kids-party.com
Hire and sale of bouncy castles, tables & chairs, balloons and party bags

Cool Quads   0844 450 0045
Electric cars, bouncy castles, slides and soft play equipment for hire

Great Jumps 020 7607 7690
www.greatjumps.co.uk
Bouncy castles with free delivery in North and Central
London. No cancellation fee

Mexicolore 020 7622 9577
www.mexicolore.co.uk
Handmade traditional papier mache Mexican party pinatas in
a wide range of colours and sizes

Playcoats 01823 270 196
www.playcoats.com
Imaginative and easy to use dressing up clothes for 3-6yrs

Seans Bouncy Castles 01295 271049
www.seansbouncycastles.co.uk

Wheelie Good Party Company 020 8386 2894
www.wheeliegoodparty.co.uk
Electric jeeps and specially designed tracks deliver to the
venue of your choice, with children enjoying hours of exciting
driving

party organisers

Children's Party Company Ltd 020 7930 3239
Emily Astor and Marie-Eve Jenkins offer a complete party
service including the catering, selecting an entertainer, table
decorations, face painting, the birthday cake, balloons and
party bags - either in your own home or at a local venue

Crechendo Events 020 8772 8140
www.crechendo.com
A fantastic range of magical parties for children from 1-16yrs
- you can choose from over 30 themes. Definitely worth
checking out

Happy Times 020 8746 4222
www.happytimes.com
Themed children's party planners and tailor-made parties

Jugglers Etc 020 8672 8468
www.jugglersetc.com
Juggling John was such a success with parents that he has
set up Jugglers Etc and can arrange everything from
selecting an entertainer to a complete party service.
Juggling, clowning, magic, face painting, games from 3-5yrs

KidzParties 020 7431 7953
www.kidzparties.biz
Professional party service for busy parents. They organise
everything and you just enjoy the party

Little People Parties 020 7358 1135
www.littlepeopleparties.co.uk
Children's party specialists

Mini Minors Birthday Parties 020 8371 9686
The cosiest, friendliest day and residential camps for children
and personalised birthday organisers. Branches: Christ
College School, East End Road, N2

Parties to Remember 020 7249 3242
A well thought through party service where children play lots
of traditional party games

Raspberry Productions 020 8952 6777
www.raspberryproductions.co.uk
Hand picked items to create your child's favourite birthday.
Entertainers, balloons, cakes, face painters, party bags

Twizzle Parties & Events 020 8789 3232
www.twizzle.co.uk
Organisers of children's parties from 2yrs+, offering a range
of different activities and themes for small children

party shops

Balloonland 020 8906 3302
12 Hale Lane, NW7
www.balloonland.co.uk

Bounce Away 020 8336 9090
Bouncy castles, tables, chairs for hire

Carnival 020 8567 3210
129 Little Ealing Lane, W5

Circus Circus 020 7731 4128
176 Wandsworth Bridge Road, SW6

Just Balloons 020 7434 3039
127 Wilton Road, SW1

It's My Party 020 7350 2763
23 Webbs Road, SW11

Oscar's Den 020 7328 6683
127-129 Abbey Road, NW6

Partyworks 0870 240 2103
www.partybypost.co.uk

Party Party 020 7267 9084
11 Southampton Road, NW5

Purple Planet 020 8969 4119
www.purpleplanet.co.uk

Party Plus 020 8987 8404
4 Acton Lane, Chiswick, W4

Party Superstore 020 7924 3210
268 Lavender Hill, SW11

Non Stop Party Shop
214-216 Kensington High Street, W8 020 7937 7200
694 Fulham Road, SW6 020 7384 1491

Surprises   020 8343 4200
82 Ballards Lane, N3

The Party Shop   020 8676 7900
67 High Street, Penge, SE20

party venues

Aquatic Experience (Syon Park)   020 8847 4730
www.aquatic-experience.org
Tour the rain forest and meet snakes, lizards, frogs and baby
crocs. Similar parties take place in the Butterfly House for the
less squemish. From 4yrs+

Blue Kangaroo   **020 7371 7622**
555 King's Road, SW6
www.thebluekangaroo.co.uk
Restaurant and party venues

Bramley's Big Adventure   020 8960 1515
136 Bramley Road, W10
www.bramleysbig.co.uk
One hour in the playground followed by tea in the party room.
Goody bags also provided

Golden Hinde   08700 118700
www.goldenhinde.co.uk
Pirate fun for 4-11yrs aboard Sir Francis Drake's 16th century
galleon. Includes treasure hunt, hoisting the anchor and
adventure tales

Highgate Newtown   020 7272 7201
Community Centre Skate and Bounce
Wonderful indoor and outdoor space for birthday parties

Horniman Museum   020 8699 1872
100 London Road, SE23
www.horniman.ac.uk
Parties in the Dutch Barn set in lovely landscaped gardens

The Party Bus   07836 605 032
www.childrenspartybus.co.uk
Up to 24 children accommodated for games, jokes and
magic tricks. Includes drinks and snacks

Puppet Theatre Barge   020 7249 6876
35 Blomfield Road, Little Venice, W9
www.puppetbarge.com
In addition to a puppet show you can hire the barge for
private parties

Science Museum Sleepover   020 7942 4747
www.sciencemuseum.org.uk
Book well in advance for these spectacular sleepovers

Wetlands Centre   020 8409 4407
www.wwt.org.uk
This Wetlands centre in Barnes can host a "pond-dipping"
party - great for nature enthusiasts

The Wonderbus   020 8968 3798
www.wonderbus.co.uk
From 2-7yrs for up to 15 children. Games, drawing, painting,
ball pool and slide. Includes food and drinks

london postcodes

© The Baby Directory

In order to help you find your nearest nursery, use this map to pinpoint where you live and which are your neighbouring postcodes.

nurseries

In this section we have listed all **independent** (ie private) Nursery Schools, Day Nurseries, Montessori and Bilingual Nurseries, in postcode order to help parents find places that offer high quality childcare and an early education. Compulsory education in the UK starts at 5yrs, but before that the following categories of care are on offer:

Day Nurseries: ages 3mths-5yrs; open 8am-6pm and for 48 or more weeks of the year. This includes catering for breakfast, lunch and tea, following the sleep routines set by parents, and gradually being introduced to a more structured day of music, play, painting, stories and outdoor games.

Nursery Schools: ages 2-5yrs; offers sessional care (ie 9am-12pm and/or 2pm-4pm), and are open on a termtime basis. Activities include music, play, painting, stories, games as well as early number and letter learning.

Montessori: many nurseries use Montessori methods, a system devised by Maria Montessori in 1907, which emphasises training of the senses and encouragement rather than a rigid academic curriculum

Bilingual Nurseries: these offer care either on a day nursery or nursery school basis, but have the additional advantage of your child being exposed to two languages. Children are gradually introduced to their second language through songs and simple instructions and within a term are happily conversing in either language.

Pre-Prep Schools which prepare your child for big school at 7, have been listed under Schools, pre-prep (page x) although some offer places for 3-4yr olds - so if you are looking for continuity then consult this category as well.

We have not listed **playgroups** as the parent or carer remains in attendance. If you are looking to meet local parents of similar aged children we recommend joining your local NCT group (see page x). For registered mother & baby groups (this doesn't exclude fathers) your local Council (see page 34) will provide a list.

For nearly all nurseries and schools in the private sector, early registration is recommended, so ring, visit and inform yourself in time, even if you later decide not to pursue that option. For a list of state-run nurseries and state primary schools with nursery classes contact your local council Early Years Education department (see councils) or check them out online via www.childcare.gov.uk

E1
Spitalfields Nursery   020 7375 0775
21 Lamb Street, E1 6EA
www.brighthorizons.co.uk
3mths-8yrs. full day. 8am-6pm. 50wks. (see advert on opposite page)

Alice Model Nursery   020 7790 5425
14 Beaumont Grove, E1 4NQ

Animal House Nursery   020 74807166
(Busy Bees)
69 Royal Mint Square, Cartwright Street, E1 8NB
3mths-5yrs. Full day

Buffer Bear at Barts   020 7641 4361
& The London (Whitechapel)
71 Varden Street, E1 1JB
3mths-5yrs. Full day

Dreammakers Nurseries Ltd   020 7480 7166
65-69 Cartwright St, E1 8NB

Green Gables Montessori School   020 74882374
St Paul's Institute, 302 The Highway, E1 9DH
18mths-5yrs. Full day

Kids Today   020 7709 0709
1 Knighten Street, Wapping Pier Head, E1W 1PW

The Nursery   020 7265 0098
St. Paul's Church, Dock St, E1 8JN

E2
Bethnal Green   020 7739 4343
Montessori School
68 Warner Place, E2 7DA

Columbia Market   020 7739 4518
Nursery School
Columbia Rd, E2 7PG

The Happy Nest Nursery Ltd   020 7739 3193
Fellows Court Centre, Weymouth Terrace, E2 8LR

Rachel Keeling Nursery school   020 8980 5856
Bullards Place, Morpeth Street, E2 0PS

Noah's Ark   020 7613 6346
Mildmay Hospital, Hackney Road, E2 7NA

Building children's futures...

Bright Horizons Family Solutions has nurseries throughout the London area and has been looking after the child care needs of London's parents for over ten years.

Our nurseries are places for listening to children and parents, for learning and teaching and for allowing children to grow and develop at their own pace. Our nurseries are OFSTED registered and our broad curriculum is in line with and approved by the National Daycare Standards for Childcare. All our nurseries have glowing OFSTED reports and we have seen children move onto school as confident learners.

Our nurseries are open-plan, purpose-designed buildings which allow children to move freely within a child-centred environment; all nurseries have their own garden for outdoor play. The staff at Bright Horizons Family Solutions nurseries are qualified, child-focused individuals who have additional training in areas such as first aid, child protection, special educational needs and curriculum for early years.

We accommodate children from 3 months to 5 years and full-time and part-time places are available 50 weeks of the year.

We have nurseries in the City, Dulwich, Chingford, Finchley, Highgate, Islington, Rainham, Waterloo and Wembley.

Call us on 020 7253 9620 and we'll be delighted to arrange a visit and send you an information pack.

www.brighthorizons.co.uk

Bright Horizons
FAMILY SOLUTIONS®

E3
Bow Nursery Centre　　　020 8981 0483
1 Bruce Rd, Bromley by Bow, E3 3HN

Childsplay　　　020 8983 4645
75 Kenilworth Road, E3 5RJ
3mnths - 5yrs

Overland Day Nursery　　　020 8981 1619
60 Pardell Rd, E3 2RU

Pilla Box Gardens Nursery Ltd　　　020 8983 7431
49 Fairfield Rd, E3 2QA

Pillar Box Montessori　　　020 8980 0700
Nursery School
107 Bow Road, E3 2AN
0-7yrs. Full day

E4
Ainslie Wood Nursery　　　020 8523 9910
140 Ainslie Wood Road, E4 9DD

Amhurst Nursery　　　020 8527 1614
13 The Avenue, E4 9LB
2-5yrs. Full day

Billet's Corner Nursery　　　**020 8523 3823**
11 Walthamstow Avenue, E4 8ST
www.brighthorizons.com
3mths-5yrs. Full day. 8am-6pm. 50wks (see advert on page 109)

Chingford Activity Nursery　　　020 8527 2902
22 Marborough Road, Chingford, E4 9AL
0-5yrs. Full day

Chingford Childrens Day Centre　　　020 8529 4067
Titley Close, E4 8PL
6mths-5yrs. Full day

College Gardens Nursery School　　　020 8529 3885
College Gardens, E4 7LQ
3-5yrs. Half days

Handsworth Avenue　　　020 8527 5364
Childrens Day Centre
32 Handsworth Avenue, E4 9PJ
6mths-5yrs. Full day

Jigsaw Day Nursery　　　020 8524 7063
2 Larkswood Leisure Park, 175 New Road, E4 9EY

The Marlborough　　　020 8527 2902
Activity Nursery
22 Marlborough Road, E4 9AL

Merryfield Montessori Nursery　　　020 8524 7697
76 Station Road, Chingford, E4 7BA
2-5yrs. Full day

Rocking Horse Nursery　　　020 8523 7030
1 Hatch Lane, E4 6LP
1-5yrs. Full day

Tiny Tots　　　020 8523 5046
101 Higham Station Avenue, E4 9AY

Woodlands Day Nursery　　　020 8531 0713
16a Handsworth Avenue, E4 9PJ

E5
Belz Nursery　　　020 8800 6186
96 Clapton Common, E5 9AL

Harrington Hill Nursery School　　　020 8806 9643
Wrens Park Estate, Warwick Grove, E5 9LL

Nightingale Nursery School　　　020 8985 5937
Rendlesham Road, E5 8PA

North London Rudolf　　　020 8986 8968
Steiner Nursery
89 Blurton Road, Hackney, E5 0NH

St. Michael's Nursery　　　020 8985 2886
59 Thistlewaite Road, E5 0QG

E6
Heritage Children's Day Nursery　　　020 7173 3522
116 Evelyn Dennington Road, E6 5YU

Oliver Thomas Nursery School　　　020 8552 1177
Mathews Avenue, E6 6BU

St. Stephens Nursery School　　　020 8471 1366
St. Stephens Road, E6 1AX

E7
Kaye Rowe Nursery School　　　020 8534 4403
Osborne Road, E7 0PH

E8
Independent Place Nursery　　　020 7275 7755
26-27 Independent Place, E8 2HD
6mths-5yrs. Full day
Market Nursery　　　020 7241 0978
Wilde Close, Hackney, E8 4JS

New generation　　　020 7249 9826
179 Haggerston Road, Haggerston, E8 4JA

Teddy Bear School　　　020 7249 4433
House Nursery
The Trinity Centre, Beechwood Road, E8 3DY

E9
Little Saint Nursery School Ltd　　　020 8533 6600
Wally Foster Centre, Homerton Road, E9 5QB

Wentworth Nursery School   020 8985 3491
Cassland Road, E9 5BY

E10
Alertkids Community Nursery   020 8558 8503
806 High Road, Leighton, E10 6AE
3mnths - 5yrs, 8am - 6pm, full time

Bright Kids Day Nursery   020 8558 0666
2 Leyton Mills, Marshall road, E10 5NH

Rainbow Montessori Nursery   020 8539 9005
71 Vicarage Road, Leyton, E10 5EF

Beaumont Nursery Unit   020 8518 7203
192 Vicarage Road, E10 5D

Hillcrest Nursery   020 8558 9889
Trinity Methodist Church, 274 High Road, E10 5PW

The Nappy Gang Nursery   020 8539 8359
88 Oliver Road, E10 5JY

Smilers Nursery   020 8558 1810
29 Vicarage Road, Leyton, E10 5EF
E11
Acacia Nursery school   020 8558 4444
Cecil Road, E11 3HF

Humpty Dumpty Nursery   **020 8539 3810**
24/26 Fairlop Road, Leytonstone, E11 1BN
www.ninawestnurseries.org.uk
Long established and highly recommended. 1-5yrs. Full day.
8am-6pm. See website for full details.

Just Learning Nursery   020 8988 0818
Whipps Cross Road, E11

Kiddy Care Day Nursery   020 8556 1732
62 Hainault Road, Leytonstone, E11 1EQ
Little Green Man Day Nursery   020 8539 7228
15 Lemna Road, E11 1HX

Sunbeams day Nursery   020 8530 2784
10 Bushwood, E11 3AY

Sunshine Day Nursery   020 8556 6889
167 Wallwood Road, E11 1AQ

Treehouse Nursery   020 8532 2535
35 Woodbine Place, E11 2RH
0-5 yrs

E12
Sheringham Nursery School   020 8553 2479
Sheringham Avenue, E12 5PB

Happy Faces At Wisdom   020 8478 2805
Kids Nursery
524 High Street, E12 6QN
2-5 yrs

E13
Coccinelle   020 8552 3340
663 Barking Road, E13 9EX

Foundation for Learning   020 7473 1412
Foster Road Nursery, Foster Road, E13 8bT
3mnths - 5yrs

Smarty Pants Day Nursery   020 8471 2620
1 Plashet Road, E13 0PZ

Stepping Stones Childcare   020 7476 8321
Kingsford Community School, Woodside Road, E13
4mths-5yrs. Full day, termtime only

E14
Bushytails Private   **020 7537 7776**
Day Nursery
Wood Wharf Business Park, Docklands, E14 9LZ
www.bushytailsdaynursery-school.co.uk
0-5yrs. Full day

Elizabeth Lansbury   020 7987 4358
Nursery School
Cordelia Street, E14 6DZ
Lanterns Nursery & Pre-School   020 7363 0951
F4-F6 Lanterns Court, Millharbour, E14 9TU

Unicorn Day Nursery   020 7513 0505
13 Columbus Courtyard, Canary Wharf, E14 4DA
3mnths-5yrs. Full day
E15
Rebecca Cheetham   020 8534 3136
Nursery School
Marcus Street, E15 3JT

Ronald Openshaw Nursery   020 8534 6196
Education Centre
Henniker Road, Stratford, E15 1JP

Stepping Stones Childcare   020 8534 8777
Brickfields Centre, Welfare Road, E15 4HT
6mths-5yrs. Full day

Ultimate Montessori   020 8519 2100
Day Nursery
9 Brydges Road, E15 1NA

E16
Abrahams Nursery & Kids Club   020 7476 3672
1 Radland Road, E16 1LN

Ceylon Cottage Nurseries   020 7511 0759
Ceylon Cottage, Butchers Road, E16 1PH

Foundations for Learning   020 7473 1412
Kimberley Rd, Nursery Kimberley Rd, E16 4NT
3mths-5 yrs

Leapfrog Day Nursery　0207 474 7487
Royal Victoria Docks, E16 1XL
www.leapfrogdaynurseries.co.uk
3mths-5yrs. 7am-7pm. 52wks. (see advert on page 119)

Mayflower Nursery School　020 7474 5263
Burke Street, Canning Town, E16 1ET

Rosecare Nursery　020 7474 0881
Custom House Baptist Church, Prince Regent Lane,
E16 3JJ

E17
Carville Day Nursery　020 8521 7612
43a West Avenue road, E17 9SF

Chapel End Early Years Centre　020 8527 9192
Brookscroft Road, E17 4LH

Church Hill Nursery　020 8520 9196
Woodbury Road, E17 9SB

Happy Child Pre　020 8520 8880
School Nursery
The Old Town Hall, 14b Orford Road, E17 9NL

Just Learning Day Nursery　020 8527 9711
20 Sutton Road, Higham Hill, E17 5QA

Koala Bear Day Nursery　020 8520 0762
Ross Wylde Hall, Church Hill, E17 3AA

Magic Roundabout Nursery　020 8523 5551
161 Wadham Road, E17 4HU

Rascals Day Nurseries　020 8520 2417
34 Verulam Avnue, E17 8ER

Tom Thumb Nursery　020 8520 1329
20 Shirley Close, 1-7 Beulah Road, E17 9LZ
www.ninawestnurseries.org.uk
Long established and highly recommended. 2-5yrs. Full day.
8am-6pm. See website for full details.

Tinkerbells Nursery　020 8520 8338
185 Coppermill Lane, Walthamstow, E17 7HU

Walthamstow Montesorri　020 8523 2968
School
Penrhyn Hall, Penrhyn Avenue, E17 5DA

E18
ABC Nursery and Pre-School　020 8530 8688
52-54 Chigwell Road, E18 1NN

Cleveland's Park Montessori　020 8518 8855
71 Cleveland Road, E18 2AE
3 mths to 5 yrs

Fareacres Nursery　020 8505 3248
1 Chelmsford Road, E18
3 mths to 5 yrs

Fullers Hall Community　020 8505 5779
Nursery
64a Fullers Road, South Woodford, E18 2QB
2-5 yrs

Heritage Childrens　020 8530 8688
Day Nursery
52-54 Chigwell Road, E18 1NN
Rainbow Kids Nursery　020 8504 1036
2 Malmesbury Road, E18 2NN

Treehouse Nursery　020 8504 1036
2 Malmesbury Road, E18 2NN
under 5

Woodlands Babies　020 8559 1247
194 Maybank Road, E18 1EL
3 mths to 2 yrs

EC1
Bright Horizons Family Solutions　020 7253 9620
Morelands, 5-23 Old Street, EC1V 9HL
www.brighthorizons.com

Leapfrog Day Nursery　020 778 0100
Weddel House, 13-21 West Smithfield, EC1A 9HU
www.leapfrogdaynurseries.co.uk
3mths-5yrs. Full day

Hopes and Dreams　020 7833 9388
339-341 City Road, EC1V 1LJ
www.hopesanddreams.co.uk
3mths-5yrs. Full day. The place to learn and grow (see advert
opposite)

EC2
Broadgate Nursery　020 7247 3491
21 Curtain Road, EC2 3LW
www.brighthorizons.co.uk
3mths-5yrs Full day. 8am-6pm. 50wks. (see ad on page 109)

Leapfrog Day Nursery　020 7422 0088
49 Clifton Street, EC2A 4EX
www.leapfrogdaynurseries.co.uk
3mths-5yrs. Full day. 7am-7pm. 52 wks. (see advert on page
119)

Newpark Childcare Centre　020 7638 5550
1 St Giles' Terrace, Barbican, EC2Y 8DU
www.newparkchildcare.co.uk
4mths-5yrs. 7am - 7pm. 50 weeks.

NORTH LONDON

N1

Beckett House   020 7278 8824
Montessori Nursery
98 Richmond Avenue, N1 0HR
2½-5yrs. Full day

The Children's House   020 7354 2113
77 Elmore Street, N1 3AQ
www.thechildrenshouseschool.co.uk
Nursery school and reception for children 2½-6yrs. Sessional.
Term-time only.

Floral Place Nursery   020 7354 9945
2 Floral Place, Northampton Grove, N1 2PL
www.brighthorizons.co.uk
3mths- 5yrs. Full day. 8am-6.30pm. 50wks.

The Grove Pre-School   020 7226 4037
& Nursery
3 Shepperton House, 91 Shepperton Road, N1 3DF
3mths-5yrs. Full day

Mace Montessori Nursery   020 7704 2805
327 Upper Street, N1 2XQ
2-5yrs. Full day

Mars Montessori Nursery   020 7704 2805
4 Collins Yard, Islington Green, N1 2XU
2-5yrs. 8am-6pm. 52 wks.

Rosemary Works   020 7613 5500
Early Years Centre
Unit 2a, Branch Place, N1 5PY
3mths-3yrs. Full day

St Andrew's Montessori   020 7700 2961
St Andrew's Church, Thornhill Square, N1 1BQ
3-5yrs

N2

Annemount Nursery School   020 8455 2132
18 Holne Chase, N2 0QN

Fortis Green Nursery   020 8883 1266
70 Fortis Green, N2 9EP
6 mths-5yrs. Full day

N3

Pentland Nursery   020 8970 2441
224 Squires Lane, Finchley, N3 2QL
www.brighthorizons.com
3mths-5yrs. full day. 8.30am-6pm. 50wks. (see advert on
page 109)

N4

Asquith Court Finsbury Park 020 7263 3090
Dulas Street, Islington, N4 3AF
www.asquithcourt.co.uk
3mths-5yrs. Full day. 8am-6pm. 51 wks. (see advert on page
117)

Hopes and Dreams...

MONTESSORI NURSERY SCHOOL

Superior care for children
aged 3 months to 5 years

Highly acclaimed Ofsted Report
and Quality Counts accreditation

Flexible hours and
drop-in facility available

Freshly prepared healthy,
organic meals

339 - 341 City Road,
Islington, London EC1V 1LJ
t: 020 7833 9388
e: office@hopesanddreams.co.uk
w: www.hopesanddreams.co.uk

Hopes and Dreams also run a professional Nanny
and Babysitting Agency

Crouch Hill Day Nursery   020 7561 1533
33 Crouch Hill, N4 4AP
3mths-5yrs. Full day

Finsbury Park Playgroup   020 7263 8397
The Hideaway, Ennis Road, N4 3HD

Holly Park Montessori   020 7263 6563
Holly Park Methodist Church Hall, Crouch Hill, N4
2-11yrs

Little Jewel Pre School   020 8341 27433
St Paul's Church Hall, Cavendish Road, N4 1RT
18mths-5yrs. Full day

North London   020 8986 8968
Rudolf Steiner School
0-7yrs

N5

Little Angels Day   020 7354 5070
Nursery & Pre-School
217 Blackstock Road, N5 2LL
3mths-5yrs. Little Angels independent day nursery and pre-
prep school - learning through play in a warm, secure
environment.See advert on page 115)

New Park Montessori   020 7226 1109
School & Nursery
67 Highbury New Park, N5 2EU
www.newparknursery.com
4mths-5yrs. 7.30am-6.30pm. 50wks.

N6

Avenue Nursery School   **020 8348 6815**
2 Highgate Avenue, N6 5RX
www.avenuenurseryschool.com
2½-7yrs. Sessional 9.30am-12pm or 1-3pm – then 9.30am-3pm for older children. Successful, long established school, large garden, caring and stimulating environment

Highgate Activity Nursery   020 8348 9248
1 Church Road, N6 4QH
Full day

Ladybird Montessori   020 7586 0740
The Scout Hall, Sheldon Avenue, N6 4ND
2½-5yrs. Mornings

Rainbow Montessori   020 7328 8986
Highgate United Reform Church, Pond Square, N6
2½-5yrs

N7

The Gower School   020 7700 2445
18 North Road, N7 9EY
3mths-5yrs

Mary Seacole Nursery   020 7281 6712
Tollington Way, N7 6QX
3mths-5 yrs. Full day

Sam Morris Centre Nursery   020 7609 1735
Parkside Crescent, Isledon Road, N7 7JG
6mths-5yrs. Full day

N8

Adventure Land Day Nursery   020 8347 6951
18 Gisburn Road, N8 7BS
2½-5yrs. Full day

Ark Montessori   020 8881 6556
Nursery School
42 Turnpike Lane, Hornsey, N8 0PS
2-5yrs. Full day

Claremont Day Nursery   020 8340 3841
7 Harold Road, N8 7DE
2-5yrs. Full day
Hollybush Nursery   020 8348 8537
5 Redston Road, N8 7HL
2-5yrs. Full day

Little Tree Montessori   020 8342 9231
143 Ferme Park Road, N8 9SG
2½-5yrs
Playland Day Nursery   020 8341 5199
40 Tottenham Lane, N8 7EA
2-5yrs.

Ruff 'N' Tumble   020 8348 2469
51 Crouch Hall Road, N8 8HH
2-5yrs. Full day

Starshine Nursery   020 8348 9909
Hornsey Club, Tivoli Road, N8 8RG
2-5yrs. Full day

N9

Blossoms   020 8351 0874
85 Bounces Road, Wapping Wall, N9 8LD

Edmonton Community   020 8807 9649
Day Nursery
24 Cyprus Road, N9 9PG
2½-5yrs. Full day
New Horizons Nursery   020 8351 8280
Walbrook House, 1 Huntingdon Road, N9 8LS
2-5yrs. Full day

Rainbow Nursery Firs Farm   020 8807 9078
1-4 Kipling Terrace, Great Cambridge Road, N9
2½ -5yrs
Tara Kindergarten   020 8804 4484
310-314 Hartford Road, N9 7HB
3mths-5yrs. Full day

N10

Montessori House   **020 8444 4399**
5 Princes Avenue, N10 3LS
www.montessori-house.co.uk
Full Montessori education for ages 2-5yrs+ in Central Muswell Hill

3-4-5 Pre-School   020 8883 1902
United Reform Church,Tetherdown, N10 1NB
2½-3yrs

3-4-5 Pre-School   07966 541889
Friends Meeting House, Church Crescent, N10 3NE
2½-5yrs

Grey Gates Nursery   020 8883 5640
182 Muswell Hill Road, N10 3NG
6mths-5yrs. 8.10am-5.45pm. 51 wks

Nursery Montessori   020 8883 7958
24 Tetherdown, Muswell Hill, N10 1NB
2-5yrs. Full day

Rosemount Nursery School   020 8883 5842
6 Grosvenor Road, Muswell Hill, N10 2DS
2-5yrs. Full day

N11
Teddies Nursery   **0800 980 3801**
60 Beaconsfield Rd, New Southgate, N11 5AE

N12
Finchley Nursery   020 8343 8500
David Lloyd Leisure, Finchley High Road, N12

"It was their excellent OFSTED report that impressed me"

Little Angels

Child centred day nursery
and pre-prep school

217 Blackstock Road, Highbury, London N5 2LL
New Highgate school opening in September

Little Angels independent day nursery and pre-prep school provides a warm, caring environment for your child.

We have created an exciting and stimulating framework based on learning through play. The rich and varied curriculum will take children from 3 months to 5 years through to reception. And there is a range of additional activities including French, Spanish, gym time, cooking, music and drama at no extra cost.

The staff to child ratio ensures constant supervision, with one to one care available when necessary. Our premises have both a bright open plan interior and secure garden play area and with all meals cooked fresh on the premises, we provide a home from home for the children of busy working parents.

For a personal introduction, individual guided tour and to view the OFSTED Report, call Caroline Thompson on **020 7354 5070** or email: **littleangels@btconnect.com**

Opening times: 8.30 am – 6.00 pm Monday – Friday
(By arrangement 8.00 am – 6.30 pm)
Minimum 3 half-days per week

N14

Asquith Court Salcombe Pre-School 020 8882 2136
33 The Green, Southgate, N14 6EN
www.asquithcourt.co.uk
2-5yrs. Full day. 8am-6pm. 51wks. (see advert on page 117)

Shining Eyes & Busy Minds Pre-School 020 8350 4584
West Grove Primary School, Chase Road, N14 4LR
2-5yrs. Full day

Southgate Day Nursery 020 8886 2824
25 Oakwood Avenue, N14 6QH
3mths-5yrs. Full day

Wonderland Day Nursery 020 8886 6163
2-16 Burleigh Parade, Burleigh Gardens, N14 5HN
3mths-5yrs. Full day

N15

Sugar Plum Nursery 020 8800 7560
255 West Green Road, N15 5JN
2-5yrs. Full day

Under 5s Centre 020 8808 9194
The Green, Phillips Lane, N15 4GZ
2-5yrs. Full day

N16

Coconut Nursery 020 7923 0720
133 Stoke Newington Church Street, N16 0UH
2-5yrs

Mini Home 020 7249 0725
14 Allen Road, N16 8SD
3mths-5yrs. Full day 8am-6pm. 51 wks

Sunrise Nursery 020 8806 6279
1 Cazenove Road, N16 6PA
2-4½yrs. Full day

Thumbelina Nursery 020 7354 1278
169-171 Green Lanes, N16 9DB
www.ninawestnurseries.org.uk
Long established and highly recommended. 2-5yrs. Full day.
8am-6pm. See website for full details.

N17

Blossoms Nursery 020 8808 0178
Unit 10, Imperial House, 64 Willoughby Lane, N17
2-5yrs. Full day

Penn Nursery 020 8808 7373
33 Forester Road, N17 6QD
2-5yrs. Full day

Sunrise Nursery　　020 8885 3354
55 Coniston Road, N17 0EX
2½-5yrs

N18
Ashland Private Day Nursery　　020 8345 5752
36 Weir Hall Road, N18 1EJ
2-5yrs

Tinkerbells Nursery　　020 8372 7682
2 Amersham Avenue, N18 1DT
0-5yrs. Full day

N19
Chameleon Nursery　　020 7272 9111
76 Dartmouth Park Hill, N19 5HU
3mths-5yrs. Full day

Montpelier Nursery　　020 7485 9813
115 Brecknock Road, N19 5AH
3-5yrs. Full day

N21
Leapfrog Day Nursery　　**020 8360 6610**
2 Florey Square, Highlands Village, N21 1UJ
www.leapfrogdaynurseries.co.uk
3mths-5yrs. Full day. 7am-7pm. 52wks.(see advert on page 119)

Visit our lovely Day Nurseries and see happy children at work and play...

Nurseries at Chiswick, Winchmore Hill, High Barnet and Staines

FREEPHONE
0800 731 6644
www.childbase.com
CHILD BASE Nurseries
NDNA

Bumble Bees Montessori　　020 8364 3647
Day Nursery
8 Uplands Way, Winchmore Hill, N21 1DG
2-5yrs

Highfields Day Nursery　　020 8360 6101
698 Green Lanes, N21 3RE
2-5yrs. Full day

Teddys Day Nursery　　020 8364 3842
18 Green Dragon Lane, N21 2LD
3mths-5yrs. Full day

Woodberry Day Nursery　　**020 8882 6917**
63 Church Hill, Winchmore Hill, N21 1LE
www.childbase.com
6wks-5yrs, 8am-6pm, 52 week per year. Child Base nurseries follow the Sound Foundations curriculum providing building blocks for your child's development.

N22
3-4-5 Pre-School　　07778 739319
c/o The Actual Workshop, Alexandra Park, N22
2½-5yrs

Alexandra Nursery School　　020 8374 9492
189 Alexandra Park Road, N22 7BJ
2-5yrs

Bowes Park Nursery　　020 8888 1142
63-65 Whittington Road, N22 2BQ
1-5yrs. Full day

Kids Business　　020 8881 5738
New River Sports Centre, White Hart Lane, N22
2-5yrs. Full day

Rainbow Corner Nursery　　020 8888 5862
24 Elgin Road, N22 7UE
2-5yrs. Full day

NORTH WEST LONDON
NW1
Agar Community Nursery　　020 7485 5195
Wrotham Road, NW1 9SU
2-5yrs. Full day

Alpha Beta Nursery　　020 7482 2263
16 Kentish Town Road, NW1 9NX

Bringing Up Baby:　　**020 7284 3600**
Camden Day Nursery
123-127 St Pancras Way, NW1 0SY
www.bringingupbaby.co.uk
A day nursery for 16 children aged 3mths - 3yrs. Open 8.15am - 6.15pm. Full year (see advert on page121).

Daisies Day Nursery -　　**020 7498 2922**
Regents Park
15 Gloucester Gate, NW1
From 3mths-5yrs. Full day 8am-6pm. 52wks. (see advert on page 127)

Asquith Nurseries

The highest quality childcare and education

We offer a safe, stimulating and happy environment for children aged 3 months to 5 years.

- Secure, caring environment
- Education through play
- Flexible schedules
- Qualified and experienced staff
- DfES/OFSTED regulated

Safe, Loved and Learning ®

For a nursery or pre-school near you, please call **0800 591 875**

Open 8am - 6pm throughout the year

Web: www.asquithcourt.co.uk

Dolphin Montessori School 020 7267 3994
Luther Tyndale Church Hall, Leighton Cresc., NW1
2½-4½yrs

St Mark's Square 020 7586 8383
Nursery School
St Mark's Church, St Mark's Square, NW1 7TN
2-5yrs. Full day

NW2
Fordwych Nursery 020 8208 2591
107 Fordwych Road, NW2 3TL
2-5yrs
The Little Ark Montessori 020 7794 6359
Nursery School
80 Westbere Road, NW2 3RU
2-5yrs. Full day

Montessori Nursery School 020 8209 0813
St Cuthberts Church, Fordwych Road, NW2 3TG
2½-5yrs

Neasden Montessori 020 8208 1631
St Catherine's Church Hall, Dudden Hill Lane, NW2
2½-5yrs

NW3
Belsize Square Synagogue 020 7431 3823
Nursery School
51 Belsize Square, NW3 4HX
2½ -5yrs

Chalcot Montessori School 020 7722 1386
9 Chalcot Gardens, NW3 4YB

Cherryfields Preschool Nursery 020 7431 0055
523 Finchley Road, NW3 7BD
2-5yrs

Church Row Nursery 020 7431 2603
Hampstead Parish Church, Church Row, NW3 6UP
2-5yrs

Eton Nursery 020 7722 1532
Montessori School
45 Buckland Crescent, NW3 5DJ
2-5yrs. Full day

Hampstead Hill Nursery School 020 7435 6262
St. Stephens Hall, Pond Street, NW3 2PP
2-5yrs. Full day

Maria Montessori 020 7435 3646
Children's House
26 Lyndhurst Gardens, NW3 5NW
www.montessori-ami.org
2½-6yrs. Full day

Octagon Nursery School 020 7586 3206
Saint Saviour's Church Hall, Eton Road, NW3 4SU
2½-5yrs

Oak Tree Nursery 020 7435 1916
2 Arkwright Road, NW3 6PD
www.devonshirehouseschool.co.uk
2½-11yrs Girls, 13yrs Boys. Part of Devonshire House
School.

Olivers Montessori 020 7435 5898
Nursery School
52 Belsize Square, NW3 4HN
2-5yrs

Peter Piper Nursery School 020 7431 7402
St Luke's Church Hall, Kidderpore Avenue, NW3
2-5yrs. 9am-1.00pm. Friendly and stimulating spacious
nursery environment.

Primrose Nursery 020 7794 5865
(Rudolph Steiner)
32 Glenilla Road, NW3 4AN
3-5yrs

Ready, Steady, Go 020 7586 6289
12a King Henry's Road, NW3 3RP
2½-5yrs

North Bridge House 020 7435 9641
Stepping Stone School
33 Fitzjohn's Avenue, NW3 5JY
2½-5yrs

NW4
Asquith Court 020 8203 9020
Nursery Hendon
46 Allington Road, NW4 3DE
www.asquithcourt.co.uk
18mths-5yrs. Full day (see advert on page 117)

Asquith Court Hill Park 020 8201 5817
5 Sunningfields Road, Hendon, NW4 4QR
www.asquithcourt.co.uk
18mths-5yrs. Full day. (see advert on page 117)

NW5
Brining Up Baby – 020 7284 3600
Kentish Town
37 Ryland Road
www.bringingupbaby.co.uk
A day nursery for 55 children aged 3mths-5yrs. open 8am-
6.15pm. 50 wks. (see advert on page 121)

Highgate Children's Centre 020 7485 5252
Highgate Studios, 53-79 Highgate Road, NW5
www.brighthorizons.com
3mths-5yrs. Full day. 8am-6.30pm. 50wks. (See advert on
page 109)

Leapfrog Day Nurseries...
for the BEST
in childcare!

We offer the best service to our parents
and the best care for 0–8 year olds!

All of our Nurseries have fantastic facilities, including
- Safe, fun environments
- Individual play areas
- CCTV and Secure Access Systems
- Open 7am - 7pm, Monday to Friday
- Full and part time places available for 0-5 year olds
- Holiday Club for 3-8 year olds
- OFSTED Registered

little things matter more!

Contact your nearest **Leapfrog Day Nursery** now!

Central London, EC2A ☎ 0207 422 0088
Smithfield, EC1A ☎ 0207 778 0100
Royal Victoria Docks, E16 ☎ 0207 474 7487
Chiswick, W4 ☎ 0208 742 0011
Enfield, N21 ☎ 0208 360 6610
Mill Hill, NW7 ☎ 0208 906 9123

leapfrogdaynurseries.co.uk

Bluebells Nursery   020 7284 3952
Our Lady Help of Christians Church Hall, Lady
Margaret Rd, NW5
2½-5yrs

Chaston Place Nursery   020 7482 0701
Chaston Place, off Grafton Terrace, NW5 4JH
3mths-7yrs. Full day

Cresswood Nursery   020 7485 1551
215 Queen's Crescent, NW5 4DP
2-5yrs. Full day

Rooftops Nursery   020 7267 7949
Priestley House, Athlone Street, NW5 4LN
2-4yrs. Full day

Truro Street Nursery   020 7485 0276
7-12 Truro Street, NW5 3PX
2½-5yrs

York Rise Nursery   020 7485 7962
St Mary Brookfield Church Hall, York Rise, NW5
1SB
2-5yrs. Full day

NW6
Asquith Court   020 7328 4787
West Hampstead
11 Woodchurch Road, NW6 3PL
www.asquithcourt.co.uk
18mths-5yrs. Full day 8am-6pm. 51 wks (see advert on page
117)

Beehive Montessori   020 8969 2235
147 Chevening Road, NW6
2-5yrs. Full day

Chaston Nursery School   020 7372 2120
30-31 Palmerston Road, NW6 2JL
3mths-5yrs. Full day

Crickets Montessori   07811 102 085
Nursery School
Milverton Road, NW6 7AR
2½-5yrs. 9am-3pm. Termtime only. Unique setting within the
extensive grounds of a cricket club where parking is problem
free.

Happy Child Day Nursery   020 7328 8791
2 Victoria Road, NW6 6QG
3mths-5yrs

Happy Child   020 7625 1966
Church Hall, 125 Salusbury Road,NW6 6RG
2-5yrs. Full day

The Learning Tree Nursery 020 7372 7213
Quex Road, Methodist Church, NW6 4PR
2½-5yrs

Mackenzie Day Nursery   020 7624 0370
St Mary's Church Hall, Abbey Road, NW6 4SR
2-5yrs. Full day

Rainbow Montessori School 020 7328 8986
(Sherriff Road)
St James's Hall, Sherriff Road, NW6 2AP
2½-5yrs

Sington Nursery   020 7431 1279
Portakabins Comm. Centre, 160 Mill Lane, NW6
3-5yrs. Full day

Teddies Nurseries   **020 7372 3290**
West Hampstead
2 West End Lane, NW6 4NT
www.teddiesnurseries.co.uk
3mths-5yrs. Full day (See advert on page 139)

NW7
Leapfrog Day Nursery   **020 8906 9123**
30 Millway, Mill Hill, NW7 3RB
www.leapfrogdaynurseries.co.uk
3mths-5yrs. Full day 7am-7pm. 52 wks (see advert on page
119)

NW8
Buffer Bear Nursery   020 7641 4491
86 Carlton Hill, NW8 0ER
6mths-5yrs. Full day

St John's Wood   020 7286 3859
Synagogue Kindergarten
37/41 Grove End Road, NW8 9NA
2-5yrs

Toddler's Inn Nursery School 020 7586 0520
Cicely Davies Hall, Cochrane Street, NW8 7NX
2-5yrs. Full day

NW9
Joel Nursery   **020 8200 0189**
214 Colindeep Lane, NW9 6DF
www.ninawestnurseries.org.uk
Long established and highly recommended. 2-5yrs. Full day.
8am-6pm. See website for details.

Gower House School   020 8205 2509
& Nursery
Blackbird Hill, NW9 8RR
2-11yrs

NW10
Almost Big School   020 8453 0136
32 Crouch Road, NW10 8HR
2-4yrs. Full day

Happy Child Day Nursery   020 8961 3485
15 Longstone Avenue, NW10 3TY
3mths-5yrs. Full day

bringing up baby

We offer your child the best start in life

High quality Day Nursery provision for 3 months to 5 year olds
Qualified staff to meet all emotional, social and cultural needs

Safe, welcoming, child friendly premises
Open minimum 50 weeks, 10 hour days

Nurseries in
Brentford • Hammersmith • Kentish Town • Wembley

Limited places available • Corporate discounts
web • www.bringingupbaby.co.uk • e-mail • office@bringingupbaby.co.uk

020 7622 5552

INVESTOR IN PEOPLE

Kindercare Montessori 020 8838 1688
Bridge Park Sports Centre, Harrow Road, NW10
2-5yrs. Full day

NW11
Asquith Court Pre-School, 020 8458 7388
Golders Green
212 Golders Green Road, NW11 9AT
www.asquithcourt.co.uk
12mths-5 yrs. Full day 8am-6pm. 51 wks (see advert on page 117)

Clowns 020 8455 7333
153 North End Road, Golders Green, NW11 7HX
1-5yrs. Full day.

Hellenic College 020 8455 8511
Montessori Nursery
Greek Orthodox Cathedral of Holy Cross & St Michael, NW11
2½-5yrs

Hoop Lane Montessori School 020 8209 0813
31.5 Hoop Lane, Unitarian Church Hall, NW11 8BS
2½-5yrs. Mornings only

Pardes House Kindergarten 020 8458 4003
Golders Green Synagogue, 41 Dunston Rd, NW11
2-4. Full day

SOUTH EAST LONDON
SE1
Waterloo Nursery 020 7721 7432
The Chandlery, 50A Westminster Bridge Road, SE1
www.brighthorizons.com
3mths-5yrs. Full day. 8am-6pm. 50wks. (see advert on page 109)

Coral Day Nursery 020 7928 0597
Windmill House, Wootton Street, SE1 8LY
0-5yrs. Full day

Kintore Way Nursery 020 7237 1894
Grange Road, SE1 3BW
3-5yrs. Part & full time

St Patrick's Creche, 020 7928 5557
Nursery and Montessori School
91 Cornwall Road, SE1 8TH
3mths-5. Full day.

SE2
Croft Day Nursery 01322 431045
75 Woolwich, SE2 0DY
4mths-5yrs. Full day

SE3
Blackheath Day Nursery 020 8305 2526
The Rectory Field, Charlton Road, SE3
6mths-5yrs. Full day

Blackheath Nursery and Prep 020 8858 0692
4 St German Place, SE3 8SW
3-11yrs
Blackheath Montessori Centre 020 8852 6765
Independents Road, Blackheath, SE3 9LF
Co-ed 3-5yrs. Full day

Greenwich Steiner School 020 8318 7787
3 North Several, SE3 0QR
3-6_. Mornings

Lingfield Day Nursery 020 8858 1388
37 Kidbrooke Grove, SE3 0LJ
18mths-5yrs. Full day

SE4
Catherine House Day Nursery 020 8692 5015
71 Tressillian Road, Brockley, SE4 1WA
3mths-5yrs. Full day.

Chelwood Nursery School 020 7639 2514
Chelwood Walk, Turnam Road, Brockley, SE4 2QQ
3-5yrs.

Cherry Li Nursery 020 8691 0497
40 Tyrwhitt Road, Brockley, SE4 1QT
2-5yrs. Full day

Dressington Pre-School 020 8690 9845
30 Rushey Mead, Brockley, SE4 1GG
2-5yrs. Full day

Hillyfields Day Nursery 020 8694 1069
41 Harcourt Road, Brockley, SE4 2AJ
2-5yrs. Full day

Lillingtons' Montessori 020 8690 2184
Nursery School
20 Chudleigh Road, Ladywell, SE4 1JW
2½-5yrs. Full day

Little Gems 020 8692 0061
Clare Road, Brockley, SE4 6PX
2-5yrs. Full day

SE5
Our Precious Ones 020 7701 9857
Clemance Hall, Brisbane Street, SE5 7NL
2-5yrs. Full day

South East Montessori 020 7737 1719
40 Ivanhoe Road, SE5 8DJ
2-5yrs. Full day

St John's Montessori Nursery 020 7737 2123
Crawford Tenants Hall, Denmark Road, SE5 9EW
2-5yrs. Full day

The Nest Playgroup   020 7978 9158
& Pre-School
Longfield Hall, 50 Knatchbull Road, SE5 9QY
2½-5yrs.

SE6
Beechfield Nursery   020 8690 2447
35 Beechfield Road, SE6 4NG

Broadfields Nursery   020 8697 1488
96 Broadfield Road, SE6 1NG

Little Learners Day Nursery   020 8291 3994
Rubens Street, Catford, SE6 4TH
18mths-5yrs. Full day

Thornsbeach Day Nursery   020 8697 7699
Thornsbeach Road, Catford, SE6
2-5yrs. Full day

Little Acorns Day Nursery   020 8690 9507
13 Exbury Road, SE6 4NB

Pavilion Day Nursery   020 8698 0878
The Pavilion, Penerley Road, SE6 2LQ

Peter Pan Nursery   020 8695 0082
353 Bromley Road, SE6 2RP

SE7
Pound Park Nursery School   020 8858 1791
Pound Park Road, Charlton, SE7 8AS
3-4½yrs. Part time

SE8
Bunny Hop Day Nursery   020 8691 7171
1 King Fisher Square, Deptford, SE8
2-4½yrs. Full day

Clyde Nursery School   020 8692 3653
Alverton Street, Deptford, SE8 5NH
3-5yrs.

Rachel McMillan   020 8692 4041
Nursery School
McMillan Street, Deptford, SE8 3EH

Rainbow Nursery   020 8692 1224
44 Alverton Street, SE8
2-5yrs. Full day

SE9
Asquith Court New Eltham   020 8851 5057
699 Sidcup Road
www.asquithcourt.co.uk
3mths-5yrs. Full day 8am-6pm. 51 wks (see advert on page 117)

Coombe Nursery   020 8850 4445
467 Footscray Road, New Eltham, SE9 3UH
2-5yrs. Full day

Elizabeth Terrace Day Nursery   020 8294 0377
18-22 Elizabeth Terrace, Eltham, SE9 5DR
4mths-5yrs. Full day
Willow Park Day Nursery   020 8850 8988
13 Gleneck Road, SE9 1EG
2mths-2yrs. Full day

SE10
Mrs Bartlett's Nursery   020 8692 1014
The Church of the Ascension, Dartmouth Row,
SE10
2½-5yrs

Sommerville Day Nursery   020 8691 9080
East Side Stage, Sparta Street, SE10 8DQ
2-4yrs. Full day

Teddies Nursery   0800 980 3801
Chevening Rd, Greenwich, SE10 0LB

SE11
Ethelred Nursery School   020 7582 9711
10, Lollard Street, Lollard Street, SE11 6UT
3-4yrs.

Toad Hall Nursery School   020 7735 5087
37 St Mary's Gardens, SE11 4UF
2mths-5yrs. Full day

Vauxhall Christian Centre   020 7582 2618
Playgroup
Tyers Street, Vauxhall, SE11 6UT
2½-5yrs. Mornings

William Wilberforce   020 7735 6317
Day Nursery
Longton House, Lambeth Walk, SE11 6LU
6mths-5yrs. Full day

SE12
Asquith Court   020 8856 1328
Kidbrooke Park Creche
Kidbrooke Park Rd, corner of Weigall Road, SE12
www.asquithcourt.co.uk
Full day (see advert on page 117)

Colfe's Prep School   020 8852 2283
Horn Park Lane, Lee, SE12 8AW
3-18yrs. Full day

Grove Park Pre-School   020 8857 8258
353 Baring Road, Grove Park, SE12 0EE
3mths- 5yrs. Full day

Lingfield Day Nursery   020 8851 7800
155 Baring Road, SE12 0LA
18mths-5yrs. Full day

Riverston Prep School   020 8318 4327
63-69 Eltham Road, SE12 8UF
1-16yrs. Full day

SE13
The Coach House Montessori   020 8297 2021
30 Slaithwaite Road, Lewisham, SE13 6DL
2-5yrs. Full day

Little Gems Day Nursery   020 8692 0061
Clare Road, Barclay, Barclay, SE13 6PX
2-4½yrs. Full day

Mother Goose Nursery   020 8694 8700
113 Brooke Bank Road, SE13
1-5yrs. Full day

Sandrock Day Nursery   020 8692 8844
10 Sandrock Road, SE13 7TR
2-5yrs. Full day

Saplings Day Nursery   **020 8852 8071**
83a Belmont Hill, Lewisham, SE13 5AX
4mths-5 yrs. Full day. Where birth to 3 matters just as much
as laying the foundations for school.

Step by Step Day Nursery   020 8297 5070
Dindon House, Monument Garden, SE13 6TP
3mths-5yrs. Full day

Village Nursery   020 8690 6766
St Mary Centre, Ladywell Road, SE13 7HU
2-5yrs. Full day

SE14
Stars of Hope Nursery   020 7639 1777
74 Wildgoose Drive, SE14 5LL
2-5yrs. Full day

Stepping Stones   020 7277 6288
Montessori Nursery
Church of God of Prophecy, Kitto Road, SE14 5TW
6mths-5yrs. Full day

Woodpecker Early Years   020 8694 9557
20 Woodpecker Road, SE14 6EU
2-5yrs. Full day

SE15
Bellenden Day Nursery   020 7639 4896
198 Bellenden Road, SE15
2-5yrs. Full day

Colourbox Day Nursery   020 7277 9662
385 Ivydale Road, SE15 3ED
6mths-5yrs. Full day

Goslings Day Nursery   020 7639 5261
106 Evelina Road, SE15 3HL
6mths-5yrs. Full day

Ladybird Nursery   020 7639 5943
143 Peckham Rye, SE15 3UL
2-5yrs. Full day

Mother Goose Nursery   020 7277 5956
54 Linden Grove, Nunhead, SE15 3LF
3mths-2yrs. Full day

Mother Goose Nursery   020 7277 5951
34 Waveney Avenue, Nunhead, SE15 3UE
18mths-5yrs. Full day

Nell Gwynn Nursery   020 7252 8265
Meeting House Lane, Peckham, SE15 2TT
3-5yrs. Full & part-time places

Peckham Rye Day Nursery   020 7635 5501
24 Waveney Avenue, Peckham Rye, SE15 3UE
4mths-5yrs. Full day.

Playaway Dulwich Daycare   020 7277 9662
385 Ivydale Road, Peckham, SE15 3ID
6mths-5yrs. Full day

Sankofa Day Nursery   020 7277 6243
14 Sharratt Street, SE15
2-5yrs. Full day

The Villa Nursery   020 7703 6216
54 Lyndhurst Grove, SE15 5AH
6mths-7yrs. Full day

SE16
Five Steps Community Nursery   020 7237 2376
51-52 Alpine Road, SE16 2RE
2-5yrs. Full day

Little Acorns   020 7252 2300
St. James's Church Hall, 30 St. James's Rd, SE16

Playschool Montessori Nursery   020 7394 3389
Lambourne House, Eugenia Road, SE16 2QT

Scallywags Day Nursery   020 7252 3225
St Crispin's Church Hall, Southwark Park Rd, SE16
2-5yrs. Full day

Trinity Childcare   020 7231 5842
Holy Trinity Church Hall, Bryan Road, SE16 1HB
2-5yrs. Full day

SE17
Elephant & Castle Day Nursery   020 7277 4488
15 Hampton Street, SE17 3AN
6mths-5yrs. Full day

St Wilfrid's Montessori   020 7701 2800
Pre-School
101-105 Lorrimore Road, Kennington, SE17 3LZ

Hours 8-6, 49 weeks, 'a home from home'

SE18

Cyril Henry Nursery School   020 8854 0178
St Mary Street, Woolwich, SE18 5AT
3-5yrs. Full day

Plumstead Manor Pre-school   020 8855 0124
Old Mill Road, SE18 1QF
3-5yrs.

Simba Day Nursery   020 8317 0451
Artillery Place, Woolwich, SE18 4AB
2-4yrs. Full day

Woolwich Common Nursery   020 8854 3695
Woolwich Common, SE18 4DG
3-5yrs.

SE19

Crown Point Nursery   020 8766 7737
316 Beulah Hill, Upper Norwood, SE19 3HF
2-5yrs. Full day

Downsview Nursery   020 8764 4611
Biggin Way, Upper Norwood, SE19 3XE
$3_{1/2}$ - $4_{1/2}$yrs. Sessional

Little Crystal Day Nursery   020 8771 0393
49 Maberley Road, Upper Norwood, SE19 2GE
2-5yrs. Full day

Norwood Playgroup   020 8766 6227
Crown Dale, SE19 3NX
$2_{1/2}$-5yrs.

SE20

Anerley Montessori   020 8778 2810
45 Anerley Park, SE20
2-5yrs. Full day

Norris Day Nursery   020 8778 9152
1 Thornsett Road, Amerley, Amerley, SE20 7XR
2-5yrs. Full day

SE21

Asquith Court Dulwich   **020 8761 6750**
Chancellor Grove, West Dulwich, SE21 8EG
www.asquithcourt.co.uk
18mths-5yrs. Full day 8am-6pm. 51wks (see advert on page 117)

Chellow Dene Day Nursery   020 8670 9001
134 Croxted Road, SE21 8NR
18mths-5yrs. Full day

Clive Hall Day Nursery   020 8761 9000
54 Clive Road, SE21 8BY
3mths-5yrs. Full day 8am-6pm. 51 wks

Ducks in Dulwich   **020 8693 1538**
Eller Bank, 87 College Road, SE21
3mths-7yrs. Full day.

Dulwich Montessori   **020 8766 0091**
St Stephen's Church, College Road, SE21
$2_{1/2}$-5yrs

Dulwich College Prep   **020 8670 3217**
42, Alleyn Park, Alleyn Park, SE21 7AA
$2_{1/2}$-5yrs. Full day

Dulwich Village Pre-school   **020 8693 2402**
Old Alleynian Club, Dulwich Common, SE21 7HA
3-5yrs

Nelly's Nursery   **020 8761 4178**
27 Turney Road, SE21 8LX
3-5yrs. Mornings only

SE22

Dulwich Nursery   **020 7738 4007**
80 Dog Kennel Hill, SE22 8BD
www.brighthorizons.com
3mths-5yrs. Full day 8am-6pm. 50 wks (see advert on page 109)

Bojangles Nursery School   **020 8693 2076**
New Life Assembly Church, Upland Rd, East Dulwich, SE22
18mths-5yrs. Full day

Buds Pre-School   **020 8299 2255**
Marlborough Cricket Club, Dulwich Common
$2_{1/2}$-5yrs. Part-time

First Steps Montessori   **020 8299 6897**
254 Uplands Road, East Dulwich, SE22
2-5yrs. Full day

Mother Goose Nursery   **020 8693 9429**
248 Upland Road, East Dulwich, SE22
1-5yrs. Full day 8am-6pm

Puddleduck Nursery   **020 8291 4735**
Goose Green Centre, East Dulwich Road, SE22 9AT
$2_{1/2}$-5yrs

SE23

Bojangles   **020 8693 2076**
St Saviour Church Hall, 69 Brockley Road, SE23

Cottage Day Nursery   **020 8291 7117**
St Hilda's Church Hall, Courtrai Road, SE23 1PL
15mths-5yrs. Full day

Sydenham Pre-School   **0117 967 3942**
Macklin House, Shackleton Close, SE23 3YP

Woodmount Nursery School   020 8699 6625
118 Malham Road, SE23 1AN

SE24
Halfmoon Montessori Nursery   020 7326 5300
155 Half Moon Lane, SE24
2½-5yrs. Full day

Herne Hill School   020 7274 6336
Old Vicarage, 127 Herne Hill, SE24 9LY
3-7yrs

Heron Day Nursery   020 7274 2894
St Jones Hall, Lowden Road, SE24 0HZ
2-5yrs. Full day

Little Fingers   020 7274 4864
Montessori Nursery
The Edward Alleyn Club, Burbage Rd, Herne Hill,
SE24
2½-5yrs

Ruskin House School   020 7737 4317
48 Herne Hill, SE24 9QP
3mths-5yrs. 7am-7pm. 51wks.

SE25
Andrews Montessori   020 8239 0049
95 Selhurst Road, SE25 6LH

Children's Paradise   020 8654 1737
Day Nursery
2-4 Crowther Road, South Norwood, SE25 5QW
3mths-5yrs. Full day

The Mulberry Kindergarden   020 8656 4945
10 Howard Road, SE25 5BU

Very Young Village   020 8665 0595
Day Nursery
18 Selhurst Place, Selhurst, SE25

Crossfield Nursery School   020 8654 7566
Elborough Road, SE25 5BD

Children's Paradise   020 8654 1737
Day Nursery
2-4 Crowther Road, SE25 5QW

SE26
Cornerstone Day Nursery   020 8676 0478
& Pre-school
2 Jews Walk, SE26 6PL
2-5yrs

Crystal Day Nursery   020 8659 6417
202 Venner Road, Sydenham, SE26 5HT
2-5yrs. Full day

Little Cherubs Nursery   020 8778 3232
Bell Green Lane, 127 Herne Hill, SE26 5TB
3mths-5yrs. Full day

Puzzle House Nursery   020 8291 9844
Trinity Path, Sydenham, SE26 4EA
2-5yrs

Sydenham Hill Kindergarten   020 8693 6880
Sydenham Hill Community Hall, Sydenham Hill,
SE26
2½-5yrs

SE27
Noah's Ark Nursery   020 8761 1307
St Cuthberts Church, Elmcourt Road, SE27 9BZ
2-7½yrs

Norwood Manor Nursery   020 8766 0246
48 Chapel Road, West Norwood, SE27 0UR
www.manortreenurseries.co.uk

Norwood Day Nursery   020 8766 6899
Co-Operative
Gypsy Road, SE27 9TG
3mths-5yrs. Full day (until 5pm)

One World Nursery   020 8670 3511
11 Thurlby Road, SE27 0RL
2-4yrs. Full day

SE28
Triangle Day Nursery   020 8311 4685
61 Kellner Rd, West, SE28
6wks-5yrs. Full day

SOUTH WEST LONDON
SW1
Daisies Day Nursery   **020 7498 2922**
- Pimlico
St James the Less School, Moreton Street, SW1V
From 3mths-5yrs. full day. 8am-6pm. 52wks.

Knightsbridge Kindergarten   020 7371 2306
St Peter's Church, Eaton Square, SW1W 9AL
2-5yrs

Little House at Napier Hall   020 7592 0195
Hide Place, Vincent Square, SW1P 4NJ
18mths-5yrs

Miss Morley's Nursery School   020 7730 5797
Fountain Court, Buckingham Palace Rd, SW1
2½-5yrs

Moreton Day Pre-School   020 7821 1979
18 Churton Street, SW1V 2LL
6mths-5yrs

Moreton Day Nursery   020 7233 8979
Lower Ground Floor, 31 Moreton Street, SW1V 2PA
2½-5yrs. Full day. Also Moreton Day Pre-School

Ringrose Kindergarten Pimlico   020 7976 6511
32a Lupus Street, SW1V 3DZ
2½-5yrs.

Thomas's Kindergarten   020 7730 3596
St Barnabas Church, 14 Ranelagh Grove, SW1W
2_-4yrs

Young England Kindergarten   020 7834 3171
St Saviour's Hall, St George's Square, SW1V 3QW
2½-5yrs
SW2
Elm Park Montessori   020 8678 1990
Nursery School
Brixton Hill Methodist Church, Elm Park, SW2 2TX
2-5yrs

Little Trees Nursery   020 8674 6912
Streatham & Clapham High School, Wavertree Rd,
SW2
Co-ed 3-5yrs. Girls 5-18yrs. Senior school: Abbotswoood
Road, SW16

Nightingale Montessori   020 7924 6100
Nursery School
St Luke's Community Hall, 194 Ramsden Rd, SW2

2-5yrs. Geared to the enjoyment of learning. Music, dance,
French, art and garden play.

Streatham Montessori   020 8674 2208
Nursery
66 Blairderry Road, SW2 4SB
2½-5yrs. Full day

Tiny Hands   020 7737 4371
Brockwell Park Community Centre, Effra Parade,
SW2
2-5yrs. Full day

SW3
The Noah's Ark   020 7924 7808
Nursery School/L'Arche de Noe
TAVR, Duke of York's HQ, King's Road, SW3
3-5yrs

Ringrose Kindergarten   020 7352 8784
St Luke's Church Hall, St Luke's Street, SW3 3RP

SW4
Abacus Pre-School   020 7720 7290
Kindergarten
Clapham United Reform Church, Grafton Square,
SW4
2-5yrs. Full day

HYDE PARK NURSERY IN W2 OPENS SEPT 04

DAISIES

DAY NURSERIES
& SCHOOLS

**Beautiful nurseries,
happy children!**

loving attention and
pre-school education

8am-6pm Open all year

3mths - 5 years

020 7498 2922

HYDE PARK · PIMLICO · REGENTS PARK · STOCKWELL

Ark on the Park Nursery School   020 8673 5736
Windmill Drive, Clapham Common, SW4 9DE
2-5yrs. Termtime.

Clapham Montessori   020 7498 8324
St Paul's Church Hall, Rectory Grove, SW4 0DX
2-6yrs. 9.15am-3.45pm. 34 wks

Clapham Park Montessori   020 7498 8324
St James Church House, 10 West Road, SW4 7DN
2½-6yrs

Daisies Day Nursery   020 7738 8606
& School
Stockwell Methodist Church, Jeffreys Road, SW4
18mths-5yrs. Excellence in education and daycare

Elm Park Nursery   020 8678 1990
90 Clarence Avenue, Clapham, SW4 8JR
6mths-5yrs. Full day

Eton House, The Manor   020 7924 6000
Nursery School
58 Clapham Common Northside, SW4 9RU

Magic Mind   020 8674 5544
4 Helby Road, SW4 8BU
1-5yrs. Full day

Parkgate Montessori School   020 7350 2452
80 Clapham Common Northside, SW4 9SD
2½-5yrs.

Squirrels Nursery School   020 8673 1277
Agnes Riley Gardens, Poynders Road, SW4 8PR
2-5yrs. Termtime, mornings.

SW5
Ladybird Nursery School   020 7244 7771
Crypt, St Jude's Church, 24 Collingham Road, SW5
3-5yrs. Mornings

SW6
Bobby's Playhouse   020 7386 5265
16 Lettice Street, SW6 4EH
www.bobbysplayhouse.co.uk
3mths-5yrs. Family run day nursery in modern premises

Bumpsa Daisies Nursery   020 7736 7037
Broomhouse Lane, Fulham, SW6 3DR
www.bumpsadaisies.com
3mths-4yrs. Full day. Family run day nursery with enclosed
outdoor area. Full-time and part-time place availabe.

Dawmouse Montessori   020 7381 9385
Nursery
Brunswick Club, 34 Haldane Road, SW6 7EU
2-5yrs

Home From Home   020 7736 9029
56 Quarrendon Street, SW6 3SU
age range 6mths-4yrs. 8am-6pm.

Kiddi Caru Day Nursery   0800 028 4500
2 Piazza Buildings, Empress State, SW6 1TR
www.kiddicaru.com
Brand new purpose built nursery providing childcare at its
best.

Little People of Fulham   020 7386 0006
250A Lillie Road, SW6 7PX
6mths-5yrs. Full day

Little Tug Boat Day Nursery   020 7731 6648
3 Finlay Street, Fulham, SW6 6HE
3mths-5yrs. Full day

Peques Nursery School   020 7385 0055
St John's Church, Waltham Green, North End Rd, SW6
www.peques-nursery.co.uk
3mths-5yrs. 8am to 6pm. 50 weeks per year. For a safe,
happy, secure, learning and developing environment.

Petits Enfants   020 7381 2409
344 Fulham Palace Road, SW6 6HT
3mths-5 yrs

Playhouse Nursery School   020 7385 6053
17 Burnthwaite Road, SW6 5BQ
www.theplayhousenursery.co.uk
First class teaching and care in a homely environment with
lots of love and fun.

Pippa Pop-ins   020 7385 2458
430 Fulham Road, SW6 1DU

Puffins   020 7736 7442
60 Hugon Road, SW6 3EN
3-5yrs. Sessional 9am-12pm and 1pm-3.30pm. Termtime.

Rising Star Montessori School   020 7381 3511
St Clement Church Hall, 286 Fulham Palace Rd,
SW6
2-5yrs

Roche School   020 7731 8788
70 Fulham High Street, SW6 3LG
www.therocheshcool.co.uk
3-11yrs

Rocking Horse Kindergarten   020 8772 0181
14 Effie Road, Eelbrook Common, SW6 1TB
2½-5yrs

Saplings Nursery   020 7610 6900
233 New Kings Road, SW6 4XE

Saplings Nursery   **020 7610 6900**
219 New Kings Road, Parsons Green
3mths- 5yrs. Full day. Where birth to 3 matters just as much as laying the foundations for school.

Scribbles 2   **020 7381 8794**
St Peter's Church Hall, 2 St Peter's Terrace
1-5yrs

Seahorses   **020 7385 7173**
Montessori Nursery I
William Thompson Memorial Hall, Burnthwaite Rd
2½-5yrs. Full day

Childcare

219 & 233 New Kings Road, SW6 4XE
Telephone: 020 7610 9900/020 7610 6900
Age Range: 3 months – 5 years. Full day.
Established 1999

Also at:
Bromley, Kent 020 8464 0965 established 1996
Croydon, Surrey 020 8681 7579 established 1997
Lewisham, SE13 5AX 020 8852 8071 established 1991

Head Office: 48 Sydenham Road, Croydon 020 8681 8484

the playhouse nursery

Experts in child day care and pre-school
education, we welcome babies and children
from 3 months upwards.
Registered with OFSTED.
Grant funding available.

Call 020 7385 6053 or visit our website:
www.theplayhousenursery.co.uk
17 Burnthwaite Road, Fulham SW6
Email: info@theplayhousenursery.co.uk

Paint Pots
MONTESSORI NURSERY SCHOOLS
IN CHELSEA AND BAYSWATER
AGED 2½- 5 YEARS
EST. 1988
Also Arts, Crafts, Music + Drama
Classes 18m - 6years

Tel: 0207 376 4571

Home from Home

Parsons Green

Personal Homely Childcare
In a fun interactive learning environment

Full & Part time childcare from 6mths

Please contact: Charlotte Winham (NNEB)
OFSTED Registered Childminder
Telephone: 020 7736 9029

FULHAM'S PREMIER
ANGLO-SPANISH NURSERY SCHOOL
"Providing Learning & Development
for Your Child"
020 7385 0055

Child Day Care leading to Pre-School Education
From 6 months to 5 years
Grant funding for 3 & 4 year olds
Ofsted Approved
50 weeks per year - 8am to 6pm
Spanish optional

2 Minutes walk from Fulham Broadway Tube
St Johns Church Hall, North End Rd, Fulham Broadway SW6
www.peques-nursery.co.uk info@peques-nursery.co.uk

Seahorses Montessori   **020 7385 7173**
Nursery II
St Etheldreda's Church Hall, Cloncurry Street, SW6
2-5yrs. Full day

Studio Day Nursery   **020 7736 9256**
93 Moore Park Road, SW6
2-5yrs. 8am-7pm.

Studio Day Nursery   **020 7736 9256**
93 Moore Park Road, SW6 2DA
2-5yrs. Full day

Teddies Nurseries Fulham   **020 7384 3197**
316 Wandsworth Bridge Road, SW6 2TZ
www.teddiesnurseries.co.uk
3mths-5yrs. Full day

Zebedee Nursery School   **020 7371 9224**
Sullivan Hall, Parsons Green, SW6 4TN
2-5yrs. Mornings

SW7

Hampshire School   **020 7370 7081**
5 Wetherby Place, SW7 4NX
3-6yrs. Sessional 8.55am-3.25pm. 35 wks.

Knightsbridge Nursery School   **020 7584 2766**
51 Thurloe Square, SW7 2SX
2½-5yrs

Miss Willcocks'   **020 7937 2027**
Nursery School
Holy Trinity Church, Prince Consort Road, SW7
2½-5yrs

Ovenstone House   **020 7584 7955**
22 Queensbury Place, SW7 2DZ
2-5yrs. Full day

Pooh Corner Kindergarten   **020 7373 6111**
St Stephens Church Hall, 48 Emperor's Gate, SW7
2-5yrs (See advert on page 134)

Ravenstone House Pre-Preparatory
School and Nursery   **020 7584 7955**
22 Queensberry Place, SW7 2DX
www.ravenstonehouse.co.uk
2mths-2½yrs. Full time 8am-6pm. 44wks.. First class
education for children, first rate service for parents (see ad on
page 137)

Ravenstone House Pre-Preparatory
School and Nursery   **020 7584 7955**
24 Elvaston Place
www.ravenstonehouse.co.uk
2mths-11yrs. Full time 7.30am-6.30pm. 48wks.
Zebedee Nursery School I   **020 7584 7660**

St Pauls Church Hall, Onslow Square, SW7 3NX
2-5yrs

SW8
Nine Elms Day Nursery   **020 7627 5191**
Savona Club House, Askalon Street, SW8 4DL
1-5yrs. Full day

Oval Montessori Nursery   **020 7735 4816**
88 Fentiman Road, SW8 1LA
3-5yrs

Springtime Day Nursery   **020 7720 5255**
200 Wandsworth Road, SW8 2JU
2-5yrs. Full day

St Monica's Nursery   **020 7582 0840**
83-87 Clapham Road, SW8
2-5yrs. Full day

The Willow Nursery   **020 7498 0319**
Clapham Baptist Church, 823-5 Wandsworth Rd,
SW8
2½-5yrs

SW9

Asquith Court Lambeth   **020 7793 9922**
50 Groveway, Lambeth, SW9 0AR
www.asquithcourt.co.uk
3mths-5yrs. Full day. (see advert on page 117)

Bunnies on the Green   **020 7738 4795**
United Reform Church, 60 Stockwell Road, SW9
2-5yrs. Full day

Wiltshire Nursery   **020 7274 4446**
85 Wiltshire Road, SW9 7NZ
18mths-5yrs. Full day

SW10
Ashburnham Day Nursery   **020 7376 5085**
Ashburnham Community Centre, Tetcott Rd, SW10
2-5yrs. Full day

Boltons Nursery School   **020 7351 6993**
262b Fulham Road, SW10 9EL
2½-5yrs. Full day

Chelsea Kindergarten   **020 7352 4856**
St Andrew's Church, Park Walk, SW10 0AU
2-5yrs

Paint Pots   **020 7376 4571**
Montessori School
Chelsea Christian Centre, Edith Grove, SW10 0LB
2½-5yrs. Developing confidence, independence, self-esteem,
concentration social skills and self-discipline

Tadpoles Nursery School   020 7352 9757
Park Walk Play Centre, Park Walk, SW10 0AY
2½-5yrs

Worlds End Pre-School   020 7351 1641
18 Blantyre Street, SW10 0DS
2½-5yrs. 9.30am-1.25pm. Termtime.

SW11

**Asquith Court Pre-School
and Nursery Battersea**   020 7228 7008
18/30 Latchmere Road, SW11 2DX
www.asquithcourt.co.uk
3mths-5yrs. Full day.(see advert on page 117)

Barnaby Bright   020 7978 4109
Nursery School
St. Barnabas Church, 12 Lavender Gardens, SW11
www.barnabybright.org.uk
2-5yrs. 9.30am-12.30pm. Termtime only

Blundells Traditional   020 7924 4204
Teaching Nursery
The Old Court, 194-196 Sheepcote Lane, SW11
18mths-5yrs

Bridge Lane Nursery   020 7564 3425
18 Bridge Lane, SW11 3AD
3mths-5yrs. 7am-7pm. 51wks.

Bumble Bee School   020 7350 2970
Church of the Ascension, Pountney Road, SW11
2½-5yrs

Clapham Junction Nursery   020 7924 1267
Asda Precinct, 204 Lavender Hill, SW11 1JG
1-5yrs. Full day

Happy Times   0800 652 2424
40 Park Gate Road, SW11 4NP
www.happytimes.co.uk
Great day nursery in London for children aged 3mths - 5yrs.
(see advert on page 145)

Little Red Hen   020 7738 0321
Church of the Nazarene, 2 Grant Road, SW11 2NU
2½-5yrs

Mini Me Montessori   020 7622 7049
6 Cupar Road, SW11 4JW
2½-4½yrs. 9.15am-12pm and 1.15pm-3.30pm. Timetime.

Mouse House Nursery   020 7924 1893
25-27 Mallinson Road, SW11 1BW
2-5yrs

Noah's Ark   020 7228 9593
St Michael's Church Hall, Cobham Close, SW11

Park Kindergarten   01622 833 331
St Saviour's House, 351 Battersea Park Rd, SW11
2-5yrs. Termtime (see advert on page134)

Plantation Wharf Day Nursery   020 7978 5819
18 Cinammon Row, Plantation Wharf, SW11 3TW
3mths-5yrs. Full day

Somerset Nursery School   020 7223 5455
157 Battersea Church Road, SW11 3ND
3-5yrs

Sparkies Playschool   07939 268861
St Vincent de Paul, 36 Altenburg Gardens, SW11
2-5yrs

Thomas's Kindergarten   020 7738 0400
St Mary's Church, Battersea Church Road, SW11
2½-4yrs. Caring environment in beautiful riverside location.
Government Early Years Curriculum

Victory Day School   020 7207 1423
140 Battersea Park Road, SW11 4NB
3mths-5yrs. Full day

SW12

Abacus Day Nursery   020 8675 8093
135 Laitwood Road, SW12 9QH
18mths-5yrs. Full day

Asquith Court Balham   020 8673 1467
36 Radbourne Road, Balham, SW12 0EF
www.asquithcourt.co.uk
3mths-5yrs. Full day 8am-6pm. 51 wks

Caterpillar I Nursery School   020 8673 6058
74 Endlesham Road, SW12 8JL
2½-5yrs

Caterpillar II Nursery School   020 8265 5224
14a Boundaries Road, SW12 8EX
2½-5yrs.

Crescent Kindergarten III   01622 833 331
The Grafton Tennis Club, 70aThornton Road, SW12
2-5yrs. Term-time.

Gateway House   020 8675 8258
Nursery School
St Jude's Church Hall, Heslop Road, SW12 8EG
2½-4yrs

Les Petits Benjamins   020 8673 8525
Oldridge Road, Clapham South
www.ecoledesbenjamins.com
5mths-2yrs. Full day 7.30am-6.30pm

Nightingales Nursery   020 8772 6056
St Francis Xavier College, Malwood Road, SW12
3mths-5 yrs. Full day

Noah's Ark   020 8772 0432
Church of the Ascension, Malwood Road, SW12

Noah's Ark Nursery School   020 7228 9593
Endlesham Church Hall, 48 Endlesham Rd, SW12

Oaktree Nursery School   020 8870 8441
21 Ramsden Road, SW12 8QX
2½-5yrs

Second Step Day Nursery   020 8673 6817
60 Ravenslea Road, SW12 8RU

Yukon Day Nursery   020 8675 8838
Yukon Road, SW12 9DN
2-5yrs. 8am-6pm or sessional.

Wainwright Montessori School   020 8673 8037
102 Chestnut Grove, SW12 8JJ
2½-5yrs.

SW13
The Ark Nursery School   020 8741 4751
Kitson Hall, Kitson Road, SW13 9HJ
3-5yrs

Ladybird Day Nursery   020 8741 1155
Trinity Church Road, SW13 SEU

Montessori Pavilion   020 8878 9695
Vine Road Recreation Ground, SW13 0NE
3-8yrs

St Michael's Nursery School   020 8567 8037
Elmbank Gardens, SW13 0NX
2-5yrs. Mornings

Village Nursery School   020 8878 3297
Methodist Church Hall, Station Road, SW13 0LP
2½-5yrs

SW14
Ladybird Montessori Nursery   020 8741 1155
Trinity Hall, Trinity Church Road, SW14 8ES
2-5yrs. 8am-6pm. 52 wks

New Spring Nursery School   07944 040 894
All Saints Church Hall, Park Avenue, SW14 8AR

Parkway Nursery School   020 8878 3955
55 St Leonard's Road, SW14 7NQ
3-5yrs. Termtime, mornings.

Parkside School   020 8876 8144
459B Upper Richmond Road West, SW14 7PL
16mths-4yrs. Full day

Playhouse Nursery School   020 8392 2877
East Sheen Baptist Church, SW14 7RS

Rainbow Nursery School   020 8546 0324
The Pavilion, Sheen Common, Fife Road, SW14

St Magdalene Montessori   020 8878 0756
61 North Worple Way, SW14 8PR

Working Mums Day Care   020 8392 9969
and Pre-School Centre
Mortlake Green School, Lower Richmond Rd, SW14
3mths-5yrs

SW15
Asquith Court Putney   **020 8246 5611**
107-109 Norroy Road, SW15 1PH
www.asquithcourt.co.uk
9mths-5yrs. full day. 8am-6pm. 51wks. (see ad on page 117)

Beehive Nursery School   020 8780 5333
St Margaret's Church Hall, Putney Park Lane, SW15
2½-5yrs

Bees Knees Nursery School   020 8876 8252
12 Priory Lane, SW15 5JQ
2½-5yrs

Busy Bee Nursery   020 8780 1615
106 Felsham Road, SW15

Busy Bee Nursery School   020 8789 0132
19 Lytton Grove, SW15

Gwendolen House   **020 8704 1107**
Nursery School
39 Gwendolen Avenue, SW15 6EP
Montessori based teaching plus music, dance, yoga and french. Nutritious menu (principally organic ingredients.) Beautiful garden.

Kingston Vale Montessori   020 8546 3442
Robin Hood Lane, Kingston Vale, SW15 3PY
2-5yrs. Mornings

Noddy's Nursery School   020 8785 9191
2 Gwendolen Avenue, Putney, SW15 6EH
4mths-5yrs. Full day

Riverside Nursery   020 8780 9345
95 Lacy Road, SW15 1NR
3mths-5yrs. Full time

Ro's Nursery   020 8788 5704
Putney Leisure Centre, SW15 1BL
6mths-5yrs. 8am-6pm or sessional

Schoolroom Montessori   020 7384 0479
St Simon's Church Hall, Hazlewell Road, SW15 6LU

2½-5yrs.

Tiggers Nursery School   020 8874 4668
87 Putney Bridge Road, SW15 2PA
2½-5yrs

SW16
Abacus Early Learning Nursery   020 8677 9117
7 Drewstead Road, SW16 1LY
18mths-5yrs. Full day

Blossomtime Montessori   020 7564 8295
Nursery School
130 Sunnyhill Road, SW16 2UN

Carey Days Nursery   020 8679 4009
496 Streatham High Road, SW16 3QB
www.careydays.com
New specialised baby nursery catering for children aged
3mths-3yrs. Open 8am-6pm (Mon-Fri) 51 weeks per year.

Stepping Stones Day Nursery   020 8679 4009
496 Streatham High Road, SW16 3QF

Elm Park Nursery   020 8696 7737
27 Aldrington Road, nr.Tooting BecCommon, SW16
3mths-5yrs

Monti's Day Nursery   020 8876 4115
6 Lilian Road, SW16 5HN
18mths-5yrs. Full day

Teddies Nurseries   0800 980 3801
Streatham
113 Blegborough Road, SW16 6DL
www.teddiesnurseries.co.uk
3mth-5yrs. Full day. 8am-6pm. (see advert on page 139)

Waldorf School of   020 8769 6587
South-West London
16-18 Abbotswood Road, SW16 1AP
3½-14yrs

SW17
Crescent Kindergarten I   01622 833 331
10 Trinity Crescent, SW17 7AE
2-5yrs. Termtime (see advert on page 134)

Crescent Kindergarten II   01622 833 331
74 Trinity Road, SW17 7SQ
2-5yrs. Termtime

Eveline Day Nursery School   020 8672 7549
30 Ritherdon Road, SW17 8QD
3mths-5yrs. Full day.

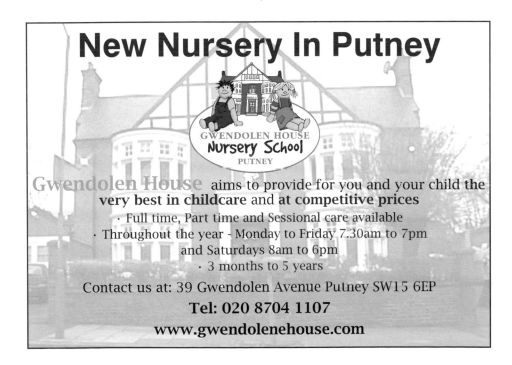

New Nursery In Putney

GWENDOLEN HOUSE
Nursery School
PUTNEY

Gwendolen House aims to provide for you and your child the
very best in childcare and at competitive prices
· Full time, Part time and Sessional care available
· Throughout the year - Monday to Friday 7.30am to 7pm
and Saturdays 8am to 6pm
· 3 months to 5 years
Contact us at: 39 Gwendolen Avenue Putney SW15 6EP
Tel: 020 8704 1107
www.gwendolenehouse.com

Eveline Day Nursery School   020 8672 0501
Seely Hall, Chillerton Road, SW17 9BE
3mths-5yrs. Full day

Headstart   020 8947 7359
St Mary's Church Hall, 46 Wimbledon Road, SW17
2-6rs. 845am-3.30pm Termtime

Red Balloon   020 8672 4711
St Mary Magdalen Church, Trinity Road, SW17 7SD
2½-5yrs.

Teddies Nurseries Balham   020 8672 4808
272 Balham High Road, SW17 7AJ
www.teddiesnurseries.co.uk
3mths-5yrs. Full day (see advert on page 139)

Toots Day Nursery   020 8767 7017
214 Totterdown Street, SW17 8TD
1-5yrs

We Care Day Nursery   020 8767 5501
83 Beechcroft Road, SW17

SW18
Andrea's Montessori Nursery   020 8877 9554
All Saints Wandworth Parish Hall, Lebanon Rd, SW18
2-5yrs

Colour Box Montessori   020 8874 4969
Nursery School
Earlsfield Baptist Church, Magdelen Road, SW18 3

Eveline Day Nursery School   020 8870 0966
East Hill United Reformed Church Hall, Geraldine **Road, SW18**
3mths-5yrs. Full day

The Gardens   020 8947 7058
343 Wimbledon Park Road, SW18
2½-5yrs.

Jigsaw Day Nursery   020 8877 1135
Dolphin House, Riverside West, Smugglers Way, SW18
www.jigsawgroup.com
Come and see for yourself why we are the best

Launch Pad Nursery School   020 8877 9554
All Saints Community Hall, Lebanon Road, SW18
2-5yrs. 9am-3.30pm. Termtime only.

Melrose House Nursery School   020 8874 7769
39 Melrose Road, SW18 1LX
2½-5yrs

THE KINDERGARTENS

The Crescent 1 Kindergarten, Trinity Crescent, Balham, SW17
The Crescent 11 Kindergarten, Trinity Road, Balham, SW17
The Crescent 111 Kindergarten, Thornton Road, Streatham, SW12
The Park Kindergarten, Battersea Park Road, Battersea, SW11
Pooh Corner Kindergarten, Kensington, SW7

We hope you will come and visit us to see how each child will reach their potential with us academically, socially and emotionally whilst having lots of fun and laughter along the way.

Also on offer:
● *Ballet, Music and French* are all taught by specialist staff as part of the curriculum.
● *Spacious Facilities* include a large garden.

**For details please contact: Philip Evelegh on 01622 833 331
or email: pe@thekindergartens.com**

Noah's Ark **020 7228 9593**
Westside Church Hall, Melody Road, SW18 2QQ
2½-5yrs

Roche School **020 8877 0823**
11 Frogmore, SW18 1HW
www.therocheshcool.co.uk
3-11yrs

Schoolroom Two **020 8874 9305**
Southfields Lawn Tennis Club, Gressenhall Rd, SW18
2½-5yrs

Sticky Fingers Montessori **020 8871 9496**
Day Nursery
St John the Divine Church Hall, Garratt Lane, SW18
18mths-5yrs. Full day

Teddies Southfields **020 8870 2009**
Duntshill Mill, 21 Riverdale Drive, SW18 4UR
www.teddiesnurseries.co.uk
3mths-5yrs. Full day (see advert on page 139)

Three-Four-Five **020 8870 8441**
Fitzhugh Community Hall, Trinity Road, SW18 3SA
3-5yrs. Sessional Termtime.

Two-to-Three **020 8870 8441**
Fitzhugh Community Hall, Trinity Road, SW18 3SA
2-3yrs. Afternoons Tues/Wed/Thurs. Termtime.

Wee Ones Nursery School **020 8870 7729**
St Anne's Church Hall, St Ann's Hill, SW18
2_-5yrs

Wimbledon Park Montessori **020 8944 8584**
Nursery School
206 Heythorp Street, SW18 5BU
2_-5yrs

SW19
Buffer Bear Nursery **020 8944 5618**
Wimbledon Traincare Depot, Durnsford Rd, SW19 8
3mths-5yrs. Full day

Castle Kindergarten **020 8544 0089**
20 Henfield Road, SW19 3HU

Crown Kindergarten **020 8540 8820**
Coronation House, Ashcombe Road, SW19 8JP
2-5yrs
Cosmopolitan Day Nursery **020 8544 0758**
65-67 High Street, Colliers Wood, SW19 2JF
2_yrs. Full day

Dees Day Nursery **020 8944 0284**
2 Mansel Road, SW19 4AA
3mths-5yrs. Full day

Eveline Day Nursery School **020 8545 0699**
89a Quicks Road, SW19 1EX
3mths-5yrs. Full day

Herbert Day Nursery **020 8542 7416**
52a Dundonald Road, SW19 3PH
Full day

The Hill Kindergarten **020 8946 7467**
65 Wimbledon Hill Road, SW19 7QP
2_-3yrs

Little Hall Gardens **020 8947 7058**
49 Durnsford Avenue, SW19 8BH
1-5yrs. Full day

Maria Montessori Nursery **020 8543 6353**
122-124 Kingston Rd, SW19
2-5yrs. Mornings

Noddy's Nursery School **020 8785 9191**
Trinity Church Hall, Beaumont Road, West Hill,
SW19 6SP

Nutkins Nursery **020 8246 6400**
Beaumont Road, (off West Hill), SW19 6TF
2-5yrs. Full day

Playdays **020 8946 8139**
58 Queens Road, SW19 8LR
3mths-5yrs. Full day. 8am-6pm. 51 wks

Playdays **020 8944 8959**
100 Wimbledon Hill Road, SW19
3mths-5yrs. Full and part tme care from 8am-6pm. 51wks.

Sunny-side Nursery School **020 8337 0887**
ATC Hall, 192 Merton Road, SW19
2½-5yrs. Mornings

St Mark's Montessori **07956 346938**
St Mark's Church, St Mark's Place, SW19 7ND
2_-5yrs. Mornings

Trinity Nursery School **020 8540 3868**
Holy Trinity Church Centre, SW19 1AX
2_-5yrs. Mornings only

Wimbledon Jewish Nursery **020 8946 4836**
1 Queensmere Road, SW19 5QD

SW20
Coombe Montessori Nursery **020 8946 3822**
Wimbledon College Playing Fields, 183 Coombe
Lane, SW20
2_-5yrs. Full day

Eveline Day Nursery Schools   020 8544 9832
Grand Drive, SW20 9NA
www.evelinedaynurseryschools.co.uk

Lollypops Nursery   020 8296 3731
Nelson Hospital, Kingston Road, SW20
6mths-5yrs

Raynes Park Nursery   020 8543 9005
Bushey Road, Raynes Park, SW20 8TE

Ursuline Convent Prep   020 8947 0859
18 The Downs, SW20 8HR
Boys 3-7yrs. Girls 3-11yrs

TWs
The Children's Garden   020 8968 4605
The Old Chapel, Grove Gardens, off Lower Grove
Rd, TW
3½-6yrs. Mornings. Steiner kindergarten.

Just Kidding Day Nursery   020 8568 4447
44 Boston Park Road, Brentford, TW8 9JF
3mths-5yrs. Full day

Happy Times   020 8746 4222
Grena Road, Richmond, TW9 1XS
www.happytimes.co.uk
Great day nurseries in London for children aged 3mths-5yrs.
Full day. (advert on page 145)

Brentford Day Nursery   020 8568 7561
(Bringing up Baby)
Half Acre, Brentford, TW8 8BH
www.bringingupbaby.co.uk
A day nursery for 42 children aged 3mths-5yrs. Open 8am -
6.15pm.

Buttercups   020 8568 4355
The Garden House, Syon Park, Brentford, TW8 8JF

Buttercups Day Nursery   020 8568 4355
& Montessori School
The Garden House, Syon Park, Brentford, TW8 8JF
3mths-5yrs. Pre-prep 4-7yrs. Full day

WEST LONDON
W1
Great Beginnings   020 7486 2276
Montessori School
82a Chiltern Street, W1M 1PS
2-6yrs

Jumbo Nursery School   020 7935 2441
St James's Church Hall, 22 George Street, W1U
2-5yrs. Mornings

W2

Buffer Bear at Westminster/   020 7641 4361
Warwick Nursery
Cirencester Street, W2 5SR
1-5yrs. Full day

Dr Rolfe's Montessori School   020 7727 8300
10 Pembridge Square, W2 4ED
2_-5yrs

Kinderland Montessori   020 7792 1964
Nursery School
47 Palace Court, W2 4LS
2-5yrs

Linden Gardens Pre-School   020 7229 2130
73b Linden Gardens, W2 4HQ
2_-5yrs. 9.30am-12.30pm. Termtime

Paint Pots   020 7792 0433
Montessori School
Bayswater United Reform Church, 12 Newton Rd, W2
2½-5yrs. Developing confidence, independence, self-esteem,
concentration social skills and self-discipline

Ravenstone House Pre-Preparatory
School and Nursery   020 7262 1190
The Long Garden, Albion Street, W2 2AX
www.ravenstonehouse.co.uk
2½mths-7yrs. First class education for children, first class
service for parents

St John's Montessori   020 7402 2529
Nursery School
St John's Church Hall, Hyde Park Crescent, W2
2-5yrs

Toddlers & Mums Montessori   020 7243 4227
St Stephens Church, Westbourne Park Road, W2
14mths-5yrs

W3
Bizzy Lizzy Day Nursery   020 8993 1664
c/o The Priory Community Centre, Acton Lane, W3
2-5yrs. Full day

Buffer Bear Nursery   020 8743 7249
10 Stanley Gardens, W3 7SZ
3mths - 5yrs. Full day

Buttercups Day Nursery   020 8740 7109
27 Old Oak Road, W3 7HN
3mths-4½yrs. Full day

Carousel Nursery   020 8896 3663
Acton Hill Church Centre, Woodlands Avenue, W3
2-5yrs. Full day

RAVENSTONE HOUSE
Pre-Preparatory School & Nursery

"First class education for children, first rate service for parents"

HYDE PARK W2

- Babies from 2 months to children of 7 years
- Open 7.30am - 6.30pm, 48 weeks a year

The Long Garden, Albion Street, London, W2 2AX

Telephone: 020 7262 1190

ELVASTON PLACE SW7

- Babies from 2 months to children of 11 years
- Open 7.30am - 6.30pm, 48 weeks a year

24 Elvaston Place, London, SW7 5NL

QUEENSBERRY PLACE SW7

- Babies from 2 months to children of 2½ years
- Open 8.00am - 6.00pm, 44 weeks a year

22 Queensberry Place, South Kensington, London, SW7 2DZ

Telephone: 020 7584 7955

For a prospectus please call
or email **info@ravenstonehouse.co.uk**

www.ravenstonehouse.co.uk

Cybertots   020 8752 0200
1 Avenue Crescent, W3
2-5yrs. Full day

Ealing Montessori School   020 8992 4513
St Martin's Church Hall, 5 Hale Gardens, W3 9SQ
2½-5yrs

Happy Child Day Nursery   020 8992 0855
St Gabriel's Church, Noel Road, W3 0JE
6mths-5yrs. Full day

Village Montessori Nursery   020 8993 3540
All Saints Church Centre, Bollo Bridge Road, W3
Aged 2_-5yrs. Full day nursery. Walled garden area. Music,
art, French, dance. OFSTED registered.

Violet Melchett Family Centre   020 7361 3334
30 Flood Walk, W3 5RR
1-4yrs. 8am-6pm. 51wks.

W4
Ark Montessori   020 8932 4766
Rugby Road, W4
2½-6yrs. Mornings

Buttercups Day Nursery   020 8995 6750
38 Grange Road, W4 4DD
3mths-5yrs. Full day

Caterpillar Montessori Nursery   020 8747 8531
St Albans Church Hall, South Parade, W4 5JU
2½-5yrs

Chiswick Community Nursery   020 8995 2180
53 Barrowgate Road, W4 4QT
6mths-5yrs. Full day

Chiswick Toddlers World   020 8995 7267
St Paul's Church Hall, Pyrmont Road, W4 3NR
1-5yrs. Full day

Devonshire Day Nursery   020 8995 9538
2 Bennett Street, W4 2AH
www.childbase.com
6wks-5yrs, 8am-6pm, 52 weeks per year. Child Base
nurseries follow the Sound Foundation curriculum providing
building blocks for your child's development.(see advert on
page 116)

Elmwood Montessori   020 8994 8177
St Michaels Centre, Elmwood Road, W4 3DY
2½-5yrs. 9am-12pm and 1pm-4pm. 34 wks.

Imaginations   020 8994 5422
Methodist Church Hall, Sutton Court Road, W4
2-5yrs

Leapfrog Day Nursery   020 8742 0011
4 Marlborough Road, W4 4ET
www.leapfrogdaynurseries.co.uk
3mths-5yrs. 7am-7pm. 52wks. (see advert on page 119)

Meadows Montessori   020 8742 1327
Dukes Meadow Community Hall, Alexandra
Gardens, W4 2TD

Our Lady Queen of Peace   020 8994 2053
Day Nursery
10 Chiswick Lane, W4 2JE
2½-4yrs

Parkside Nursery School   020 8995 4648
Homefield Lodge, Chiswick Lane North, W4 2KA
2-6yrs. Mornings only

Riverside Children's Centre   020 8995 9299
Cavendish School, Edensor Road, W4 2RG
2-5yrs. Full day

Riverside Teddies   020 8987 1831
Day Nursery
Riverside Club, Dukes Meadow, W4 2SX
www.teddiesnurseries.co.uk
3mths-5yrs. Full day. (see advert on page 139)

Tara House Nursery School   020 8995 5144
opposite 3 Wilson Walk, off Prebend Gardens, W4
2-5yrs

Tic-Toc Day Nursery   020 8995 7585
Turnham Green Church Hall, Heathfield Gardens
3mths-5yrs. Full day 8am-6pm.

Teddies Chiswick Park   020 8995 4766
The Old Chapel, Evershed Walk, W4 5BW
www.teddiesnurseries.co.uk
3mths-5yrs. Full day

Westside Day Nursery   020 8742 2206
Steele Road, W4 5AF
3mths-2_ yrs. Full day

W5
Buttercups Day Nursery   020 8840 4838
9 Florence Road, W5 3TU
3mths-5yrs

Caterpillar Day Nursery   020 8579 0833
8th Ealing Scout Hall, Popes Lane, W5 4NB
2-5yrs. Full day

Happy Child Day Nursery   020 8992 0209
Woodgrange Avenue, W5 3NY
3mths-5yrs. Full day

Happy Child Day Nursery   020 8567 2244
283-287 Windmill Road, W5 4DP

Teddies
Nurseries

"*It was the best start possible for my child*"

- Excellence in all areas of care and development

- Qualified, experienced and caring staff

- Fun, exciting and imaginative environment

- Nurturing individual development for children aged from 3 months to 5 years

Open 8am-6pm Mon-Fri, with flexible hours and full-time, part-time and half-day sessions.

With over 40 nurseries, Teddies Nurseries is one of the UK's leading childcare providers.

For more information call

0800 980 3801

www.teddiesnurseries.co.uk

3mths-5yrs. Full day

Happy Child   020 8840 9936
Montessori School
Welsh Chapel, Ealing Green, W5 5EN
2-5yrs. Full day

Happy Child Day Nursery   020 8567 4300
2b The Grove, W5 5LH
3mths-5yrs. Full day

Happy Child Day Nursery   020 8566 1546
2a The Grove, W5 5LH
1-5yrs. Full time.

New World Montessori   020 8810 4411
Nursery School
St Barnabus Millenium Church Hall, Pitshanger
Lane, W5
2-5yrs

Nursery Land Daycare Centre   020 8566 5962
9th Ealing Scouts Hut, Northfield Avenue, W5 4UA
2-4yrs

Resurrection Day Nursery   020 8998 8954
84 Gordon Road, W5 2AR
2-5yrs. Full day

St Matthew's   020 8579 2304
Montessori School
St Matthew's Church Hall, North Common Road,
W5
2-5yrs

Jumpers Nursery   020 8799 4871
YMCA, 25 St Mary's Road, W5 5RE
2½-5yrs. Full day

W6
Bayonne Nursery School   020 7385 5366
50 Paynes Walk, W6
3-5yrs

The Beanstalk Montessori   020 8740 7891
Nursery School
St Peter's Church, Black Lion Lane, W6 9BG
2½-5yrs

Bringing Up Baby: 020 8746 1015
Richford Street Day Nursery
50 Richford Gate, 61-69 Richford Street, W6 7HZ
www.bringingupbaby.co.uk
A day nursery for 58 children aged 3mths - 5yrs. Open
8.15am - 6.15pm. Full year.

Flora Nursery   020 8748 0750
Community Centre, Flora Gardens, W6 0HR
2½-5yrs. Full day

Happy Times   0800 652 2424
The Stamford, Ravenscourt Park, W6 0TN
www.happytimes.co.uk
Great day nurseries in London for children aged 3mths-5yrs.
7am-7pm (see advert on page 145)

Howard House Nursery School   020 8741 5147
58 Ravenscourt Road, Ravenscourt Park, W6 0UG
2½-5yrs. Mornings

Jigsaw Day Nursery   020 8563 7982
Centre West, Hammersmith Broadway, W6 9YD
www.jigsawnurseries.com
3mths-5yrs. Full day 8am-6pm. 52wks.

Jordans Nursery School   020 8741 3230
Lower Hall, Holy Innocents Church, Paddenswick
Road, W6 0UB

Step By Step Day Nursery   020 8748 1319
1 Bridge Avenue, W6 9JA
2-5yrs

W7
Bunny Park Day Nursery   020 8567 6142
37 Manor Court Road, W7 3EJ
Registered by Ofsted for children aged 2-5yrs. Large
secluded garden, French lessons. Open 8am to 6pm.
Buttons Nursery School   020 8840 3355
99 Oaklands Road, W7 2DT
www.buttonsdaynursery.co.uk
3mths-5yrs. 8am-6pm. 51wks.

Fairytale Day Nursery   020 8840 2851
Leighton Hall, Elthorne Park Road, W7
2-5yrs. Full day

Sticky Fingers Day Nursery   020 8566 4606
Bernard Sunley Hall, Greenford Avenue, W7 1AA
2-5yrs. Full day

W8
Holland Park Pre-School   020 7603 2838
Stable Yard, Ilchester Place, W8 6LU
2½-5yrs. 9.30am-3.30pm. Termtime

Iverna Gardens Montessori   020 7937 0794
Nursery School
Armenian Church Hall, Iverna Gardens, W8 6TP
www.iverna.com
2½-5yrs

The Playroom   020 7376 1804
Etheline Hall, Denbigh Road, W8
2-5yrs. Afternoons

The Playroom   020 7376 1804
Christchurch Vestry, Victoria Road, W8 5RQ

2-5yrs Mornings

W9

Buffer Bear at Westminster/ 020 7641 4346
St Stephens Nursery
The Annexe, Essendine Road, W9 2LR
6mths-5yrs. Full day

Buffer Bear at Westminster/ 020 7641 5837
St Jude's
88 Bravington Road, W9 3BE
1-5yrs. Full day

Little Sweethearts Montessori 020 7266 161
St Saviour's Church Hall, Warwick Avenue, W9 2PT
2-7yrs

Windmill Montessori 020 7289 3410
Nursery School
Former Caretaker's Cottage, Oakington Road, W9
2-5yrs

W10

Spanish Day Nursery
152 Clapham Manor Street
18mths-5yrs. Full day

Buffer Bear at Westminster/ 020 7641 5835
Katharine Bruce Nursery
Queens Park Court, Ilbert Street, W10 4QA
1-5yrs. Full day

Dalgarno Pre-School 020 8969 1463
1 Webb Close, W10 5QB
2½-5yrs. Sessional 9.30am-12pm. 39 wks

Garden House Nursery School 020 8968 2922
210 Latimer Road, W10 6QY
2-5yrs

Kids Unlimited 01625 586333
34 Ladbroke Grove, W10

Little Butterflies 020 8961 8501
Ladbroke Grove, W10
2½-5yrs

Lloyd Williamson School 020 8962 0345
12 Telford Road, W10|
2-6yrs, 7.30am-6pm 50 wks

Maxilla Nursery Centre 020 8969 6494
4 Maxilla Walk, W10 6NQ

New Studio Pre-School 020 8960 6661
Kelfield Mews, Kelfield Gardens, W10 6LS
2½-5yrs. 9.25am-1.25pm. Termtime

Sunrise Pre-School 020 8968 2921
The Moberly Centre, 101 Kilburn Lane, W10 4AH
2-5yrs

Swinbrook Nursery 020 8968 5833
39-41 Acklam Road, W10 5YU
2-8yrs. 8am-6pm. 51wks.

Venture Pre-School 020 8960 3234
103A Wornington Road, W10 5YB
2½-5yrs. 9.30am-12pm. Termtime

Tiny Tots Nursery 020 8960 2020
St Quintin Health Centre, St Quintin Avenue, W10
3mths-4yrs.

W11

Cherry Tree Pre- 020 8961 2081
Nursery School
St Francis of Assisi Community Centre, Pottery
Lane, W11
18mths-3½yrs

Delaney's Nursery School 020 7603 6095
Norland Church, St James's Gardens, W11 4RB
2-5yrs old

Dr Rolfe's Montessori School 020 7727 8300
206-208 Kensington Park Road, W11 1NR
2½-5yrs. Full day 9am-3.15pm. Termtime

Gardens Pre-School Group 020 7727 2725
349 Westbourne Park Road, W11 1EG
2½-5yrs. Sessional 9.30-12pm

Gate Nursery School 020 7221 2094
Gordon flat, 77 Clarendon Road, W11 4JF
2-4yrs

Ladbroke Square 020 7229 0125
Montessori School
43 Ladbroke Square, W11 3ND
2½-5yrs

Maria Montessori Children's 020 7221 4141
House Notting Hill
All Saints Church, 28 Powis Gardens, W11 1JG
www.montessori-ami.org
2½-5yrs

The Mynors' Nursery School 020 7727 7253
Garden flat, 4 Chepstow Villas, W11 2RB
2_-5yrs

The Square Montessori 020 7221 6004
School
18 Holland Park Avenue, W11 3QU

www.thesquareschool.co.uk
2-5yrs. 9.15am-12.15pm or 3.45pm. A cosy environment with excellent teaching standards.

St Peters Nursery School 020 7243 2617
59a Portobello Road, W11 3BD
2½-5yrs

Strawberry Fields 020 7727 8363
Nursery School
5 Pembridge Villas, W11 3EN
2-5yrs. 9am-3pm. Termtime.

Miss Delaney's Too 020 7727 0010
St Clement's Church, 95 Sirdar Road, W11 4EQ
2½-5yrs.

Miss Delaney's Nursery 020 7603 6095
Norland Church, St James's Gardens, W11 4RB
2½-5yrs

Villas Nursery School 020 7602 6232
32 St Ann's Villas, Holland Park Avenue, W11 4RS
www.daycare.co.uk
2-5yrs. Full day

W12
Ladybird Day Nursery 020 8741 3399
277 & 287 Goldhawk Road, W12 8EU
6mths-5yrs. Full day

PLAY DAYS

Day Nurseries & Nursery Schools

Quality childcare for children aged
3 months to 5 years
Full and part time care / 51 weeks a year

13 Barton Rd. W.Kensington W14
Tel: 020 7386 9083
45 Comeragh Rd. W.Kensington W14
Tel: 020 7385 1955
58 Queen's Rd. Wimbledon SW19
Tel: 020 8946 8139
100 Wimbledon Hill Rd. Wimbledon SW19
Tel: 020 8944 8959

Ladybird Montessori: 020 8846 8519
Baby Unit
277 Goldhawk Road, W12 8EU
6mths-2yrs

Little People of 020 8749 5080
Shepherds Bush
61 Hadyn Park Road, W12 9AQ
6mths-3yrs. Full day

Little People of Willow Vale 020 8749 2877
9 Willow Vale, W12 0PA
3-5yrs. Full day

Stepping Stones 020 8742 9103
Nursery School
St Saviour's Church, Cobbold Road, W12 9LN
2-5yrs. 9.30am-12.30pm. Offering excellence for your child and you.

Vanessa Nursery School 020 8743 8196
14 Cathnor Road, W12 9JA
3-5yrs

W13
Children's Corner 020 8840 5591
29 Hastings Road, W13 8QH
18mths-5yrs. Full day

Corner House Day Nursery 020 8567 2806
82 Lavington Road, W13 9LR
3mths-5yrs. 8am-6pm. 51 wks. Expert care and education provided by only qualified staff

Happy Child Baby Nursery 020 8566 5515
Green Man Passage (off Bayham Road), W13 0TG
3mths-2½yrs
Happy Child Day Nursery 020 8566 5515
Green Man Passage (off Bayham Road), W13 0TG
1-5yrs. Full day

Home from Home Day Nursery 020 8566 7706
St Luke's, Drayton Grove, W13 0LA
2-5yrs. Full day

Jigsaw 020 8997 8330
1 Courtfield Gardens, W13 0EY
18mths-5yrs. Full day

Playways Early 020 8998 2723
Learning School
2 Amhert Road, W13 8ND
3mths-5yrs. Full day

West London YMCA 020 8810 6769
Noah's Ark Nursery
2a Drayton Green, W13 0JF
2-5yrs

W14
Bright Sparks 020 7371 4697
Montessori School
25 Minford Gardens, W14 0AP
2½-5yrs

Busy Bee Nursery 020 7602 8905
Addison Boys Club, Redan Street, W14 0HD
3-5yrs

Holland Park Day Nursery 020 7602 9066
9 Holland Road, W14 8HJ
3mths-2yrs. Full day

Little Lillies 020 7381 0670
76-80 Lillie Road, W14 6YS
2½-5yrs. Mornings

Playdays **020 7386 9083**
13 Barton Road, W14 9HB
3mths-5yrs. Full day 8am-6pm. 51 wks (see advert on page 138)

Playdays **020 7385 1955**
45 Comeragh Road, W14 9HT
3mths-5yrs. Full day 8am-6pm. 51 wks (see advert on page 139)

Ripples Montessori School 020 7602 7433
St John the Baptist Church, Holland Rd, W14
2½-5yrs

School House Nursery 020 7602 9066
5 Holland Road, W14 8HJ
2-8yrs. Full day

Sinclair Montessori 020 7602 3745
Nursery School
Garden flat, 142 Sinclair Road, W14 0NL
2½-5yrs
Warwick Pre-School Group 020 7602 3080
78 Warwick Gardens, W14 8PR
2-5yrs. 9.30am-1.25pm. Termtime

WC1
Coram Fields Nursery 020 7833 0198
93 Guildford Street, WC1N 1DN
3-5yrs

The Mango Tree 020 7278 2214
25 Easton Street, WC1X 0DS
From 3mths-4 yrs. Full day

Thomas Coram 020 7520 0385
Early Childhood Centre
49 Mecklenburgh Square, WC1N 2NY
6mths-5yrs. Full day

Corner House Day Nursery
Established 1989
Specialised, professional care and education from fully qualified staff.
For children aged 3 months to 5 years
Tel: 020 8567 2806

WC2
Chandos Day Nursery   020 7836 6574
47 Dudley Court, 36 Endell Street, WC2H 9RF
3mths-5yrs. Full day

Kingsway Children's Centre   020 7831 7460
4 Wild Court, WC2B 5AU
From 3mths.Full day.

MACE Montessori   020 7242 584
Nursery School
38-42 Millman St, WC1N 3EW
2-5½yrs. 8am-6pm. 48wks

french nursery schools

NW5
L'île aux Enfants   020 7267 7119
22 Vicars Road, NW5
3-11yrs

NW11
Pomme d'Api   020 8455 1417
86 Wildwood Road, NW11
1-4yrs. Mornings only

SW1
French Nursery School   020 7584 3964
77-79 Kinnerton Street, SW1
2-5yrs

SW4
L'ecole du Parc   **020 8671 5287**
12 Rodenhurst Rd, Clapham, SW4 8AR
1-5 yrs.

SW6
Ecole des Petits   020 7371 8350
2 Hazlebury Road, SW6

SW12
Les Petits Benjamins   **020 8673 8525**
Oldridge Road, Clapham South, SW12
www.ecoledesbenjamins.com
Open 7.30-6.30pm. 5mths-2yrs. 51 weeks

L'Ecole des Benjamins   **020 8673 9951**
Oldridge Road, Clapham South, SW12
www.ecoledesbenjamins.com
Term time 2-6yrs

W10
Petite Ecole Française   020 8960 1278
90 Oxford Gardens, W10
21mths-6yrs

W6
Ecole Française de Londres:
Jacques Prévert   **020 7602 6871**
59 Brook Green, W6
4-11yrs

Le Hérisson   **020 8563 7664**
The Methodist Church, Rivercourt Road, W6
2-6yrs

L'Ecole du Parc welcomes children of 1 to 5 years in
a warm and friendly environment
• Private house and garden
• Qualified and dynamic teaching staff
• French educational programme and activities in English
• Nursery grants for all 3 and 4 year-olds
• Regulated by OFSTED and the DfES
12 Rodenhurst Road - Clapham - London SW4 8AR
Tel/Fax: 020 8671 5287

l'école·des
Benjamins
école bilingue
bilingual éducation

Oldridge Road
Clapham South
London
SW12 8PP
Full Day care & schooling
7.30am-6.30pm
Crèche: children 5 mnths to 2 yrs
School: children 2 to 6 years
All non-French speaking
children are welcome

020 8673 8525
020 8675 9951
www.ecoledesbenjamins.com
eb@ecoledesbenjamins.com

happy times

Georgina is an NNEB qualified Carer with a background in nursing and over 15 years childcare experience. But more importantly, she is a mother of two grown up children and knows what it means to be a mum. At Happy Times we recruit our Carers for their experience as parents as well as for their childcare qualifications – that's what makes us unique.

Rosemarie with grandchildren, Arami and Chyna

Rosemarie has an NVQII in childcare and lots of experience of working with under-fives. Rosemarie also understands what it means to be a mum as she has two grown up children of her own. And now she is a grandma too! At Happy Times we understand that maturity, experience and a love of children are as important as childcare qualifications – that's what makes us unique

Georgina with her son Leslie

Alice returned to work part-time in January when her daughter, Ruby was 7 months old. Ruby is now looked after in the baby room by Alice's colleagues on the days that she works. At Happy Times we help our carers to return to work when they are ready – that's what makes us unique.

Wendy with Tyler

Wendy is a Team Leader at Happy Times after more than 5 years as a Senior Carer. The baby room she runs has benefited from Wendy's expertise as a mother to Tyler as well as from her childcare training. Tyler adores all the messy activities and can't get enough of the sand and mousse play. At Happy Times we recruit Carers who understand what children enjoy most – that's what makes us unique.

Alice with Ruby

We're unique...
Because they're unique...

Fantastic Day Nurseries in London for children aged 3 months to 5 years.

For Happy's Guide or to visit a Happy Times nursery please call

0800 652 2424
www.happytimes.co.uk

spanish nursery schools

SW4
Anglo Spanish Nursery   020 7622 5599
152 Clapham Manor Street
18mths-5yrs. Full day

SW6
Peques Nursery School   020 7385 0055
St John's Church, Walham Green,
North End Road, Fulham
www.peques-nursery.co.uk
2-5yrs. Open 8am-6pm. 50wks. For a secure, happy and
safe environment with qualified staff (see advert on page 118)

W10
Spanish Day Nursery   020 8960 6661
317 Portobello Road
2-5yrs. Full day

schools, pre-prep

(see also helplines, nurseries)

For a list of state schools in your area, contact your
local council (see councils). ISC offer advice and
information on private schools in your area. The
following schools have a nursery section

East London
E4
Normanhurst School   020 8529 4307
68-74 Station Road, Chingford
co-ed 2-16yrs

E7
Grangewood Independent School 020 8472 3552
Chester Road, Forest Gate
co-ed 4-11yrs

E17
Forest School   020 8520 1744
Nr Snaresbrook
co-ed 7-18yrs

E18
Snaresbrook College   020 8989 2394
75 Woodford Road
co-ed 3-11yrs

EC2
City of London School for Girls 020 7628 0841
St Giles Terrace, Barbican
girls 7-18yrs

EC4
St Paul's Cathedral School   020 7248 5156
2 New Change
boys 7-13, girls 4-7yrs

North London
N1
St Paul's Steiner Project   020 7226 4454
1 St Paul's Road, Islington
3-9yrs. Also toddler and playgroups

N2
Kerem School   020 8455 0909
Norrice Lea
4-11yrs

N6
Channing School   020 8340 2328
Highgate
girls 4-18yrs

Highgate Junior School   020 8340 9196
3 Bishopswood Road
co-ed 3-7yrs, boys 8-13yrs

N10
Norfolk House Prep School   020 8883 4584
10 Muswell Avenue
co-ed 4-11yrs

Prince's Avenue School   020 8444 4399
5 Prince's Avenue
co-ed 5-7yrs

N11
**Woodside Park
International School**   020 8368 3777
Friern Barnet Road
co-ed 2-18yrs

N14
Salcombe Prep School   020 8441 5282
224-226 Chase Side, Southgate
co-ed 4-11yrs

N21
Keble Prep School   020 8360 3359
Wades Hill, Winchmore Hill
boys 4-13yrs

Palmers Green High School   020 8886 1135
Hoppers Road, Winchmore Hill
girls 3-16yrs

North West
NW1
The Cavendish School   020 7485 1958
179 Arlington Road
girls 3-11yrs

NW2
Mulberry House School   020 8452 7340
7 Minster Road
co-ed 2-8yrs

NW3

Devonshire House School   020 7435 1916
2 Arkwright Road

Hall School   020 7722 1700
23 Crossfield Road
boys 5-13yrs

Heathside Preparatory School   020 7794 5857
16 New End
co-ed 2½-13½yrs

Hereward House School
14 Strathray Gardens. 020 7794 4820
boys 4-13yrs

Lyndhurst House Prep School   020 7435 4936
24 Lyndhurst Gardens, Hampstead
boys 7-13yrs

Phoenix School   020 7722 4433
36 College Crescent
co-ed 3-7yrs

Royal School Hampstead   020 7794 7708
65 Rosslyn Hill
girls 4-18yrs (boarders from 7yrs)

Sarum Hall   020 7794 226
15 Eton Avenue1
girls 3-11yrs

St Anthony's School   020 7435 0316
90 Fitzjohns Avenue
boys 5-13yrs

St Christopher's School   020 7435 1521
32 Belsize Lane
girls 4-11yrs

St Margaret's School   020 7435 2439
18 Kidderpore Gardens
girls 5-16yrs

St Mary's School, Hampstead   020 7435 1868
47 Fitzjohn's Avenue
boys 2-7yrs, girls 2-11yrs

South Hampstead High School   020 7794 7198
5 Netherhall Gardens
girls 4-18yrs

Southbank International School   020 7431 1200
16 Netherhall Gardens
co-ed 3-14yrs

Trevor-Roberts Prep School   020 7586 1444
55-57 Eton Avenue
co-ed 5-13yrs

Village School   020 7485 4673
2 Parkhill Road
4-11yrs

NW4

Hendon Preparatory School   020 8203 7727
20 Tenterden Grove
co-ed 2-13yrs

NW6

Broadhurst School   020 7328 4280
19 Greencroft Gardens
co-ed 2½-7yrs

Islamia Primary School   020 7372 2532
Salusbury Road
5-16yrs

Rainbow Montessori School   020 7328 8986
13 Woodchurch Road
5-11yrs

NW7

Belmont   020 8959 1431
Mill Hill
co-ed 7-13yrs

Goodwyn School   020 8959 3756
Hammers Lane, Mill Hill
3-11yrs

Mill Hill Pre-Prep School   020 8959 6884
Winterstoke House, Wills Grove
3-7yrs

The Mulberry House School

An established independent school for 2-8 year olds, offering a stimulating and caring environment that meets the needs of individuals, while preparing them for the next stage of their schooling at 4+ or 7+. Extended day, full and part time places available.

For brochures and details of open evenings please telephone

020 8452 7340

E-mail: tmhs@rmplc.co.uk.

7 Minster Road,
West Hampstead, NW2 3SD

Mount School 020 8959 3403
Milespit Hill, Mill Hill
girls 4-18yrs

NW8
American School in London 020 7449 1200
1 Waverley Place
www.asl.org
An independent co-educational day school for students aged
4-18yrs

Abercorn Place School 020 7286 4785
28 Abercorn Plac e
co-ed 2 ¹/₂-13yrs

Arnold House 020 7266 6982
1 Loudon Road
boys 5-13yrs

**St Christina's RC
Preparatory School** 020 7722 8784
25 St Edmund's Terrace
boys 3-7yrs, girls 3-11yrs+

**St John's Wood
Junior Prep School** 020 7722 7149
St John's Hall, Lord's Roundabout
co-ed 3-8yrs

NW9
St Nicholas School 020 8205 7153
22 Salmon Street
co-ed 2-11yrs

NW11
Goldershill School 020 8455 2589
666 Finchley Road
co-ed 2-7yrs

King Alfred School 020 8457 5200
Manor Wood, North End Road
co-ed 4-18yrs

South East
SE3
Blackheath High School 020 8852 1537
Vanbrugh Park
girls 3-18yrs

Pointers Nursery + Prep 020 8293 1331
19 Stratheden Road, Blackheath
2³/₄-11yrs, co-ed. Full day

SE6
St Dunstan's College 020 8516 7200
Stanstead Road
co-ed 4-18yrs

SE9
St Olave's Prep School 020 8829 8930
106-110 Southwood Road, New Eltham
co-ed 3-11yrs

SE12
Colfe's Prep School 020 8852 2283
Horn Park Lane
co-ed 3-11yrs

Riverston School 020 8318 4327
63-69 Eltham Road, Lee
co-ed 1-16yrs

SE19
Virgo Fidelis Prep School 020 8653 2169
Central Hill, Upper Norwood
co-ed 2-11yrs

SE21
Dulwich College Prep School 020 8670 3217
42 Alleyn Park
boys 3-13yrs, girls 3-5yrs. Nursery in Gallery Road

Oakfield Prep School 020 8670 4206
125-128 Thurlow Park Road
co-ed 2-11yrs

**Rosemead Preparatory
School** 020 8670 5865
70 Thurlow Park Road
co-ed 3-11yrs

SE22
Alleyn's School 020 8693 3457
Townley Road, Dulwich
co-ed 4-18yrs

James Allen's Prep School 020 8693 0374
East Dulwich Grove
girls 4-11yrs, boys 4-7yrs

SE24
Herne Hill School 020 7274 6336
127 Herne Hill
co-ed 3-7yrs

SE26
Sydenham High School 020 8778 8737
15 & 19 Westwood Hill
girls 4-18yrs

South West
SW1
Eaton House School 020 7730 9343
3-5 Eaton Gate
boys 4-9yrs

Eaton Square Pre-Prep School 020 7823 6217
30 Eccleston Street
co-ed 2 ¹/₂-6yrs

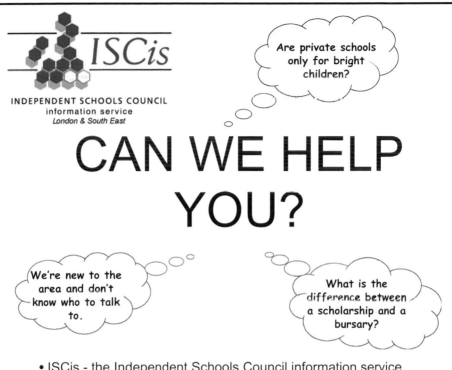

- ISCis - the Independent Schools Council information service, was set up specifically to help parents find information about independent schools in their area.

- Contact us for a copy of our FREE guide to 570 Independent schools or visit our website to search for schools in your area and find out more on how to find the right school for your child.

- Whether you are short of time or just need someone to talk to, join the hundreds of families who have found the support and information they needed through our consultancy service.

Tel: **020 7798 1560**
Fax: 020 7798 1561
Email: southeast@iscis.uk.net
Website: **www.iscis.uk.net/southeast**

Eaton Square Prep School 020 7931 9469
79 Eccleston Square
co-ed 2½-11yrs

Francis Holland School 020 7730 2971
39 Graham Terrace
girls 4-18yrs

Garden House School 020 7730 1652
53 Sloane Gardens
co-ed 3-11yrs

Hellenic College of London 020 7581 5044
67 Pont Street
co-ed 2-18yrs

Hill House School 020 7584 1331
17 Hans Place
co-ed 4-13yrs

Sussex House 020 7584 1741
68 Cadogan Square
boys 8-13yrs

Westminster Under School 020 7821 5788
Adrian House, 27 Vincent Square
boys 7-18yrs (including Westminster School)

SW3
Cameron House 020 7352 4040
4 The Vale
co-ed 4-11yrs

SW4
Eaton House, The Manor 020 7924 6000
58 Clapham Common Northside
2 ½-5yrs, co-ed; boys-8yrs

Parkgate House School 020 7350 2452
80 Clapham Common Northside
co-ed 2 ½-11yrs

SW6
Sinclair House School 020 7736 9182
159 Munster Road
co-ed 2-8yrs. Probably the most adventurous pre-prep
school in SW London

Eridge House 020 7371 9009
1 Fulham Park Road

Fulham Prep 020 7371 9911
47a Fulham High Street
co-ed 5-13yrs

Kensington Preparatory
School for Girls 020 7731 9300
596 Fulham Road
girls 4–11yrs

SW7
Ravenstone House
Pre-Preparatory School 020 7584 7955
22 Queensberry Place
www.ravenstonehouse.co.uk
2½-8yrs. First class education for children, first rate service
for parents (see advert on page 121)

Falkner House Girls School 020 7373 4501
19 Brechin Place
co-ed 3-4yrs, girls 4-11yrs

Glendower Preparatory School 020 7370 1927
87 Queen's Gate
girls 4-12yrs

Hampshire Schools 020 7584 3297
63 Ennismore Gardens
co-ed 2-13yrs

Hampshire Schools 020 7370 7081
5 Wetherby Place
co-ed 3-6yrs

Lycée Français
Charles de Gaulle 020 7584 6322
35 Cromwell Road
co-ed 4-18yrs

Queen's Gate School 020 7589 3587
133 Queen's Gate
girls 4-18yrs

St Nicholas Preparatory School 020 7225 1277
23 Princes Gate
co-ed 3-13yrs

St Philip's School 020 7373 3944
6 Wetherby Place
boys 7-13yrs

Vale School 020 7584 9515
2 Elvaston Place
co-ed 4-11yrs

SW8
Newton Prep 020 7720 4091
149 Battersea Park Road
co-ed 3-13yrs

SW10
Parayhouse School 020 8740 6333
St John's, World's End, King's Road
co-ed 5-17yrs with learning difficulties

Redcliffe School 020 7352 9247
47 Redcliffe Gardens
girls 3-11yrs, boys 3-8yrs

SW11

Thomas's Prep School 020 7978 0900
28-40 Battersea High Street
co-ed 4-13yrs

Thomas's Prep School 020 7978 0900
Battersea Church Road

Thomas's Prep School 020 7326 9300
Broomwood Road
co-ed 4-13yrs. A flourishing and energetic co-educational
school with excellent facilities

Dolphin School 020 7924 3472
106 Northcote Road
co-ed 4-11yrs

South London
Montessori School 020 7730 9546
Trott Street, Battersea
2¹/₂12yrs

SW12

Broomwood Hall School 020 8673 1616
74 Nightingale Lane
boys 4-8yrs, girls 4-13yrs

Woodentops Pre-Preparatory
School & Kindergarten 020 8674 9514
The White House, 24 Thornton Road
2 ¹/₂-11yrs

SW13

Colet Court 020 8748 3461
Lonsdale Road
7-13yrs. Junior St Paul's School

Harrodian 020 8748 6117
Lonsdale Road
co-ed 5-15yrs

SW14

Tower House School 020 8876 3323
188 Sheen Lane
boys 4-13yrs

SW15

Hall School Wimbledon 020 8788 2370
Stroud Crescent, Putney Vale
3-11yrs co-ed. Senior school at 17 The Downs, SW20.
020 8879 9200. 11-16yrs

Hurlingham School 020 8874 7186
95 Deodar Road
co-ed 4-11yrs

Ibstock Place School 020 8876 9991
Clarence Lane, Roehampton
co-ed 3-16yrs

Lion House School 020 8780 9446
The Old Methodist Hall, Gwendolen Avenue
coed- 3-8yrs

Prospect House School 020 8780 0456
75 Putney Hill
co-ed 3-11yrs

Putney High School 020 8788 4886
35 Putney Hill
girls 4-18yrs

Putney Park School 020 8788 8316
11 Woodborough Road
boys 4-11yrs, girls 4-16yrs

SW16

Streatham Hill &
Clapham High School 020 8677 8400
Abbotswood Road
3-18yrs girls

Beechwood School 020 8677 8778
55 Leigham Court Road

SW17

Bertrum House School 020 8767 4051
290 Balham High Street
2-8yrs

Eveline Day School 020 8672 4673
14 Trinity Crescent
3-11yrs. Full day

Finton House School 020 8682 0921
169-171 Trinity Road
co-ed 4-11yrs

SW18

Highfield School 020 8874 2778
256 Trinity Road
co-ed 2-11yrs

St. Michael Steiner School 020 8648 5758
5 Merton Road
co-ed 3-14yrs

SW19

Kings College School 020 8255 5300
Southside, Wimbledon Common
boys 7-13yrs

Study Preparatory School 020 8947 6969
Wilberforce House, Camp Road
girls 4-11yrs

Willington School 020 8944 7020
Worcester Road, Wimbledon
boys 4-13yrs

Wimbledon High School 020 8971 0900
Mansel Road
girls 4-18yrs

Wimbledon House School 020 8544 1523
1b/1c Dorset Road
co-ed 3-11yrs

SW20

Rowans   020 8946 8220
19 Drax Avenue
3-9yrs

Full listings for TW schools can be found in the
Local Baby Directory:
Surrey & S. Middlesex. See order form at the front
of this Directory

TW9

Kew College   020 8940 2039
24-26 Cumberland Road, Kew, Richmond
3-11yrs

Unicorn School   020 8948 3926
238 Kew Road, Richmond
co-ed 3-11yrs

W1

Queen's College   020 7291 7070
61 Portland Place
girls 4-10yrs+

**St Nicholas
Pre-Preparatory School**   020 7493 0165
18 Balderton Street
2–7yrs

**West London
W2**

**Ravenstone House Pre-Preparatory
School and Nursery**   **020 7262 1190**
The Long Garden, Albion Street
hydepark@ravenstonehouse.co.uk
www.ravenstonehouse.co.uk
2½mths-7yrs. First class education for children, first class
service for parents (see advert on page 121)

Connaught House School   020 7262 8830
47 Connaught Square, Hyde Park
boys 4-8yrs, girls 4-11yrs

Hampshire Schools   020 7229 7065
9 Queensborough Terrace
co-ed 4-13yrs

Pembridge Hall School for Girls   020 7229 0121
18 Pembridge Square
girls 5-11yrs

Wetherby School   020 7727 9581
11 Pembridge Square
boys 4-8yrs

W3

International School of London   020 8992 5823
139 Gunnersbury Avenue
co-ed 4-18yrs. English + Arabic, etc.

King Fahad Academy   020 8743 0131
Bromyard Avenue
Muslim. Parallel classes for boys and girls 6-18yrs

W4

Falcons School for Boys   020 8747 8393
2 Burnaby Gardens
The Falcons School for Boys educates 3-8 years old boys

**Chiswick and Bedford
Park Prep School**   020 8994 1804
Priory House, Priory Avenue
boys 4-8yrs, girls 4-11yrs

Orchard House School   020 8742 8544
16 Newton Grove
co-ed 3-11yrs

W5

Falcons School for Girls   **020 8992 5189**
15 Gunnersbury Avenue
The Falcons School for Girls educates girls from 4-11 years

St Augustine's Priory   020 8997 2022
Hillcrest Road
admin@saintaug.demon.co.uk
www.saintaug.demon.co.uk
An ideal school environment fostering academic curiosity,
independence and kindness

Aston House School   020 8566 7300
1 Aston Road
co-ed. 2-11yrs

Clifton Lodge Prep School   020 8579 3662
8 Mattock Lane
boys 4-13yrs

Durston House School   020 8997 0511
12 Castlebar Road
boys 4-13yrs

Harvington School   020 8997 1583
20 Castlebar Road
girls 3-16yrs; boys 3-5yrs

St Benedict's Junior School   020 8862 2050
5 Montpelier Avenue
boys 4-18yrs, girls 16-18yrs

W6

Bute House School   020 7603 7381
Luxembourg Gardens
girls 4-11yrs

Godolphin & Latymer   020 8741 1936
Iffley Road

Larmenier Infant School   020 8748 9444
Great Church Lane
3-7yrs

Latymer Preparatory School   020 8748 0303
36 Upper Mall
boys 7-18yrs, girls 16-18yrs. Introducing co-ed throughout

Ravenscourt Park Prep School   020 8846 9153
16 Ravenscourt Avenue
co-ed 4-11yrs

St Paul's Girls' School 020 7603 2288
Brook Green
girls 11-18yrs

W7
Manor House School 020 8567 4101
16 Golden Manor, Hanwell

W8
Hawkesdown House School 020 7727 9090
27 Edge Street
hawkesdown@hotmail.com
Boys 4-8yrs. First class academic education in a kind and caring school

Thomas's Prep School 020 7361 6500
17-19 Cottesmore Gardens
co-ed 4-13yrs. A lively co-educational school in the heart of Kensington

Lady Eden's School 020 7937 0583
39-41 Victoria Road
girls 3-11yrs

W10
Bassett House School 020 8969 0313
60 Bassett Road
co-ed 3-8yrs

W11
Norland Place School 020 7603 9103
162-166 Holland Park Avenue
girls 4-11yrs, boys 4-8yrs

Southbank International School 020 7229 8230
36-38 Kensington Park Road
co-ed 4-18yrs

W13
Avenue House School 020 8998 9981
70 The Avenue
2 ½-11yrs. Full day

**Notting Hill and Ealing
High School** 020 8991 2165
2 Cleveland Road
girls 5-18yrs

W14
St James Independent School 020 7348 1777
Earsby Street
boys & girls 4-10yrs, separate schools

gifted children

Gifted Monthly
28 Wallis Close, SW11
www.giftedmonthly.com
online newsletter for parents with gifted children

**National Association for
Gifted Children** 0870 770 3217

learning difficulties
(see also helplines)

Willoughby Hall Dyslexia Centre 020 7794 3538
1 Willoughby Road, NW3
6-12yrs

David Mulhall Centre 020 7223 4321
31 Webbs Road, SW11

left-handedness

Anything Lefthanded 020 8770 3722

www.RU-lefthanded.co.uk 0800 781 5338
Small range of products and advice on how to help left handed children start to write correctly

speech therapists

**Speech, Language
and Hearing Centre** 020 7383 3834
1-5 Christopher Place, Chalton Street, NW11.
www.speech-lang.org.uk
Specialist centre for babies/toddlers with hearing or speech impairment

tuition

Southgate Tutorial School 020 8446 5216

**Victoria Page
Private Tuition** 020 7381 9911
Fulham, SW6
3-11yrs scholarship, maths, english, reasoning, remedial reading, common entrance. Also reached on 07050 240 810

Fleet Tutors 020 8580 3911
One-to-one tuition at home.

VICTORIA PAGE
Est.1982

PRIVATE TUITION
Children 3yrs – 11+
Remedial Reading
Maths & English
Adult Students of English
Preparatory School &
Common Entrance

**07050
246 810
Fulham**

adventure playgrounds

Usually for 5yrs+ but some are perfect for energetic 3-5yr olds. Open between 10am–6pm weekends and holidays, and 3.30pm–7pm term time. The following are a combination of private organisations which may require advance booking and the best council-run adventure playgrounds

EAST

Apples & Pears   020 7729 6062
28 Pearson Street, E2

Brooks Farm   020 8539 4278
Skeltons Lane Park, Leyton, E10

Discover Story Garden   020 8536 5563
1 Bridge Terrace, Stratford, E15
Designed to inspire 2-7yrs olds to create their own stories - sliding down a monster's tongue, dressing up and an interactive sound and light installation

NORTH

Timbuktu   020 7272 2183
Grenville Road, N19

SOUTH

Home Park   020 8659 2329
Winchfield Road, SE23

Loughborough   020 7926 1049
Moorland Road, SW9

Battersea Park   020 8871 7539
Sun Gate Entrance, Albert Bridge Road, SW11

York Gardens   020 7223 3269
Lavender Road, SW11

Kimber BMX   020 8870 2168
Kimber Road, SW18

Tiger's Eye   020 8543 1655
42 Station Road, SW19

Creative wiz kids!

- Ages 1-3
- Art, Music and movement
- Ages 2-6 holiday camps
- Birthday parties 1-12 years
- Primrose Hill

020 7794 6797

WEST

White City   020 8749 0909
Canada Way, W12

Log Cabin   020 8840 1506
259 Northfield Avenue, W5 4UA

Distillery Lane Children's Centre   020 8748 9224
Distillery Lane, W6
(book in advance)

art workshops

The organisations listed below are where young children can go to experience all types of art media, materials and craft projects with something to take home at the end of the day. See also ceramic cafés and castings for preserving your baby's hand or foot print

NORTH & WEST

Brush Strokes   020 8346 1486
St Peter Le Poer Church Hall, Muswell Hill, N10
Christ Church Hall, 620A High Road, Finchley N12
Painting, stencils, jigsaws, drawing, sticking, cooking etc.
Also art birthday parties. 18mths–4yrs

Art 4 Fun
212 Fortis Green Road, N10   020 8444 4333
172 West End Lane, NW6   020 7794 0800
444 Chiswick High Road, W4   020 8994 4100
196 Kensington Park Road, W11   020 7792 4567
www.Art4Fun.com
Make, design, decorate ceramics, wood, glass, mosaic, etc.
Great for parties. Under 4s can get really messy with clay, dough, plaster and papier mâché

Creative Wiz Kids   020 7794 6797
NW3
Classes and holiday activities. A fun and relaxed environment that brings out the artist!

Nellie's young@art Classes   01298 872 752
NW1/W8

**London International
Gallery of Children's Art**   020 7435 0903
02 Centre, 255 Finchley Road, NW3 6LU
Workshops at this London gallery exhibiting children's art

Arties, N8   020 8343 8722

SOUTH

**Penny Poppins
Musical Paint & Create**   020 8741 8016
SW3/SW6/SW15/SW13/W4
Newborn–4yrs experience the fun and development benefits music and creative art have to offer

Paint Pots Art Classes   **020 7376 4571**
SW10
18mths–6yrs art and craft classes during the holidays

Tulse Hill Pottery   **020 8674 2400**
93 Palace Road, SW2

**Mira Stevanoska's
Art Classes**   **020 7386 8015**
53 Walham Grove, SW6 1QR
4yrs+ teaching of fine art skills, drawing, painting, portraiture, landscape. Termtime courses after school and on Saturdays

Art Yard   **020 8878 1336**
318 Upper Richmond Road West, SW14

baby research

The Babylab   **020 7631 6258**
Centre for Brain & Cognitive Development,
FREEPOST, 32 Torrington Square, WC1E 7BR
www.cbcd.bbk.ac.uk
Together with your baby you can have fun making discoveries about brain development

chess

You might ask why we have included chess in the Baby Directory, but it's been a long-term category and where else would you go to find such useful information? It is recommended that chess is only considered for young children (4-6yrs+) who have already mastered Snakes & Ladders, Ludo and other family board games. The www.chesskids.com website is a font of information including an online course for parents.

British Chess Federation
www.bcf.ndirect.co.uk

Chess Kids
www.chesskids.com

Richmond Junior Chess Club
13 Rosslyn Road, East Twickenham
www.rjcc.org.uk

Barnet Knights Chess Club
www.chessclub.demon.co.uk

ceramic cafés

(see also castings)

Ceramic cafés are definitely one of London's unique offerings. For a basic studio fee and a whole range of ceramic shapes you can take your baby's hand or footprint, book a party (5yrs+), make jewellery, or if your bathroom accessories are getting tired, design and paint your own

NORTH & WEST
Art 4 Fun
212 Fortis Green Road, N10	020 8444 4333
172 West End Lane, NW6	020 7794 0800
444 Chiswick High Road, W4	020 8994 4100
196 Kensington Park Road, W11	020 7792 4567

www.Art4Fun.com
Make, design, decorate ceramics, wood, glass, mosaic, etc
(see advert on page 7)

Ceramic Coffee House   **020 8444 6886**
452 Muswell Hill Broadway, N10

The Clay Café   **020 8905 5353**
8-10 Monkville Parade, Finchley Road, NW11
www.theclaycafe.co.uk
Original keepsake. Painted hand/footprints on a glazed ceramic plate

The Ceramics Café
6 Argyle Road, W13	**020 8810 4422**
215 King Street, W6	**020 8741 4140**

Colour Me Mine   **020 8444 4333**
212 Fortis Green Road, N10
www.muswellhill.colourmemine.com

SOUTH
Pottery Café   **020 7736 2157**
735 Fulham Road, SW6
www.pottery-café.com
Decorate your own English pottery - parties, baby's footprints, children's activities

Crawley Studios   **020 8516 0002**
39 Wood Vale, Forest Hill, SE23

Brush and Bisque-it
41 Northcote Road, SW11	020 7738 9909
77 Church Road, SW13	020 8503 1515

Ceramic Magic   **020 8255 2484**
40 Sheen Lane, SW14 8LW

Pottery Café   **020 8744 3000**
323 Richmond Road, TW1

cookery

It's 4pm 'sugar levels are falling' so you decide to rustle up a delicious tea, open the fridge door and stare blankly at ingredients, which just wouldn't be good together in the pan. The key is getting an arsenal of ideas from books, friends - or one of our recommended cookery sessions to get everyone inspired (kids and adults)

Books for Cooks Workshop   **020 7221 1992**
4 Blenheim Crescent, W11

Cookie Crumbles 0845 691 4173
www.cookiecrumbles.net
5-16yrs

Cooking for Coco
This cookery book: by trained chef and mother, Sian Blunos, provides parents with recipes that baby and parents find tasty. Most can be cooked in advance and frozen

Dodo Book for Cooks 0870 900 8004
www.dodopad.com
Indodispensible family organiser. An ideal place to save your recipes.

Gill's Cookery Workshops 020 8458 2608
6yrs+

Kids' Cookery School 020 8992 8882
107 Gunnersbury Lane, W3 8HQ
3-18yrs

Les Petits Cordons Bleus 020 7935 3503
114 Marylebone Lane, W1U 2HH
www.cordonbleu.net
7yrs+

Sticky Mitts 0870 240 6892
www.stickymitts.co.uk
Inspiring cookery courses you can do at home with your children

cycling and scooters

You can start from 2yrs+ with a little LikeaBike from Yo-Yo Trading. Thereafter, get a good fitting hat from your local Halfords or cycle shop to minimise the cuts and bruises when the stabilizers come off

Cycle Training UK 020 7582 3535
www.cycletraining.co.uk
Individual tuition for beginners including accompanied school journeys

Herne Hill Stadium 020 7737 4647
Burbage Road, SE24
Opened in 1948 for the Olympics, the track offers serious opportunities for the keen cyclist. Also mountain bike track and camps run during holidays

LikeaBike from YoYo 01444 831 064
www.yoyotrading.co.uk

London Cycling Campaign 020 7928 7220
30 Great Guildford Street, SE1
www.lcc.org.uk
Available from cycling shops the LCC London cycling maps show routes across London. The publication London Cycle Guides (£8.99) is the best for family routes

Safe Routes to Schools 0117 929 0888
www.saferoutestoschools.org.uk
Campaigning to increase the number of children cycling to school

Two plus Two UK 01273 480 479
twoplustwo@pavilion.uk.com
Stocking the complete range of bicycle trailers for children up to age 5.

dance

(see also art workshop, drama, gyms:mini and music groups)

Dance teachers tend to hold classes in different halls within a broad area, so check neighbouring postcodes, as the teacher may be listed there. Most ballet classes are for children from 3yrs+ unless otherwise stated

Royal Academy of Dancing 020 7326 8000
www.rad.org.uk
Ballet classes from 3yrs

Imperial Society of 020 7377 1577
Teachers of Dancing
22-26 Paul Street, EC2A 4QE
www.istd.org.uk
Find out about other types of dancing available to you locally.

International Dance 01273 685 652
Teachers' Association
International House, 76 Bennett Road, BN2 5JL
You can ring for a list of local ballet teachers in your area.

Stagecoach 01923 254 333
www.stagecoach.co.uk
Stagecoach, Britain's largest part-time theatre school, offers drama, dance and singing tuition at weekends to young performers from 4-16 all across London.(see advert on inside front cover)

Little Magic Train 01865 739 048
For 2-4yr olds the Little Magic Train is a dance and drama session at the Holmes Place Health Clubs across London.

EAST LONDON

Chantraine School of Dance 020 8989 8604
E11

Chisenhale Dance Space 020 8981 6617
64-84 Chisenhale Road, E3
www.chisenhaledancespace.co.uk

NORTH LONDON

Finchley Ballet School   020 8449 3921

Carol Straker Dance Foundation   020 8985 1221
www.csdf.co.uk
Dance for under 5 year olds as well as toddler and parent classes.

City Dance Academy   020 7359 2273
N1

Islington Ballet School   01992 813572
149 Grosvenor Avenue, N5 2NH
Ballet classes and creative dance for children from 3 years.

Lauderdale House   020 8348 8716
Highgate Hill, Waterlow Park, N6 5HG
www.lauderdale.org.uk

Chalk Farm School of Dance   020 8348 0262
N6
Ballet classes for 3-5yrs on Thurs pm and Sat am. Term-time only. Locations in Primrose Hill and Hampstead

Islington Arts Factory   020 7607 0561
2 Parkhurst Road, N7 0SF
www.islingtonartsfactory.org.uk
Ballet classes from 5yrs+ at £20 per term. Also holds art classes for 4-6yrs on Mondays 4-5pm where children learn technical drawing and painting skills

Crazee Kids   **020 8444 5333**
Jackson Lane Community Centre, Highgate, N6
From 2-10yrs. Creative movement, dance, drama and music through a wide range of exciting and magical adventures, building confidence and self-awareness.

North London Performing Arts Centre   020 8444 4544
N10
www.nlpac.co.uk
Ballet for 3-5yrs term-time. Also Drama Fun for 3-5yrs and holiday workshops.

NORTH WEST LONDON

Marylebone Ballet School   01992 813572
NW1
Ballet classes and creative dance for children from 3 years

Ready, Steady, Go   020 7586 5862
NW1

Biodanza   020 7485 2369
NW1/NW3/WC1
0-5yrs dance classes from Chile for girls and boys. Classes held all over North London and Covent Garden.

NW3 Dance Academy   01689 606 751
(formerly Stella Mann School of Dancing)

Rona Hart School of Dance   020 7435 7073
Rosslyn Hall, Willoughby Road, NW3

Abbey Community Centre   020 7435 4247
222C Belsize Road, NW6 4DJ
4-7yrs. Also drama

St John's Wood Ballet School   01992 813572
NW8
Ballet classes and creative dance for children from 3 years

SOUTH EAST LONDON

Leader School of Dance   020 8678 7828
SE27

McAlpine Dance Studio   020 8673 4992
Longfield Hall, 50 Knatchbull Road, SE5 9QU
Term-time classes from 3yrs+ for ballet, jazz, spanish and drama. Also an Easter holiday course

Laban Centre   020 8691 8600
Deptford Creekside, SE8
www.laban.org
The recently opened centre for contemporary dance offering a wide range of courses and classes for babies/toddlers & children. Includes music, dance, ballet and yoga. Very popular so book early

Greenwich Dance Agency   020 8293 9741
The Borough Hall, Royal Hill, SE10
www.greenwichdance.org.uk
Classes for 0-2yrs play & dance, and 3-5yrs First Steps. Term-time only. Pay per class. Also offers holiday summer school.

Grafton Regal   020 7394 0677
7 Village Way, Dulwich, SE21 7AW
www.graftonregal.co.uk

Campbell School of Stage Dance   020 8768 0782
SE22

Beryl Low School of Performing Arts   020 8244 9185
SE22/SE27

Campbell School of Stage Dance   020 8768 0782
Methodist Hall, Half Moon Lane, SE24
Ballet and tap classes for 3-5yrs. Tues 4.15-5.15pm and Sat 10.30-11.30am

Southfields School of Ballet   020 8674 2526

SOUTH WEST LONDON

Chelsea Ballet School   020 7351 4117
St Barnabas Church Hall, Ranelagh Grove, SW1
www.chelseaballet.co.uk
Ballet classes for 2½-5yrs held every day in the afternoon. Term-time only. Scottish dancing course held during the Christmas holidays for 5yrs+

Westminster School of Dancing   020 7828 0651
St Vincent de Paul RC Primary Sch, Morpeth Terrace, SW1
Ballet classes for 3-5yrs on Wed pm. Term-time only. Uniform

Vacani School of Dancing 020 7592 9255
SW1/SW11/SW12
Also at Belgravia, Clapham, Fulham, Bayswater, Richmond,
East Sheen

Kicks for Kids 020 7222 8873
Westminster School of Performing Art, St Andrews
Club, SW1P 2DG
Drama, singing

La Sylvaine School 020 8964 0561
SW3/SW7

Spring School of Ballet 01276 709 393
The Contact Centre, Hambalt Road, SW4
Term-time classes in Ballet, tap and jazz for 2½yrs-5yrs Mon-
Sat. Also workshops in the summer holidays. Weekend
classes also held at Clapham Manor School

First Steps School of 020 7381 5224
Dance and Drama
SW6

Snowball School of Ballet 020 8785 9219
Dance Attic Studios, 368 North End Road, SW6
www.danceattic.com
Term-time ballet classes from 3-5yrs on Mon and Fri

Wendy Bell School of 020 7371 9652
Dance and Fitness
16 Mimosa Street, SW6 4DT
2½yrs+

West London School of Dance 020 8743 3856
David Lloyd Centre, 116 Cromwell Road, SW7
www.wlsd.org
Ballet classes for boys and girls from 2½-5yrs Mon-Fri in the
afternoons. Term-time only. Classes last 45 mins and are
accompanied by a pianist. Café for parents

Childsplay 020 7727 9307
Ashburnham Community Centre, Upcerne Rd,
SW10

Fancy Footwork 020 8870 8886
Chatham Hall, Northcote Road, SW11
Parent and toddler class 2-3yrs and Baby Ballet 3-5yrs on
Mon, Wed, Fri and Sat. Term-time only for 12 weeks. Also
classes at St Luke's Community Hall, Ramsden Road,
Balham, SW12

Sam Hawkins School of Dance 020 8847 3792
Garfield Community Centre, SW11

Woolborough Academy 020 8351 7713
Woolborough House, 39 Lonsdale Road, SW13
3yrs+

London Dance School 020 8940 3793
SW13/W4/W6

Studioflex 020 8878 0556
SW14

Islington Ballet School
St John's Wood Ballet School
Creative dance for Children from 3 years,
progressing to classical Ballet
training and optional examinations.

For further information please contact:
Belinda Payne A.I.S.T.D. (Dip.)
01992 813572

Southwest School of Ballet 020 8392 9565
SW15

The Chloe James 020 8644 6532
Academy of Dance
St. Peter's Church, Leigham Court Rd, SW16

Streatham School of Dance 020 8857 4206
St Leonard's Church Hall, 8 Tooting Bec Gardens,
SW16
Classes on Wed and Sat from 3yrs+ term-time only. Ballet
until 5yrs then tap and modern available

Rainbow School of Ballet 020 8877 0703
10 Godley Road, Earlsfield, SW18
Ballet classes in Battersea/Clapham area from 2½ yrs, small
classes with pianist. Termtime only.

Cherry Dunn Dancing Classes 020 8946 1523
St John's Church Hall, Spencer Hill, SW19
2½-17yrs

Village Dancing School 020 8543 1394
4 Havelock Road, SW19 8HD

Footsteps School of Dance and Drama 020 8540
3090
SW20

CENTRAL & WEST LONDON

The Place 020 7387 7669
17 Duke's Road
www.theplace.org.uk

Pineapple Dance Studios 020 7836 4004
7 Langley Street, WC2
www.pineappleuk.co.uk
4yrs+ on Saturday and Sunday only

Dance Works 020 7629 6183
16 Balderton Street, W1
www.danceworks.co.uk

Arts Educational Schools 020 8987 6666
14 Bath Road, W4 1LY

Frances Lundy School of Dance 020 8675 0433
W4/W12

June Carlyle School of 020 8992 4122
Educational Dance
Centram Church Hall, Beaufort Road, W5
3+ yrs.

Margaret Dance Academy 020 8740 0727
Pitshanger Methodist Church, Pitshanger Lane, W5

Ruth Barber 01923 820941
Ellen Wilkinson High School, Queens Drive, W5

Ealing Dance Centre & Studio 020 8998 2283
96 Pitshanger Lane, W5 1QX
www.ealingdance.co.uk
3yrs+

Ravenscourt Theatre School 020 8741 0707
30-40 Dalling Road, W6
www.dramaschoollondon.com

Crackerjack 020 8840 3355
99 Oaklands Road, W7 2DT

Portobello School of Ballet 020 8969 4125
59A Portobello Road, W11

West London School of Dance 020 8743 3856
4 Labroke Road, ,W11
www.wlsd.org
Also at Southbank Intl School, 36-38 Kensington Park Rd,
W11

drama

If you already have a drama queen (or king) in the
family, you might as well capitalise on any natural
talents. These drama groups offer a small range of
activities for the 3yrs+ which are fun, confidence-
building, increase co-ordination and concentration

NATIONAL
Stagecoach 01923 254 333
The Courthouse, Elm Grove,
Walton-on-Thames, KT12 1LZ
www.stagecoach.co.uk
With 60 venues across London but with no more than 15 in a
group. Holiday workshops and termtime weekend sessions
are always popular so book early (4yrs+) (see advert inside
front cover)

Helen O'Grady Drama Academy 01481 200 250
Garenne House, Rue de la Cache,
St Sampsons, GY2 4AF
www.helenogrady.co.uk
With 8 groups across London, starting 5yrs+

Perform 020 7209 3805
66 Church Way, NW1 1LT
www.perform.org.uk
With more than 30 centres across London children can
attend a themed workshop to build on the 4 Cs: confidence,
communication, co-ordination and concentration. Classes
held throughout the week/weekend with a week-long course
in the holidays.

EAST
Pollyanna Children's
Training Theatre 020 7702 1937
Metropolitan Wharf, Wapping Wall, E1 9SS
3yrs+

NORTH
Hoxton Hall 020 7739 5431
130 Hoxton Street, N1
www.hoxtonhall.co.uk

North London
Performing Arts Centre 020 8444 4544
76 St James Lane, N10 3DF

Greasepaint Anonymous 020 8886 2263
4 Gallus Close, Winchmore Hill, N21 1JR
4yrs+

Hot Tin Roof Drama Project 020 8858 7324
Highbury Round House, Donalds Road, N5
4yrs+

Allsorts 020 8969 3249
www.alsorts.com
Allsorts drama for children provide after school, Saturday and
holiday courses covering all aspects of drama in a fun and
friendly environment. Ages 4-6 in Hampstead, Kensington,
Notting Hill and Fulham.

Club Dramatika 020 8883 1554
NW11

Dramarama 020 8446 0891
South Hampstead High School, Maresfield
Gardens, NW3
From 3yrs+ children can attend Sat am during termtime and
week courses during holidays. Also provide themed parties at
any location

Tricycle Theatre 020 7328 1000
269 Kilburn High Road, NW6 7JR

SOUTH
Bright Sparks Performers 020 8769 3500
SE22

Theatre Factory 020 7274 6586
St Faith's Centre, Red Post Hill, Dulwich, SE24
3-11yrs

Blackheath Conservatoire of
Music and the Arts 020 8852 0234
19-21 Lee Road, SE3 9RQ

New Peckham Varieties   020 7708 5401
Magic Eye Theatre, Havil Street, SE5 7SD
4yrs+ on Mon pm as well as sessions at weekends. Older
children can try jazz, steel bands and break dancing. A great
deal to look forward to

Rise Theatre Arts School   020 7924 1404
SW11
4-16yrs

Bounce School of Performing Arts 07870 739213
Alderbrook Primary School, Oldbridge Road, SW12
4-11yrs

**Little Players Children's
Theatre & Drama Stud**   020 8789 7655
Newlands Hall (Putney Vale Club), Putney Vale,
SW15

Drama Club   020 7231 6083
Open Door Community Centre, Beaumont Road,
SW19
5yrs+

Polka Theatre   020 8543 4888
240 The Broadway, SW19

Wimbles   020 8408 3578
SW19

Little Actors Theatre Company   020 7231 6083
Open Door Community Centre, SW19, SE16
3-10yrs. Fun acting parties designed for children aged from
3yrs. Professional actors. Games, story telling and themes.

Big Foot Theatre Company   020 8761 2111
SW2/SW18
Summer drama courses

WEST
Centrestage   020 7328 0788
33 Margaret Street, W1
www.centrestageschool.co.uk

Dramatic Dreams   020 8740 9925
W12

Barbara Speake Stage School   020 8743 1306
East Acton Lane, W3 7EG

Esta   020 8741 2843
16 British Grove, W4
From 3yrs+

Arts Educational Schools   020 8987 6666
14 Bath Road, W4 1LY

foreign language classes & clubs

FRENCH

1.2.3 Soleil   0845 085 0048
PO Box 33380, NW11 7WG
www.123-soleil.co.uk
French language classes for children in over 20 locations
across London. 8 months to 11yrs

Bonjour French Fun   020 8670 7134
After school French classes from 4yrs+ in East Dulwich,
Herne Hill and Clapham (termtime)

Club Petit Pierrot   020 7828 2129
www.clubpetitpierrot.uk.com
Fun French from 8mths. Small groups, excellent results.
Highly recommended by BBC and Daily Express

French a la carte   020 8946 4777
97 Revelstoke Road, Wimbledon Park, SW18 5NL
www.frenchandspanishalacarte.co.uk
Termtime and holiday classes from 2yrs+ and Saturday
morning classes from 5yrs in Wimbledon

French Ecole   020 8856 5131
www.frenchecole.com
French language classes for children aged 3-11yrs plus
holiday clubs in centres across London

Le Club Francais   01962 714 036
www.leclubfrancais.com
Fun clubs for children from 3yrs+ to learn French or Spanish
in venues throughout London

Le Club Frere Jacques   020 7354 0589
French classes in Barnes, Ealing, Hammersmith, Notting Hill,
West Hampstead, Muswell Hill and Islington

Le Club Tricolore   020 7924 4649
10 Bolingbroke Road, SW11 6AJ
www.leclubtricolore.co.uk
French activites for the under 5s where learning the language
is all part of the fun.

Les Petites Marionnettes   020 7637 5698
24 Weymouth Street, W1 3FA
Les Petites Marionnettes offer private French tuition in your
own home from 2yrs+ after school and during termtime only.

Les Petits Lapins   07947 823 067
86 Church Road, SW19 5AB
www.lespetitslapins.com
French from 12mths to 8yrs. Classes also held in W8, SW4,
SW6 and SW15; also holiday courses/after school clubs.

Recreation   **020 8838 0018**
St John's Church Hall, Robin Hood Lane, Kingston Vale, SW15 3PY
French termtime (2pm and 3.45pm) and holiday clubs for 3-6yrs.

GERMAN

German Parent and Toddler Group **020 7630 5940**
SW1

German Playgroup   **020 8992 7572**
W5

German Saturday School   **020 7281 8167**
N1/N5

German Saturday School   **020 7370 1278**
W2
Between 10am-12pm during school terms starting from 3yrs+

German Saturday School   **020 8942 5663**
Richmond

German Saturday School   **020 8567 8381**
W5

German School   **020 8940 2510**
Douglas House, Petersham Road, Richmond, TW10
www.etsl.demon.co.uk
5-18yrs

Hansel & Gretel   **020 8693 4152**
SE22

SPANISH

1.2.3 Sol   **0845 085 0048**
PO Box 33380, NW11 7WG
www.123-sol.co.uk
Spanish language classes for children throughout London from 8 months to 11 years

Anglo Spanish Nursery   **020 7622 5599**
152 Clapham Manor Street, SW4
18mths-5yrs

Peques Nursery School   **020 7385 0055**
St John's Church, Waltham Green, North End Road, Fulham, SW6 1PB
www.peques-nursery.co.uk

Spanish Day Nursery   **020 8960 6661**
317 Portobello Road, W10
2-5yrs. Full day. 48 wks

football

Football in the Community guarantees that all clubs organise coaching courses, fun trial days and skills workshops for children around 5yrs+. These take place at the clubs with FA qualified coaches

Little Kickers   **01235 833 854**
www.littlekickers.co.uk
Weekday football classes for pre-school children 2-5yrs. With over 10 venues across London they offer 45 min sessions geared around football fun. Sharing, waiting a turn and learning a few little football tricks are all part of the ethos

Kick It Soccer   **01895 435 571**
Football for 3-12yrs – venues across London

Super Soccer Saturdays (Fit4Kidz) **07903 148 271**
Wandsworth Common, Trinity Road, SW18
Football for boys & girls aged 4-12 from 10.30-12.00 every Saturday morning. Newcomers arrive at 10.15 for registration purposes. Professional coaching and skills training supported and run by coaches from clubs such as Chelsea, Fulham, West Ham & Wimbledon

Sports Galore   **01285 656 098**
Sunday morning, 2 hour football sessions for 4-14 yrs in Battersea Park (10am-12pm), and Paddington Recreation Ground (9am-11am). Price £132 for 11 week classes. Fully qualified FA coaches

Arsenal	**020 7704 4140**
Brentford FC	**020 8758 9430**
Charlton Athletic	**020 8850 2866**
Chelsea	**020 7957 8220**
Crystal Palace	**020 8768 6000**
Fulham	**020 7893 8383**
Queens Park Rangers	**020 8743 0262**
Leyton Orient, E10	**020 8556 5973**
West Ham United, E13	**020 8548 2707**
Milwall, SE16	**020 7231 1222**
Queens Park Rangers	**020 8743 0262**
Tottenham Hotspur	**020 8365 5000**
West Ham United	**020 8548 2707**

Limited spaces don't let your child be left on the bench!

It's one thing buying kids the latest trainers, but giving them a head start in sport is a real investment. Obviously, we can't promise you a future star, but we can offer your child the foundation needed to lead a healthy and active life.

APPROVED FOOTBALL TRAINING FOR KIDS FROM 2 TO UNDER 5

Small wonders.

call **01235 833854**

LittleKickers

gyms : mini

ACROSS LONDON

Tumble Tots
St John's Wood, Golders Green,
Muswell Hill, Highbury, Finchley   020 8381 6585
Fulham, Wimbledon,
Barnes, Victoria   020 8944 8818
Chiswick, Kew, Twickenham,
Kingston, Hampton   01932 865 100
Battersea, Dulwich, Clapham,
Blackheath   020 8464 4433
www.tumbletots.com
The leading national active physical play programme for pre-school children. (see advert on page 168)

Gymboree Play & Music   **0800 092 0911**
Business Design Centre, N1   020 7288 6657
The O2 Centre, NW3   020 7794 8719
Exchange Shopping Ctr, SW15   020 8780 3831
Whiteleys Shopping Cenre, W2   020 7229 9294
Holmes Place, Wimbledon, SW19   020 7258 1415
St George's Leisure Centre, HA1   020 8863 5191
www.gymboreeplayuk.com
(see advert on page 168)

Crechendo Playgyms   **020 8772 8120**
www.crechendo.com
Classes held throughout London

EAST LONDON

Redbridge School of Gymnastics   020 8530 3810
Pulteney Road, E18
Drop-in sessions for under 5s to encourage balancing, running, jumping.

NORTH LONDON

Little Steps Gym (Muswell Hill)   020 8883 1608
Middlesex Cricket Club, Finchley,
www.stepsgym.com
Children's activity gym classes

Active Kids   **020 7281 2604**
Fortismere School, North Gym, N10
Multi-sport classes for 3-7 year olds during weekdays, weekends and school holidays.

Highgate Newtown Community Centre Skate and Bounce   020 7272 7201
25 Bertram Street, N19 5DQ

Fit Start   020 8374 7680
Sobell Leisure Centre, Hornsey Road, N7
Mornington Sports Centre, NW1
Activity sessions for children aged 6mths-3yrs

Hornsey YMCA   020 8340 6088
184 Tottenham Lane, N8 8SG

SOUTH LONDON

Ladywell Gym Club   020 8690 7002
The Playtower, Ladywell Road, SE13 7UW

Greenwich Gym Club   020 8317 5000
Waterfront Leisure Centre, High Street Woolwich, SE18 6DL

TJ's Mini-Gym   020 8659 4561
Crystal Palace National Sports Centre, SE19
Babies' gym classes from 10mths-2yrs in soft play area, ball pit and mini trampolines. Toddler gym sessions are termtime only.

Budokwai Toddlers   020 8370 1000
4 Gilston Road, SW10 9SL
3-16yrs

The Little Gym   **020 8874 6567**
Compass House, Riverside West, SW18 1DB
www.thelittlegym.co.uk
Developing your child's skills and confidence (see advert on page 163)

TJ's Mini Gym Club Wimbledon   020 8640 2678
Church Hall, Kohat Road, SW19
Mother and toddler mini-gym sessions from 1-7yrs. Termtime only.

Tiny Tumblers   020 8542 1330
Wimbledon Leisure Centre, Latimer Road, SW19
Gym classes from 18mths+ in soft play area. Baby bounce classes from 12mths. Also at: Newham Leisure Centre, E13; Atherton Leisure Centre, E15; St Mark's Church, Becton, E6; and Froud Centre, Manor Park, E12

WEST LONDON

Tiny Tots Gym   020 7727 9747
Kensington Sports Centre, Walmer Road, W11

Tippitoes, W5   020 8566 1449

Ealing YMCA Health & Fitness Centre   020 8799 4800
25 St Mary's Road, W5 5RE
www.estlondonymca.org
Activity sessions for "Crawlers 8mths-12yrs" and "Tiny Tumbles 1-2yrs"

Crackerjack   020 8840 3355
W7
1yr+

Ready, steady, go!

Crêchendo is all about fun, fitness & confidence. Each weekly class is 45 minutes of discovery and action-packed adventure for babies and children aged 4 months to 4 years.

Come along and find out what makes Crêchendo London's favourite physical play programme and give your child the chance to gain skills & confidence which last a lifetime.

020 8772 8120
playgyms@crechendo.com
www.crechendo.com

A Big Adventure for Little People.

From 4 months to 12 years old

Curriculum based programmes:
• Gymnastics • Sports • Karate

Other activities:
• Birthday Parties • Holiday Camps

Telephone now for a free trial class
020 8874 6567

Developing your child's skills and confidence.

The Little Gym, Compass House, Riverside West,
Smugglers Way, SW18 1DB. www.thelittlegym.co.uk

BUILDING CONFIDENCE THAT LASTS A LIFETIME ....

25 years - 1979 to 2004

*Britain's leading national **active play programme**, for children from **6 months to 5 years***

➤ Classes structured to develop balance, climbing, agility and co-ordination skills that ultimately promote your child's self-confidence

➤ Develop language with action songs and rhymes

➤ **Gymbabes** classes are designed for active babies, helping develop muscles and co-ordination for crawling and promoting walking and language skills

➤ Trained staff and specially designed Tumble Tots equipment

Liane	020-8381-6585	St John's Wood; Golders Green; Muswell Hill; Highbury; Finchley (& Saturdays)
Sarah	020-8944-8818	Fulham; Wimbledon; Barnes; Victoria
Helen	01932-865100	Chiswick; Kew; Twickenham; Kingston; Hampton;
Julia	020-8464-4433	Battersea; Dulwich; Clapham; Blackheath

GYMBOREE PLAY & MUSIC

Play, Music and Arts classes for Newborn to Under 5s.

Our structured, theme-based and developmentally appropriate classes feature enthusiastic and highly trained teachers, the highest quality equipment and props and spectacular permanent sites.

Bayswater: 020 7229 9294 · Harrow: 020 8863 5191 · Highgate: 020 7272 0979 · Islington: 020 7288 6657 · Putney: 020 8780 3831 · St Margarets: 020 8607 9995 · Swiss Cottage: 020 7794 8719 · Uxbridge: 01895 252550 · Wimbledon: 020 8542 4785
MORE SITES COMING SOON: RING 0800 092 0911

GYMBOREE PLAY & MUSIC **Ring to book your trial class!**

Promoting sport, fitness and health-enhancing activity

Active:kids

- Weekly multi-sport classes for 3-7 year olds

- Weekend workshops for 3-11 year olds

- School holiday programmes for 3-13year olds

- Parties with a difference

High energy, well structured and a lot of fun. A great introduction to the world of sport and fitness developing core skills, confidence and strength. Taught by highly qualified sport specialists.

Call Greg 07939 227943 or 020 7281 2604

holiday activities

(see also drama, gyms:mini and health clubs for holiday activities)

Barracudas　　　　　　　　　**0845 123 5299**
www.barracudas.co.uk
Day camps for 5-16yrs in Essex, Surrey, Berkshire, Kent, Norfolk, Middlesex, Cambridgeshire, East London, Oxford, Herts, Bucks and Sussex

Camp Beaumont　　　　　　　**0845 608 1234**
www.daycamps.co.uk
From 3yrs+ multi activity day camps from 8.30am to 5.30pm

Creative Wiz Kids　　　　　**020 7794 6797**
NW3
www.creativewizkids.com
Fun, action packed holiday clubs for 2-6yrs

Paint Pots Holiday Classes　**020 7376 4571**
Ashburnham Centre, Tetcott Road, SW10
Arts, crafts, music and drama classes. 18mths-6yrs

Pippa Pop-ins Holiday Activities　**020 7731 1445**
430 Fulham Road, SW6 1DU
Summer holiday activites at this popular London nursery school for children aged 2-10yrs

Sports Galore Activity Weeks　**01285 656 098**
Easter and summer holiday sports and activity weeks from 10am-4pm daily including minibus transport and an out of hours club. For 4-5yr olds activities are interspersed with art, storytime and party games

The Little Gym　　　　　　　**020 8874 6567**
Compass House, Riverside West, Smugglers Way, SW18
www.thelittlegym.oo.uk
Great holiday activities developing your child's skills and confidence

indoor playcentres

Perfect for rainy days or as party venues. Supervision not provided so you have to expect a few knocks. Best for girls to wear trousers as a slim-fitting skirt is a bit restrictive. Equipment includes ball pits, climbing ropes, slides and tunnels

Space Zone　　　　　　　　　**020 8650 0233**
Beckenham Leisure Centre, 24 Beckenham Road, BR3 4PF

EAST
Shadwell Centre　　　　　　　**020 7364 5000**
The Highway, E1

Soft Play Activity Sessions　**020 8539 8343**
Cathall Leisure Centre, Cathall Road, E11 4LA

Atherton Leisure Centre　　　**020 8536 5500**
189 Romford Road, E15 4JF

Kids Mania　　　　　　　　　**020 8533 5556**
28 Powell Road, Clapton, E5 8DJ

NORTH
Clown Town　　　　　　　　　**020 8361 6600**
Coppetts Centre, Colney Hatch Lane, N12 0AQ

Fantasy Island　　　　　　　**020 8904 9044**
Vale Farm, Watford Road, Wembley, HA0

Highgate Newtown Community Centre Skate and Bounce　　　　　　　　　　**020 7272 7201**
25 Bertram Street, N19

Pirates Playhouse　　　　　　**020 7609 2166**
Sobell Leisure Centre, Hornsey Road, N7

Playstation　　　　　　　　　**020 8889 0001**
2a Brabant Road, Wood Green, N22

Paint Pots

HOLIDAY CLASSES

Arts, Crafts Music + Drama Classes 18mth - 6yrs

Tel: 0207 376 4571

Pyramid Soft Play   020 7359 5916
Highbury Roundhouse, 71 Ronalds Road, N5

Sidings Community Centre
Under 5s Soft Room   020 7625 6260
150 Brassey Road, NW6

The Fun House   020 8807 0712
Edmonton Leisure Centre, Plevna Road, N9

The Play House   020 7704 9424
The Old Gymnasium, Highbury Grove School,
Highbury New Park, N5

Toddler Bounce   020 8489 5322
Tottenham Green Leisure Centre, Phillip Lane, N15

Tropical Adventure Trail   020 8345 6666
Lee Valley Leisure Centre, Picketts Lock Lane,
Edmonton, N9

SOUTH
The Blue Kangaroo   **020 7371 7622**
555 King's Road, SW6
www.thebluekangaroo.co.uk
Family restaurant and play centre plus a great party venue

Camberwell Leisure Centre   020 7703 3024
Artichoke Place, Camberwell Church Street, SE5 8TS

Discovery Planet   020 7237 2388
Surrey Quays Shopping Centre, Redriff Road,
Surrey Quays, SE16 7LL

Kid's Corner   020 8852 3322
232 Hither Green Lane, SE13 6RT

Kidzone   020 8772 9577
Balham Leisure Centre, Elmfield Road, SW17 8AN

Peckham Pulse   020 7525 4990
Melon Road, SE15 5QN

Rascals   020 8317 5000
Greenwich Leisure, High Street, Woolwich, SE18 6DL

Rainbow Club Soft Play   020 8877 0703
Golf Club, Burntwood Lane, SW17

Spike's Madhouse   020 8778 9876
Crystal Palace National Sports Centre, SE19 2BB

Tiger's Eye   020 8543 1655
42 Station Road, Merton Abbey Mills, SW19 2LP

Toddlers' World   020 8317 5000
Arches Leisure Centre, 80 Trafalgar Rd, SE10 9UW

SOUTH WEST
Bouncers   020 8948 4228
Pools on the Park, Twickenham, TW10

Heathrow Gym   020 8570 9639
Green Lane, TW4 6DH

Little Tikes   020 8994 9596
Brentford Fountain Leisure Centre,
Chiswick High Road, TW8 0HJ

Lollipop Club   020 8332 7436
Old Deer Park, 187 Kew Road, TW9 2AZ

Snakes and Ladders   020 8847 0946
Syon Park, Brentford, TW8 8JF

WEST
Bramley's Big Adventure   020 8960 1515
136 Bramley Road, W10 6TJ

Bumper's Backyard   020 7727 9747
Kensington Sports Centre, Walmer Road, W11 4PQ

Seymour Leisure Centre   020 7723 8019
Seymour Place, W1H 5TJ

Crackerjack   020 8840 3355
99 Oaklands Road, W7

libraries

These libraries have a good selection of children's
books, both old favourites and new titles to extend
and enhance the stories you have at home. Most
organise story sessions during the week, homework
clubs during termtime and other special events for
families

EAST
North Chingford   020 8529 2993
The Green, Station Road, E4 7EN

Clapton   020 8356 2570
Northwold Road, E5 8RA

Hackney   020 8356 2562
223 Mare Street, E8

Homerton   020 8356 1690
Homerton High Street, E9 6AS

CENTRAL
Barbican Children's   020 7638 0569
Barbican Centre, Silk Street, EC2

Pimlico   020 7641 2983
Rampayne Street, SW1V 2PU

Churchill Gardens Children's   020 7931 7978
Ranelagh Grove, SW1V 3EU

Victoria   020 7641 4289
160 Buckingham Palace Road, SW1W 9UD

Chelsea   020 7352 6056
Old Town Hall, Kings Road, SW3 5EZ

St Pancras   020 7619 5833
Town Hall Extension, Argyle Street, WC1H 8NL

Holborn   020 7974 6288
32-38 Theobald Road, WC1X 8PA

Charing Cross   020 7641 4628
4 Charing Cross Road, WC2H 0HG

Westminster Reference   020 7641 4636
35 St Martin's Street, WC2H 7HP

NORTH
Islington Central   020 7527 6900
Fieldway Crescent, N1

South Isington   020 7527 7860
115-117 Essex Road, N1 2SL

Mildmay Park   020 7527 7880
21-23 Mildmay Park, N1 4NA

Shoreditch	020 8356 4350
80 Hoxton Street, N1 6LP	
East Finchley	020 8883 2664
East Finchley High Road, N2	
Arthur Simpson	020 7527 7800
Hanley Road, N4 3DL	
Highgate	020 8348 3443
Shepherd's Hill, N6 5QT	
Hornsey	020 8489 1429
Haringey Park, N8 9JA	
Edmonton Green	020 8807 3618
South Malll, Edmonton Green, N9 0NX	
Muswell Hill	020 8883 6734
Queens Avenue, N10 3PE	
Bowes Road	020 8368 2085
Bowes Road, N11 1BD	
Palmers Green	020 8379 2711
Broomfield Lane, N13 4EY	
Southgate Circus	020 8882 8849
High Street, N14 6BP	
West Green Libraries	020 8800 4676
Woodland Park Road, N15 3AA	
Marcus Garvey	020 8489 5309
Tottenham Green Centre, 1 Philip Lane, N15 4JA	
St Ann's	020 8800 4390
Cissbury Road, Tottenham, N15 4TY	
Stoke Newington	020 8356 5233
184 Stoke Newington Church Street, N16 0JS	
Stamford Hill	020 8356 2573
Portland Avenue, N16 6SD	
Coombes Croft	020 8489 5350
Tottenham High Road, N17 8AG	
Welr Hall	020 8884 2420
Silver Street, N18	
Highgate	020 7860 5752
Chester Road, N19 5DH	
Archway	020 7527 7820
Hamlyn House, Highgate Hill, N19 5PU	
Ridge Avenue	020 8360 9662
Ridge Avenue, N21 2RH	
Winchmore Hill	020 8360 8344
Green Lanes, N21 3AP	
Alexandra Park	020 8883 8553
Alexandra Park Road, N22 4UJ	
Wood Green Central	020 8888 1292
High Road, N22 6XD	

NORTH WEST

Queen's Crescent	020 7413 6243
Queen's Crescent, NW1	
Camden Town	020 7974 1563
Crowndale Centre, 218 Eversholt Street, NW1 1BD	
Regent's Park	020 7974 1530
Compton Close, off Robert Street, NW1 3QT	
Marylebone Children's	020 7641 1041
109-117 Marylebone Road, NW1 5PS	
Chalk Farm	020 7974 6526
Sharpleshall Street, NW1 8YN	
Heath	020 7974 6520
Keats Grove, NW3 2RR	
Swiss Cottage	020 7974 6522
88 Avenue Road, NW3 3HA	
Belsize Branch	020 7974 6518
Antrim Road, NW3 4XN	
Kentish Town	020 7974 6253
262-6 Kentish Town Road, NW5 2AA	
West Hampstead	020 7974 6610
Dennington Park Road, NW6 1AU	
Kilburn	020 7974 1965
Cotleigh Road, NW6 2NP	
St John's Wood	020 7641 5087
20 Circus Road, NW8 6PD	
Church Street	020 7641 5479
Church Street, NW8 8EU	

SOUTH EAST

John Harvard	020 7407 0807
211 Borough High Street, SE1 1JA	
East Street	020 7703 0395
168-170 Old Kent Road, SE1 5TY	
Durning	020 7926 8682
167 Kennington Lane, SE11 4HF	
Lewisham	020 8297 9677
199-201 Lewisham High Street, SE13 6LG	
Nunhead	020 7639 0264
Gordon Road, SE15 3RW	
Blue Anchor	020 7231 0475
Market Place, SE16 3UQ	
Rotherhithe	020 7237 2010
Albion Street, SE16 7HY	
Newington	020 7703 3324
155-157 Walworth Road, SE17	
Upper Norwood	020 8670 2551
39 Westow Hill, Crystal Palace, SE19 1TJ	
Kingwood	020 8670 4803
Seeley Drive, Dulwich, SE21 8QR	
Dulwich	020 8693 5171
368 Lordship Lane, SE22	
Grove Vale	020 8693 5734
25-27 Grove Vale, East Dulwich, SE22 8EQ	

| Forest Hill | 020 8699 2065 |
| Dartmouth Road, SE23 3HZ | |

| Carnegie | 020 7926 6050 |
| 188 Herne Hill Road, SE24 | |

| Sydenham | 020 8778 7563 |
| Sydenham Road, SE26 | |

| Blackheath Village | 020 8852 5309 |
| 3-4 Blackheath Grove, SE3 0DD | |

| Camberwell | 020 7703 3763 |
| 17-21 Camberwell Church Street, SE5 8TR | |

| Minet | 020 7926 6073 |
| 52 Knatchbull Road, SE5 9QY | |

SOUTH WEST

| Battersea | 020 8871 7471 |
| Lavender Hill, SW11 1JB | |

| York | 020 8871 7471 |
| Lavender Road, SW11 2GV | |

| Battersea Park | 020 8871 7468 |
| 309 Battersea Park Road, SW11 4NF | |

| Northcote | 020 8871 7469 |
| Northcote Road, SW11 6HW | |

| Balham | 020 8871 7195 |
| Ramsden Road, SW12 8QY | |

| Castelnau | 020 8748 3837 |
| 75 Castelnau, Barnes, SW13 9RT | |

| East Sheen | 020 8876 8801 |
| Sheen Lane, East Sheen, SW14 8LP | |

| Roehampton | 020 8871 7091 |
| Danebury Avenue, SW15 | |

| Putney | 020 8871 7090 |
| Disraeli Road, SW15 2DR | |

| Tate Streatham | 020 7926 6768 |
| 63 Streatham High Road, SW16 | |

| Tooting | 010 8871 7175 |
| 75 Mitcham Road, SW17 | |

| Westhill | 020 8871 6386 |
| West Hill, SW18 1RZ | |

| Alvering | 020 8871 6398 |
| Allfarthing Lane, Wandsworth, SW18 2PQ | |

| Earlsfield | 020 8871 6389 |
| Magdalen Road, SW18 3NY | |

| Donald Hope | 020 8542 1975 |
| Cavendish House, Colliers Wood High St, SW19 2HR | |

| Southfields | 020 8871 6388 |
| Wimbledon Park Road, SW19 6NL | |

| Wimbledon | 020 8946 7432 |
| Wimbledon Hill Road, SW19 7NB | |

| Tate | 020 7926 1056 |
| The Oval, Brixton, SW2 | |

| Raynes Park | 020 8542 1893 |
| Approach Road, SW20 8BA | |

| Clapham | 020 7926 0717 |
| The Old Town, 1 Clapham Common Northside, SW4 0QW | |

| Brompton | 020 7373 3111 |
| 210 Old Brompton Road, SW5 0BS | |

| Sands End Community Centre | 020 8576 5257 |
| 59-61 Broughton Road, SW6 2LA | |

| Fulham | 020 8576 5255 |
| 598 Fulham Road, SW6 5NX | |

| Tate South Lambeth | 020 7926 0705 |
| 180 South Lambeth Road, SW8 1QP | |

WEST

| Queens Park | 020 7641 4575 |
| 666 Harrow Road, W10 4NE | |

| Kensal | 020 8969 7736 |
| 20 Golborne Road, W10 5PF | |

| North Kensington | 020 7727 6583 |
| 108 Ladbroke Grove, W11 1PZ | |

| Shepherds Bush Children's | 020 8576 5062 |
| 7 Uxbridge Road, W12 8LJ | |

| Askew Road | 020 8576 5064 |
| 87-91 Askew Road, W12 9AS | |

| West Ealing | 020 8567 2812 |
| Melbourne Avenue, W13 9BT | |

| Baron's Court | 020 8576 5258 |
| North End Crescent, North End Road, W14 8TG | |

| St James's | 020 7641 2989 |
| 62 Victoria Street, W1E 6QP | |

| Mayfair | 020 7641 4903 |
| 25 South Audley Street, W1Y 5DJ | |

| Notting Hill Gate | 020 7229 8574 |
| 1 Pembridge Square, W2 4EW | |

| Paddington | 020 7641 4472 |
| Porchester Road, W2 5DU | |

| Acton | 020 8752 0999 |
| High Street, W3 6NA | |

| Chiswick | 020 8994 1008 |
| Duke's Avenue, W4 2AB | |

| Pitshanger | 020 8997 0230 |
| 143-145 Pitshanger Lane, W5 1RH | |

| Northfields | 020 8567 5700 |
| Northfields Avenue, W5 4UA | |

| Central | 020 8567 3670 |
| 103 The Broadway Centre, W5 5JY | |

| Hammersmith Children's | 020 8753 3817 |
| Shepherds Bush Road, W6 7AT | |

| Hanwell | 020 8567 5041 |
| Cherington Road, W7 3HL | |

| Kensington & Chelsea Central | 020 7937 2542 |
| Phillimore Walk, Hornton Street, W8 7RX | |

| Maida Vale | 020 7641 3659 |
| Sutherland Avenue, W9 2QT | |

model agencies

Childsplay　　　　　　　**020 7403 4834**
1 Cathedral Street, SE1 9DE

**Elisabeth Smith
(Model Agency) Ltd**　　　**020 8863 2331**
81 Headstone Road, Harrow, HA1 1PQ
www.elisabethsmith.com
Established in 1960 specializing in
babies/children/teenagers/families

Kids Plus　　　　　　　　**020 7737 3901**
54 Grove Park, SE5 8LG
www.kidsplus.co.uk

music groups

Most young children will be able to sing all the verses
of "Old MacDonald" before they decide to talk. These
classes and workshops are great for boosting
physical, musical and emotional development, in
addition to the CDs and tapes you might play at
home. The list is not exhaustive, and locations are
either by postcode or areas due to the increasing
number of classes available' so ring for details

Amanda's Action Kids　　**020 8578 0234**
www.amandasactionkids.co.uk
We dance, we sing, we learn through music, but most
importantly - we have FUN! 6mths-3½yrs.

Bea's Baby Music School　**020 8670 9378**
www.babymusic.co.uk
Groups 6mths to 6yrs. Stimulating, fun, educational. Live
professional musicians. SE27/SW3/SW6/SW12/SW15

Blueberry Playsongs　　　**020 8677 6871**
Barnes, Chelsea, Clapham, Hammersmith, Notting
Hill, Putney, Richmond, Wimbledon,
SW3/SW4/SW14/SW15/SW19/W
www.blueberry.clara.co.uk
9mths - 4 yrs. Guitar accompanied action songs, nursery
rhymes, instruments, games and dancing. Come and try the
Blueberry experience!

**Move and Groove
with Paint Pots**

32 Songs on tape
with song book
for children of all ages.
Price £12 inc p&p

Send cheques to:
PAINT POTS
9 Shalcomb Street
London SW10 0HZ

Tel: 020 7376 4571

Gymboree Play and Music　**0800 092 0911**
Business Design Centre, N1　　　020 7288 6657
The O2 Centre, NW3　　　　　　020 7794 8719
The Exchange Shopping Centre, SW15　020 8780 3831
Whiteleys Shopping Centre, W2　　020 7229 9294
Holmes Place Wimbledon, SW19　　020 8863 5191
www.gymboreePlayUK.com
Interactive play and music classes for newborns to the Under
5s in six centres across London

Hickory Jig Music　　　　**07966 454098|**
The Boys' Brigade Hall, Reynolds Place,
SE3/SE10/SE24 and more
www.hickoryjigmusic.co.uk
6mths-7yrs. Imaginatively planned and presented classes.
Live instruments and fabulous props. New class just opened
in Dulwich

Hickory Fiddle Violin Club　**07966 454 098**
www.hickoryjigmusic.co.uk
Violin club for children aged 2½ -3yrs. Daytime, weekday
classes, Blackheath only

Jazz-Mataz　　　　　　　**01962 717 181**
www.jazz-mataz.com
Fun clubs for under 5s to enjoy music, games and much
more.

Little Acorns　　　　　　**020 8408 0322**
www.thelittleacorns.com
Nursery music workshops for babies and young children in
Putney

London Suzuki Group　　**020 7386 8006**
www.suzukimusic.net
Locations across London teaching young children (from 3yrs)
with parental participation

Mini Crotchets　　　　　**020 8675 1052**
www.minicrotchets.co.uk
Wonderful music classes for toddlers aged 9mths-3yrs.

Monkey Music　　　　　　**01582 766 464**
www.monkeymusic.co.uk
Music classes for the under 5s throughout London.

**Move and Groove
with Paint Pots**　　　　　　**020 7376 4571**
32 songs for all ages

Music for the Young　　　**020 8765 0310**
St Luke's Church, Sydney Street, SW3
Music classes on Tues pm for 3-5yrs. Term-time only

Music House for Children　**020 8932 2652**
Bush Hall, 310 Uxbridge Road, W12 7LJ
www.musichouseforchildren.co.uk
Instrumental tuition at home. Quality dedicated teachers
since 1994. Do look at their website.

Musical Bumps　　　　　　**01732 321 217**
www.musicalbumps.com
Groups in London (East & North) 'Richmond and Kent.

Musical Express　　　　　**020 8946 6043**
www.musicalexpress.co.uk
Fun with music for pre-school children in Barnes, Putney and
Wimbledon (SW13, SW15, SW19 and SW20). Come for a
free class!

Muzsika   **020 7794 4848**
Creative and lively music classes for babies and young children (6mths-6yrs) in St John's Wood.

Paint Pots   **020 7376 4571**
Chelsea Community Church, Edith Road, SW10
Classes also held at Ashburnham Community Centre, Tetcott Road, SW10; and Bayswater United Reform Church, Newton Road, W2

Rucksack Music Inc   **020 8806 9335**
www.rucksackmusic.co.uk
Relaxed musical sessions for babies and toddlers in N1/N2/N6/N8/N10/N12/N14/N16 and Hemel Hempstead

Sing and Sign   **01273 550 587**
www.singandsign.com
Help your baby communicate before speech. Fewer tantrums, more fun!

Tiny Beats   **020 7207 5501**
www.intune.co.uk/tinybeats
Music classes for babies and toddlers. Traditional songs, instruments and movement. Nursery rhymes, action and interaction (Pimlico, SW1)

Whippersnappers   **020 7738 6633**
Brockwell Lido, Dulwich Road, SE24
Zany and zestful interactive musical workshops for the under 5s. Classes also held at The Ecology Centre in Holland Park, W8.

WHIPPERSNAPPERS

Whippersnappers run zany and zestful inter-active underfives music workshops. We use African drumming, puppets, original Pickny Beat songs, percussion, singing, props and theatricality which all combine to delight children and their parents /carers.

- Classes are themed
- Multi – cultural
- Inter - active and inclusive
- Suitable for babies/toddlers and 3–5 year olds
- Available for nursery and community bookings.

We also hold birthday parties and discos for 1-13 year olds

FOR MORE INFORMATION CALL US ON
020 7738 66 33
or visit
www.whippersnappers.org

LITTLE ACORNS
Nursery Music workshops

PARENTS AND NANNIES SAY...
"Delightful happy atmosphere"
"A great introduction to musical instruments"
"We think it's the best music class in the area"
"A fun-filled learning experience"
"A truly lively and original music group"

ST. MARY'S CHURCH PUTNEY BRIDGE
Tel: 020 8408 0322
www.thelittleacorns.com

M U Z S I K A

In St John's Wood NW8

Creative & lively Music Classes for Babies & Young Children

Inspired by the work of Zoltan Kodaly, Carl Orff & Emile Jaques-Dalcroze

For more information call
020 7794 4848
or email
MuzsikaLondon@aol.com

Sing, dance, explore musical instruments, learn basic music skills ...

Make Music Together!

RUCKSACK MUSIC INC

Presents....

"A Toddlingly Musical Time"

Come and join in with a relaxed guided
musical session for children
(Babies and Toddlers 0-3yrs)
with small percussion instruments to
experience and enjoy!
Lots of singing, marching, clapping,
stomping and just having a good time!!
No need to book - just drop-in!!

As filmed by "London Today" and the BBC.

Visit us at:
www.rucksackmusic.co.uk

For more info on times, days, locations in
each area and prices and/or for a leaflet - call

020-8806-9335 or 07957-608-151

Locations in and around London are:
North Finchley, Stoke Newington, Crouch End,
Highgate, East Finchley, Southgate, Muswell Hill,
Hemel Hempstead, Upper Clapton and Islington.
*New groups opening in Buckinghamshire, Hertfordshire
and Middlesex from Sept 2004*

Music for the Young

Classes for 2-6 year olds

Wonderful introduction to music through

Rhythm - percussion
Melody - toys
Movement - drama

*Structured classes in a fun environment
all accompanied by live piano*

Please call **Isabel Saunders** (B.Mus)
0790 661 9144 - isabel@musicfortheyoung.co.uk
020 8568 3075 - www.musicfortheyoung.co.uk

Centres: Clapham · Putney · Chelsea · Hammersmith
Richmond · Notting Hill · Barnes · Wimbledon

learning to have fun with music
for ages 9 months - 4 years

blueberry
playsongs

Guitar accompanied action songs, nursery rhymes, instruments,
games & dancing - come and try the blueberry experience!
www.blueberry.clara.co.uk · blueberry@clara.co.uk

Call: 020 8677 6871

Hickory Jig Music
for babies and children 6m – 5y

• Creative & engaging music classes
• Lively, fun packed 'Jiggity-Jig' drop-ins
• 'Hickory Fiddle' pre-school violin club
• Special occasion parties

Venues throughout SE London

Call: **07966 454 098** for details
e-mail: hickory.jig.music@virgin.net or
visit us at www.hickoryjigmusic.co.uk

Come and join the Mini Crotchet Magic!

mini crotchets

Wonderful music classes for toddlers aged 9mths-3yrs.
Fun, small, intimate groups. Live piano accompaniment. Action and
counting songs, nursery rhymes, finger puppets and instruments
led by interactive musical singing.
Classes in Balham, Battersea and Fulham.

Call Joya: 020 8675 1052
email: joya@minicrotchets.co.uk www.minicrotchets.co.uk

Why not have a Mini Crotchet Party? Joya Logan [GTCL LTCL]

BEA S BABY
MUSIC SCHOOL
Putney Leisure Centre
St. Luke s Community Hall, SW12
First Steps Dance, Fulham
Alpha Place, Chelsea
Streatham Borders
Groups 6 months - 6 years

020 8670 9378
Website: www.babymusic.co.uk

Musical Express
Get on the right track

• Instruments • Action songs & rhymes •
• Musical games • Stories •
• Puppets • Music & fun for pre-school children •
Come and have a free trial class. Contact:
Jenny Tabori, LTCL, GTCL & Dip. Music Therapy
Tel: 020 8946 6043
Website: www.musicalexpress.co.uk

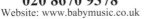

The Original

Sing and Sign

The phenomenon everyone is talking about!

"hot" "more" "finished" "clean" "drink" "get up"

Or learn at home with our video/DVD

Baby signing helps your baby to communicate BEFORE speech

Learn the fun way!

Traditional and original songs
Nursery rhymes
Puppet & Props
Instruments
Lots of fun!

(From 7-18months)

For details of our classes nationwide visit

www.singandsign.com

or call 01273-550587

RECOMMENDED BY EXPERTS

all rhythm and no blues!

To book your FREE introductory session call our central reservation no.

Tel: 01582 766464

www.monkeymusic.co.uk

Music classes for babies and young children!

**Action songs and rhymes
Music and movement
Fun with percussion
Musical games**

Monkey Music introduces music to very young children in a way they can easily understand and enjoy. Since 1992, thousands of children have participated with specialist teachers in local classes across the UK.

Classes are available at three levels:

Heigh ho - 6 months to rising 2
Jiggety jig - 2 & 3 year olds
Ding dong - 3 & 4 year olds

Call to book a FREE introductory session today!

one o'clock clubs

One of the UK's best inventions. These free weekday clubs set within parks have outdoor and indoor play facilities for children under 5. They open between 12.30pm – 4pm, but do check as some close one day in the week. A useful meeting place for parents and nannies, and also a great place to go when it's raining and energies are overflowing at home. Activities include: painting, sticking, playdough, water, sand, trikes, balls and toys (no need to book)

E1
Wapping Park　　　　　　020 7481 9321
High Street

E2
Haggerston Park　　　　　020 7729 6662
Queensbridge Road

E5
Springfield Park
Springfield Lane

E9
Victoria Park　　　　　　020 8986 6150
Cadogan Terrace

E14
Millwall Park　　　　　　020 7515 6807
Stebondale Street

N1
Barnard Park　　　　　　020 7278 9494
Copenhagen Street

St Paul's Open Space
The Playbuildings Marquess Estate

N4
Finsbury Park　　　　　　020 8802 1301
Jamboree Playhuts Seven Sisters Road

N5
Highbury Fields　　　　　020 7704 9337
The Bandstand

N16
Clissold Park　　　　　　020 8809 6700
Stoke Newington Church Street

N19
Whittington Park　　　　020 7263 6896
Yerbury Road

NW3
Parliament Hill Fields　　020 7485 6907
Peggy Jay Centre Gospel Oak Road

SE1
Geraldine Harmsworth Park　020 7820 9724
St George's Road

SE5
Kennington Park　　　　020 7735 7186
Bolton Crescent off Camberwell Road

Myatts Fields　　　　　　020 7733 3609
Cormont Road

Ruskin Park　　　　　　020 7733 6659
Denmark Hill

SE15
Leyton Square　　　　　020 7639 1812
Peckham Park Road

Peckham Rye　　　　　　020 8693 0481
Peckham Rye Road

SE16
Southwark Park　　　　020 7231 3755
Hawkstone Road

SE19
Norwood Park　　　　　020 8761 1752
Salters Hill

SE26
Crystal Palace Park　　　020 8659 6554
Crystal Palace Park Road

SW2
Brockwell Park　　　　　020 8671 4883
Arlingford Road

Hillside Gardens　　　　020 8678 0698
Hillside Road

Windmill Gardens　　　　020 8671 5587
Blenheim Gardens

SW4
Agnes Riley Gardens　　020 8673 1277
Clarence Avenue

Clapham Common　　　020 8673 5736
Windmill Drive

SW6
Bishop's Park　　　　　020 7731 4572
Rainbow Playroom Stevenage Road

SW8
Heathbrook Park　　　　020 8871 7827
St Rule Street

Vauxhall Park　　　　　020 7582 3209
Fentiman Road

SW9
Loughborough Park　　020 7926 1049
Moorland Road

Max Roach Park　　　　020 7274 6693
Wiltshire Road

SW9
Slade Gardens　　　　　020 7733 3630
Robsart Street

SW11
Battersea Park   020 8871 7541
Prince of Wales Drive

York Gardens   020 7738 0889
Lavender Road

SW12
Triangle   020 8673 4106
Tooting Bec Common off Emmanuel Road

SW16
Streatham Vale Park   020 8764 3688
Abercairn Road

SW18
Bolingbroke Grove   020 7228 6674
Chivalry Road, Wandsworth Common

Coronation Gardens   020 8874 3975
Pirbright Road

Garratt Park   020 8946 0366
Siward Road

King George's Park   020 8673 4106
Pet's Corner, Buckhold Road

Windmill   020 8874 9195
Heathfield Road

SW19
Colliers Wood
Clarendon Road

TW1 2NL
Marble Hill Park   020 8891 0641
Richmond Road, Twickenham

W10
Kensington Memorial Park
St Marks Road

Little Wormwood Scrubs
Dalgarno Gardens

Meanwhile Gardens   020 8960 7894
Elkstone Road

W12
Randolph Beresford   020 8741 8400
Australia Way

W13
Llamas Park   020 8810 0240
Elers Road

Pitshanger Park   020 8998 1918
Meadowvale Road

W3
Acton Park   020 8743 6133
East Acton Lane

W4
Rainbow Play House   020 8995 4648
Homefields Chiswick Lane

W6
Ravenscourt Park   020 8748 3180

paddling pools

☺ = recommended

E9	Victoria Park
N8	Priory Park
N16	Clissold Park
N22	Alexandra Palace Park
NW5	Parliament Hill
NW10	☺ Queen's Park
SE5	Burgess Park
	Ruskin Park
SW1	Causton Street
SW2	☺ Brockwell Park
SW4	Clapham Common
SW6	☺ Bishop's Park
SW10	Cremorne Gardens
SW13	Castelnau Recreation Ground Washington Road/Barnes Avenue
	Palewell Common East Sheen
	Vine Road Recreation Ground Vine Road, Barnes
SW18	Streatham Common
SW19	Dundonald Park
	Wimbledon Park
Kew	North Sheen Recreation Ground
W1	Hyde Park
W6	☺ Ravenscourt Park
W10	Meanwhile Gardens
W11	Memorial Park St Mark's Road
W13	Cranleigh Gardens
WC1	Coram's Fields
W12	Hammersmith Park

parks & playgrounds

E3
Mile End Park
Green Bridge

Victoria Park, Old Ford Road
Adventure playground, plus two playgrounds, deer enclosure, boating lake, café and paddling pool

E5
Springfield Park
Café, one o'clock club, pond

N2
Cherry Tree Woods
Woodland, football area, good playground, café and toilets

N4
Finsbury Park
Boating lake, adventure playground, climbing frames, Under 5's centre

N5
Highbury Fields
Good equipment for all ages. Helter skelter, huge slide, seesaw tyres (good for adults too – when no-one's looking!), water play area, sandpit with toys, cycling roundabout

N6
Highgate Woods
Muswell Hill Road
"A great playground divided into age group areas - there is an under 5 bit with its own gate and loads of great things, plus special swings for babies. Also a good café in the woods"

Waterlow Park
Three duck ponds, flowerbeds, squirrels.

N8
Campsbourne
At the foot of Alexandra Park. Tyre swings, slide, playhouse, rockers, climbing frame

Priory Park
Tarmac area for bikes and roller-skates. Enclosed playground with swings, paddling pool, refreshment kiosk

Stationers Park
Ducks, picnic tables, enclosed playground

N10
Coldfall Woods
Natural woodland area

Queen's Wood
Natural woodland, jungle walkway for 5-9yrs. Café, ecology centre

N13
Broomfield Park　　　　　**020 8379 3722**
Broomfield Lane, Palmers Green
Good playground, several complex structures

N16
Clissold Park
Good playground, paddling pool, animals, under 5's centre. Butterfly tunnel. Cafe open all year

N17
Bruce Castle Park
Lordship Lane
Tarmac trike area, toddler swings, climbing frame, rope climbing pyramid

Downhills Park & Recreation Ground
Park with squirrels. Well-designed play equipment

Lordship Lane Recreation Ground
Lake with ducks. Playground with swings, etc

Tower Gardens
Risley Avenue
Plenty of equipment, large sandpit, swings, climbing structures

N22
Alexandra Palace and Park
Alexandra Palace Way, Wood Green
Boating lake, paddling pool, sandpit, playground, deer and llama paddocks. Famous firework display in November

NW1
Camden Square
Good adventure playground for older children manned both after school and on Saturdays

Cantelowes Park
Osney Street
Playground, skateboard/BMX ramp

Lisson Gardens
Lisson Street
Small-scale toddler equipment

Primrose Hill
Useful adjunct to zoo visit. Good secure playground, plentiful roundabouts. Loos. Good helter skelter slide. Unusual play structure. Sandpit. Overlooks aviary

Regents Park
Boating lake, three good adventure playgrounds. You can see some animals if you walk round the outside of the zoo. Poor cafés

Rochester Terrace Gardens
Kentish Town Road
Playground for toddlers and for larger kids

Talacre Open Space
Prince of Wales Road
Gardens and playground

NW3
Hampstead Heath
Kite flying. Playgrounds at Constantine Road end. Under 5's centre weekdays. Swimming pools in summer

NW5
Parliament Hill
Highgate Road, Kentish Town
Part of Hampstead Heath with supervised traditional playground, playpark and Under 5's centre. Kites, views. Supervised playground near Savernake Road, with large sandpit, paddling pool May-September

NW6
Queens Park
Kingswood Avenue
Clean paddling pool. Excellent equipment including wooden castle, climbing pole, huge sandpit, helter skelter. Under 5's centre. Friendly café. Small farm with rabbits and chickens

NW8
St John's Wood Parish Park
Good climbing frames, swings, etc.

Violet Hill
Off Abbey Gardens
Helter skelter, swings, roundabout

NW10
Roundwood Park   020 8838 1414
Harlesden Road
Playground, birdcages, good café. Toys, toadstool area. "Absolutely fantastic," reader's comment

NW11
Golders Hill Park
West Heath Avenue
Flower gardens, duck and flamingo ponds. Deer, wallabies and exotic birds in small animal section. Large sandpit and climbing structure. Good but busy café

SE1
Archbishops Park
Lambeth Palace Road
Playground with slides, train

Leather Market Gardens
Western Street

SE5
Burgess Park
Camberwell Road
Contains Chumleigh Gardens with playground, wooden animals, paddling pool, go-kart track, café

Leyton Square
Peckham Park Road

Myatts Field
Knatchbull Road
Under 5's centre

Ruskin Park
Playground, paddling pool, under 5's centre

SE10
Greenwich Park
King William Way
Great views, Meridian Line, surrounded by museums, boats and all things maritime

SE11
Kennington Park
Playground, under 5's centre

SE22
Dulwich Park
Aviary and boating lakes (lots of ducks) good children's play area, recently refurbished. Dogs off leash only on outer circle. under 5's centre. Parking free. Café

SE24/SW2
Brockwell Park
Dulwich Road
Playground, under 5's centre, aviary, sandpit

SE26
Crystal Palace
Worth the occasional trip. Children's Zoo. Terrific sporting facilities. Large open space. Dinosaur trail. Easy parking (big distances to walk). Pony rides. Under 5's centre. Good playground

Sydenham Wells Park
Wells Park Road, Sydenham

SW1
Causton Street
Sandpit, paddling pool, train, playhouse

Green Park
Good for picnics

St James's Park
Pelicans fed at 3pm, bandstand, playground

SW3
St Luke's Gardens
Sydney Street
Enclosed play area with swings and rockers. Small adventure play structure, plank bridge and slide. Benches and toilets

SW4
Clapham Common
Grandison Road/Windmill Drive
Playgrounds with sandpits. Café near Nightingale Road

SW6
Bishop's Park
Large playground. One o'clock club. Enclosed swing area. Two good climbing frames, nice train. Usually a good selection of bikes and tunnels, large sandpit, clean paddling poo. Small very basic café

Normand Park
Slides, play-houses, occasionally trikes. Tough kids (and mothers). Lots of fag ends

South Park
Good playground

SW8
Larkhall Park

SW10
Cremorne Gardens
Lots Road
Small paddling pool

SW11
Battersea Park
One o'clock club. Also children's zoo (see zoos). Boating, good adventure playgrounds. Pond and fountains

SW13
Castelnau Recreation Ground
Washington Road/Barnes Avenue
Paddling pool, playground

SW13
Mortlake Green
Old-fashioned swings and slide

Palewell Common
Merry-go-round, ice cream kiosk, playground, football fields

Vine Road Recreation Ground
Vine Road
Playground, paddling pool

SW16
Streatham Common
Rockery, playground, padding pool, café

SW17
Tooting Bec Common
Good playground, pond, café

SW18
St George's Park
Mapleton Road
Animal enclosure, playgrounds, under 5's centre

SW19
Cannizaro Park
Sculptures, woodlands, azaleas

Dundonald Park
Dundonald Road
Playground, paddling pool

John Innes Park
Mostyn Road
Ornamental gardens

Quicks Road Recreation Ground
Haydons Road
Large playground

Wandsworth Common
Nature trail

Wellington Road Recreation Ground

Wimbledon Common
Windmill Road/Camp Road
Windmill

Wimbledon Park
Wimbledon Park Road/Revelstoke Road
Lake, two playgrounds, sandpit, paddling pool, café

SW20
Canon Hill Common/
Joseph Hood Recreation Ground
Pond, playground

TW
Boston Manor Park   020 8560 5441
Boston Manor Road, Brentford
Playground cunningly situated under the motorway. Nature trail and pond

Kew Royal Botanic Gardens   020 8940 1171
Worth the price of entry even in bleak midwinter to gain entrance to palm houses. Good cafés, wonderful aquarium (down a buggy- unfriendly spiral stair in the Palm House). No balls or dogs

Marble Hill House   020 8892 5115
Richmond Road
Adventure playground, under 5's centre, café (Mar-Oct)

Osterley Park   020 8232 5050
Jersey Road, Isleworth
Extensive grounds of large house. Good teas in old stables. Lake, gardens and large "wild" green areas. Cows and horses in surrounding fields. Great bluebells

Syon Park   020 8560 0883
Brentford
Lake, train in summer. Entry charge
See also outings, indoor adventure playgrounds

Richmond Park
Off the A3. Largest royal park in London. Wide open spaces, trees, lots of deer, lakes, horses etc. Also the Isabella Plantation, an enclosed area, beautiful especially in spring.

W10
Emslie Horniman Pleasance
Bosworth Road
Victorian gardens a la Teletubbies. Also lovely quiet gardens

W2
Diana Princess of Wales Memorial Playground
Kensington Gardens
Hugely popular ship playground. Prepare to queue to enter on hot summer days. Old Elfin Oak, Peter Pan statue still there too...

Paddington Gardens
Moxon Street
Two play areas. Splendid tall slide, good complex structures. Under 5's centre, café

W3
Acton Park
Uxbridge Road
Playground, play centre for under 5s

Springfield Gardens
Horn Lane
Small playground with cowboy wagon, tennis courses

W4
Dukes Meadow
Off Great Chertsey Rd, behind Chiswick New Pool
Secret and empty playground. Good climbing structure and swings, and unusual elastic climbing frame to have a boing on. Beware broken glass

Chiswick House   020 8995 0508
Burlington Lane
Great woodland with hidden pathways, excellent child-friendly café with lawn for games in front (w/e only in winter)

W5
Gunnersbury Park
Popes Lane
Two playgrounds, one for under 5s, larger one good for toddlers and older kids too. Good café, boating pond, good museum

Hanger Hill Park
Hillcrest Road
Good playground. Hill for toboganning, pitch and putt

Lammas Park
Northfield Avenue/Church Lane
Wildlife area, open fields for football

Walpole Park
Mattock Lane
Aviary, newly refurbished playground, summer café

W6
Brook Green
Rope bridges, sandpit, etc

Ravenscourt Park   020 8741 2051
Three areas for children. Good swings, slides, balancing
equipment. Under 5's centre. Unusual wooden structures.
Dog-free zones. Excellent paddling pool. Sandpit. Slow café

W7
Brent Lodge River Park   020 8758 5019
Church Road, Hanwell
Aka Bunny Park, with two playgrounds, small zoo, café

W8/W14
Holland Park
Abbotsbury Road
Sandpits, one o'clocks, woodland, excellent café, Japanese
garden, rabbits, peacocks, altogether wonderful

riding

Many stables do not recommend riding for under 3s
and leave them on the leading rein until 5yrs old

E6
Newham Riding School   020 7511 3917
Docklands Equestrian Centre, 2 Claps Gate Lane

N12
London Equestrian Centre   020 8349 1345
Lulington Garth, Woodside Park
Café. 2yrs+

N14
Trent Park Equestrian Centre   020 8363 9005
Bramley Road

SE21
Dulwich Riding School   020 8693 2944
Dulwich Common

SW15
Stag Lodge Stables   020 8974 6066
Robin Hood Gate, Richmond Park

SW19
Deen City Farm   020 8543 5858
39 Windsor Avenue, Merton Abbey
4yrs+

Ridgeway Stables   020 8946 7400
93 Ridgeway, Wimbledon Village
3¹/₂yrs+

Wimbledon Village Stables   020 8946 8579
24 High Street

W2
Ross Nye's   020 7262 3791
8 Bathurst Mews
6yrs+

Hyde Park & Kensington Stables   020 7723 2813
63 Bathurst Mews

W5
Ealing Riding School   020 8992 3808
17-19 Gunnersbury Avenue
5yrs+

W10
Westways Riding Stables   020 8964 2140
20 Stable Way

W12
Wormwood Scrubs Pony Centre   020 8740 0573
Woodmans Mews, Scrubs Lane
6yrs+

swimming classes

Aquababies   02392 460 033
www.aquababiesltd.co.uk
Classes across London. No buoyancy aids are used for these
classes which are for babies 0-4yrs

**Amateur Swimming
Association Courses**   020 8778 0131
Crystal Palace National Sports Centre, Upper
Norwood, SE19 2BB
Ante/post aquanatal parent/baby, pre-school & after school
swimming classes

Aquatots   020 8688 6488
Swimming the natural way, without buoyancy aids. 0-4yrs

Cygnets   020 8579 6973
W12/NW10
Birth to 4yrs

Dolphin Swim Schools   020 8640 4488
Wimbledon College, SW19

Dolphin Swimming Club   020 8349 1844
ULU Pool, Malet Street, WC
13yrs+

Lewisham Swim School   020 8690 2123
261 Lewisham High Street, SE13 6NJ

Little Dippers   0870 758 0302
www.littledippers.co.uk

Baby & Toddler Swimming
at LA Fitness Clubs
FINCHLEY & NEW BARNET
Developing water skills through fun activities
BOOKING & INFO
020 8240 8657
MIGHTY DUCKS SWIM SCHOOL

AQUABABIES

Teaching babies and young children to swim
(Birth to 4 years)

For Classes In Your Area
Tel: 02392-460033
Private Lessons Available

Mighty Ducks Swim School   020 8240 8657
mightyducks@virgin.net
We run fun classes for babies from 6 months, developing waterskills

**Oakleigh Park
School of Swimming**   020 8445 1911
Oakleigh Road North, N20

Splash   020 8579 6973
Vanessa Nursery, 14 Cathnor Road, W12
4yrs+

Swimming Nature   0870 900 8002
Classes held in Brondesbury Park, Chelsea, Hallam Street, Marylebone, Notting Hill, Queen's Park, Regent's Park, South Kensington and Victoria
www.swimmingnature.co.uk

swimming pools - outdoor

Usually only open during the summer months

N8
Park Road Pools   020 8341 3567
Park Road

N12
Finchley Lido   020 8343 9830
Great North Leisure Park, High Road, North Finchley.
Indoor, very small outdoor pool

NW5
Parliament Hill Lido   020 7485 3873
Parliament Hill Fields, Gordon House Road

SE18
Charlton Lido   020 8856 7180
Hornfair Park, Woolwich
July-Sept

SE24
Brockwell Park Lido   020 7274 3088
Brockwell Park, Dulwich Road

SW16
Tooting Bec Lido   020 8871 7198
Tooting Bec Common, Tooting Bec Road

TW
Hampton Heated Open Air Pool   020 8255 1116
High Street, Hampton Court

Richmond Pools on the Park   020 8940 0561
Old Deer Park, Twickenham Road, Richmond

W2
Serpentine Lido   020 7298 2100
Hyde Park

WC2
Oasis Sports Centre Outdoor Pool 020 7831 1804
32 Endell Street, Holborn

tennis - mini

The LTA (Lawn Tennis Association) has a very informative website about the game of mini tennis for the 4yrs+ agegroup.

Islington Tennis Centre   020 7700 1370
Market Road, N7 9PL
4yrs+

Holly Park Junior Tennis Club   020 8347 7550
Crouch End Playing Fields, Park Road, N8

Hampstead Heath Tennis   020 8348 9930

NW3

Rocks Lane Tennis Centre   020 8876 8330
Rocks Lane, SW13 0DG

In the Zone Jnr   07958 271 776
Tennis birthday party specialists

Toddler Tennis   020 8678 9101
Brockwell Park
Toddler Tennis from 3-5yrs is a great treat for South London.

Will To Win Tennis Centre   020 8994 1466
Chiswick House Grounds, , W4/W5/W14
www.tennis-uk.com
Coaching and play from 3-13yrs. Women's drop-in mornings

3-Up Tennis   020 8991 6755
(London School of Tennis)
The Brentham Club, Meadvale Road, W5

art centres & galleries

You can no longer claim that having children has impacted on your enjoyment of London's top galleries and art centres. There is a better reason for going to visit galleries now than ever before. You will not be disappointed by the well structured workshops, tours, facilities and goodie bags now on offer for children. More importantly, they provide an interesting insight for parents as to how to open their children's eyes to the world of art. A little tip: if you want your children not to touch priceless sculptures, it helps to have a little supply of biscuits or a favourite toy to keep the hands busy

Barbican Centre   020 7382 2333
Silk Street, EC2
www.barbican.org.uk
The arts education programme has original and hands-on workshops which embrace the arts, music and film. Try making papier mâché masks in the theme of Aladdin

Battersea Arts Centre (BAC)   020 7223 2223
Lavender Hill, SW11
www.bac.org.uk
The ever popular Saturday children's theatre (2.30pm) for 4yrs+ is a great introduction to theatre. Shows include audience participation alongside familiar themes. Arts Factory workshops are held midweek for 5yrs+ so enquire online or at the box office

Camden Art Centre   020 7435 2643
Arkwright Road, NW3
www.camdenartscentre.org
New galleries recently opened, landscaped gardens and a range of workshops and tours for children

Courtauld Institute Gallery   020 7848 2922
Somerset House, The Strand, WC2R 1LA
www.courtauld.ac.uk
Family activites on the first Saturday of the month from 11.30am are a delight for parents and children. Tours focus on a particular theme and conclude in a practical workshop. However, these are particularly popular and you need to book early. After school events are available too for the 5yrs+ age group. Wonderful winter skating and summer fountains in the courtyard, so bring a change of clothes in warm weather

Dulwich Picture Gallery   020 8693 5254
Gallery Road, SE21
www.dulwichpicturegallery.org.uk
Set in the heart of leafy Dulwich this gallery offers a quick fix for parents needing visual refreshment, and your children can spill into Dulwich Park afterwards to let off steam. Good café with highchairs. There are also family activity workshops at the weekend, and evening courses for adults both for art appreciation as well as bringing on artistic skills.

London International   020 8435 0903
Gallery of Children's Art
02 Centre, 255 Finchley Road, NW3 6LU
www.ligca.org
Open from 4-6pm Tue-Thurs, 12-6pm Fri-Sun, closed Mon. Admission free. They offer a good range of Saturday, term time and holiday activities for 2-12yrs, including mask making, musical drawings, book making and wire sculptures. Art materials are always available to create your own work of art in response the exhibition.

Jackson's Lane Centre   020 8340 5226
269A Archway Road, N6
www.jacksonslane.org.uk
Highlights for children are the Saturday shows (11am and 2pm) produced by visiting touring companies and including nursery rhymes and puppet shows. Workshops during the holidays and half term for dance and art, either drop-in or courses. Most are oversubscribed so book in advance

National Gallery   020 7839 3321
Trafalgar Square, WC2
www.nationalgallery.co.uk
Have you been on the Magic Carpet? Starting at 11.30am Wed – Fri, under 5s are taken on a $\frac{1}{2}$hr journey by the enthusiastic staff who tell spellbinding stories about a selection of paintings. "Spot the Difference" with visiting artists (Sat & Sun 11.30am and 2.30pm). Baby changing and buggy access

National Portrait Gallery   020 7306 0055
2 St Martin's Place, WC2
www.npg.org.uk
Grab a Family Activity Rucksack from the information desk, full of artistic little goodies such as jigsaws, fuzzy felt, dressing up items, and a discussion guide for parents to get the most out of the activities. Workshops and holiday activities take place in the Clore Gallery (including sculpture, masks and photography) for the 4yrs+ but book early as they are generally oversubscribed

Royal Academy   020 7300 8000
Burlington House, Piccadilly, W1
www.royalacademy.org.uk
The Art Tray (akin to a Pony Club grooming box) stacked full of paper, crayons, scissors, glue, crêpe paper and glitter is provided to all children who want to create their own works of art. The Summer Exhibition is a real favourite. If you go on a hot day, be prepared (with a change of clothes) to let little ones play in the fountain jets in the main courtyard

South Bank Centre   020 7960 4201
Belvedere Road, SE1
www.rfh.org.uk
A lot of time has been invested in choosing a fun programme for younger audiences with a good selection of concerts orientated towards families and young children, including face painting, circus performances, drumming, etc. Events are seasonal so check out the website for current events

days out

Tate Britain
020 7887 8008
Millbank, SW1P 4RG
www.tate.org.uk
The famous Art Trolley is one of the smartest ways to get children enjoying the Tate and guiding parents towards their child's early art education. Staff engage the children by focusing on a particular painting. They park the Trolley by a chosen painting, then play simple games, ask children to find shapes, and organise the sticking, cutting and drawing of their own picture. The Art Space, open weekends and weekdays during the holidays, is an area for families to relax with books, jigsaws, dressing up, simple sculptures etc

Tate Modern
020 7887 8008
Holland Street, SE1 9TG
www.tate.org.uk
Tate Tales offer exciting tours around the gallery led by visiting writers and poets (third Saturday, 11am) so be prepared to be on the ball and play word games. "Viewpoints" guides children to make their own landscape; "Transformer" is a still-life sculpture trail; and "Head, Shoulders Knees and Toes" is a sculpture trail for the Under 5s, encouraging looking, drawing, touching and creating (£1.50 daily). Baby changing facilities & pushchair access

Tricycle Theatre
020 7328 1000
269 Kilburn High Road, NW6 7JR
www.tricycle.co.uk
An amazing range of art workshops and tours offered for children by the Tricycle, including events for the 18mth age group and upwards. A new Creative Space studio offers dance and poetry classes or music lessons for 5yrs+. Saturday theatre productions are also scheduled (11.30am, 2pm). Enquire online and book early

Watermans Arts Centre
020 8232 1020
40 High Street, Brentford, TW8
Visit this riverside arts studio for children's theatre productions and art workshops

castles & soldiers

There's nothing like a few ancient battles to get imaginations going. And this selection are all within easy reach and access from London, making them a perfect day out

Bodium Castle
01580 830 436
www.nationaltrust.org.uk
Open Mid-Feb to Oct 10am-6pm/duskdaily and mid-Nov-Feb 10am-4pm/dusk on Sat and Sun. Last entry is 1hr before closing. Admission £4 adults, £2 5s-16yrs and free for Under 5s. A favourite venue for family picnics on fine days or budding knights wanting to tear around in lots of space. Their Bat Pack includes a tabard to wear, adventure trail and a good range of exciting activities. During half terms and holidays there are additional events and activities. Café/tearoom with nappy changing facilities and shop

Changing the Guard
Buckingham Palace, The Mall, SW1
Daily 11.30am from April to end of July. Alternate days in winter

Hampton Court Palace
020 8781 9500
www.hrp.org.uk
Children's trail and maze. M25 Jcn 10, A307 or Jcn 12, A308.

Hever Castle
01732 865 224
www.hevercastle.co.uk
Castle open Mar-Oct 12-6pm daily and Nov 12-4pm daily. Admission for castle & garden £8.40 adult, £4.60 5-16yrs and free for under 5s. This was the childhood home of Anne Boleyn and where she first courted Henry VIII - and the castle, garden and lakes were restored in the early 20th century. The gardens are extensive, and there's a maze, adventure playground, secret grottos and a water maze which is perfect for hot sunny days (bring a change of clothes)

Leeds Castle
0870 600 888
www.leeds-castle.com
Castle open Apr-Oct 11am-5.30pm daily and Nov-Mar 10am-3.30pm daily. Last entry 1hr before closing. Admission for castle, gardens and museum is £11 adults, £7.50 5-16yrs and free for under 4s. Built soon after 1066 Leeds castle is a fantastic day out with many family and children's events throughout the holidays and weekends. A maze, aviary, secret grottos and also children's classical concerts and open-air summer theatre to give you an excuse to visit.

Mountfitchet Castle & Norman Village
01279 813237
Open 10am-5pm daily. Admission £3.80 or £3 for 2-14yrs, free for under 2s. This castle and village take you back almost 900 years to witness a picture of medieval life. There are animals to feed as you wander around the village (goats, guinea fowl, chickens, peacocks) and plenty of places to picnic. Also café with nappy changing facilities and a shop

Tower of London
020 7709 0765
Crown Jewels, Armoury. Open Mar-Oct 9am-5pmMon-Sat, 10am-5pm Sun. Nov-Feb 10am-4pm Mon, Sun and 9am-4pm Tues-Sat. Beefeater tours half-hourly (outside only). Admission £11.50 adults, £7.50 for 5-15yrs. Free for under 5s. Despite the pricey entrance fees this really is one of London's great days out. Family trail booklets and pencils are given at the Sentry Box and costumed actors give visitors the right feel with singing, dancing and playing musical instruments. Crown Jewels, Torture at the Tower and the Armoury are all worth visiting.

cinema clubs

We are continually impressed by what the cinemas below have lined up for movie-mad kids. We recommend sitting somewhere middle to back, as it can be quite alarming for little ones to sit in the front row the first time. The workshop activities prior to the screening really extend children's whole experience of the film and make it even more memorable. Perfect for a wet weekend morning

E8
Rio Cinema   020 7241 9410
103-7 Kingsland High Street, E8
www.riocinema.co.uk
Kids Club on Sat 11am. Membership cards are stamped with a free movie and poster given after collecting 10 stamps

EC2
Barbican Centre   020 7382 7000
Silk Street, EC2
Family Fun Film Club on Sat 11am with themed workshops starting at 10am

SE1
Movie Magic at the NFT   020 7928 3232
National Film Theatre, South Bank, SE1
www.bfi.org.uk/moviemagic
Films for younger audiences are screened Sat & Sun 3pm including themed workshops (ie making Dickensian glowing lanterns and short animation films for older children). Additional holiday activites/screenings midweek at 2pm

SW2
Ritzy Cinema   020 7733 2229
Brixton Oval, Coldharbour Lane, Brixton, SW2
www.ritzycinema.co.uk
Kids Club movies on Sat at 10.30am (£1 children and £2 accompanying adult). Free newspapers, tea & coffee. During holidays themed workshops held on Tues & Thurs 10.30am

SW4
Clapham Picture House   020 7498 3323
76 Venn Street, SW4
www.picturehouses.co.uk
The Clapham Kids Club screens movies on Sat 11.45am as well as workshops and quizzes starting at 11.15am. Also Thurs 10.30am screenings for mothers with babes in arms (under 12mths)

W11
Electric Cinema   020 7908 9696
191 Portobello Road, W11
www.electrichouse.com
Kids Club screenings on Sat 11am and 1pm with themed workshops. Be filmed whilst making a Thunderbird costume and then see yourself on the big screen prior to the screening of the movie. Also kids' activities most afternoons during holidays. Mon 3pm screening for mothers with babes in arms (under 12mths)

circus

From about 2 yrs+ children will be amazed, amused and sometimes bemused by the amazing acrobatics performed by the visiting circus tropes. These days it's less about elephants and tigers, more palaminos and canaries, but it doesn't dampen the enthusiasm for the unique spectacle of clowns, candy floss and the big band sound. Check websites for locations and timing

Zippo's
www.zippo.dial.pipex.com

Chinese State Circus
www.chinesestatecircus.co.uk

Cirque du Soleil
www.cirquedusoleil.com

Moscow State Circus
www.moscowstatecircus.co.uk

Circus Schools

The Circus Space   020 7613 4141
Coronet Street, N1 6HD
www.thecircusspace.co.uk

Albert and Friends Instant Circus   020 8237 1170
www.albertandfriendsinstantcircus.co.uk

farms: city

Brooks Farm   020 8539 4278
Skeltons Lane Park, Leyton, E10 5BS
Open 10.30-5.30pm (closed Mon and between 12.30-1.30pm daily) except Bank Holidays. Shetland ponies (no riding), llamas and Monty the pig are firm favourites

Coram's Fields   020 7837 6138
93 Guilford Street, WC1N 1DN
Seven acres with pets' corner, pigs, guinea pigs. Refurbished and 'immaculately clean' (reader's comment)

Deen City Farm   020 8543 5300
39 Windsor Avenue, Merton Abbey, SW19 2RR
Good selection of farm animals, including rheas (small ostrich) and pets. Snakes and lizards also on show seasonally. Watch eggs hatch or gaze at the fish in the café. For pony rides (daily) enquire for times. Closed Mon, otherwise 10-5pm

days out

Freightliners Farm   020 7609 0467
Sheringham Road, N7 8PF
Open Tues-Sun 10–5pm. Mixture of rare-breed chickens, goats, sheep, rabbits, guinea pigs. Craft-based activity workshops for under 4s during the summer holidays

Hackney City Farm   020 7729 6381
1a Goldsmiths Row, off Hackney Road, E2 8QA
Open Tues-Sun 10-5pm. Closed Mon

Hounslow Urban Farm   020 8751 0850
Fagg's Road, Feltham
Rare breed farm featuring Highland cattle, Middle White pigs, donkeys including a new arrival, Eeyore, only six weeks old as we go to press - but no small animals. Entrance £3 adults, £1.50 children 2-16yrs. Open 10-5pm Tues-Sun (closed Mon)

Kentish Town City Farm   020 7916 5421
1 Cressfield Close, NW5 4BN
Cows, sheep, horses, pigs, chickens, ducks, rabbits and plenty of opportunities to touch. You can ride the ponies for £1 Sat & Sun at 1.30pm. Wed playgroup during termtime from 10.30am

Mudchute Farm   020 7515 5901
Pier Street, Isle of Dogs, E14 9HP
Cow, chickens, sheep, pigs, rabbits, donkeys etc. Farm tours available for 10 or more children, and holiday play activities during the summer holidays. Book in advance

Newham City Farm   020 7474 4960
King George Avenue, E16 3HR
Open Tues-Sun 10am-5pm. Closed Mon

Stepping Stones Farm   020 7790 8204
Stepney Way/Stepney High Street, E1 3DG
Open Tues-Sun 9.30am - 6pm. Closed Mon

Surrey Docks City Farm   020 7231 1010
Rotherhithe Street, SE16 1EY
Open 10-5pm. Closed Mon and Fri. Complete range of animals including donkeys, pigs, sheep, goats, rabbits and ponies

Vauxhall City Farm   020 7582 4204
24 St Oswalds Place, SE11 5JE
Open 10.30-4pm. Closed Mon & Fri. Good selection of animals

farms: out of town

Aldenham Country Park   020 8953 9602
Dagger Lane, Elstree, WD6 3AT

Bocketts Farm Park   01372 363764
Young Street, Fetcham, Nr Leatherhead, KT22 9DA
www.bockettsfarm.co.uk
Bocketts Farm has created a winning formula. All sorts of animals, accessible to feed and touch; horse rides around the orchard, and pig races which are highly competitive events and get the adults quite steamed up. But for the budding mechanics there are plenty of ride-on tractors

Burpham Court Farm Park   01483 576089
Clay Lane, Jacobs Well, Guildford, GU4 7NA
A3 to Burpham and Merrow

Godstone Farm   01883 742 546
Tilburstow Hill Road, Godstone, RH9 8LX
www.godstonefarm.co.uk
For children who need space, this is an ideal environment. An adventure playground, and ball pit adjoins the animal enclosures. Hatching eggs are mesmerising for the little ones, as are the other baby animals. Open 10-6pm, £4.30 child 2yrs+, adults free

Horton Park Children's Farm   01372 743984
Horton Lane, Epsom, KT19 8PT
www.hortonpark.co.uk
Open 10am-6pm daily. Even more suitable for younger children with small enclosures of rabbits, chicks, hamsters to touch, with lizards and snakes for the very brave. Café and picnic areas with soft toy barn if it's pouring with rain

Lockwood Donkey Sanctuary   01428 682409
Farm Cottage, Sanhills, Wormley, nr Godalming, GU8 5UX

Marsh Farm Country Park   01245 321552
South Woodham Ferrers, CM3 5WP

Odds Farm Park   01628 520188
Woburn Common, High Wycombe, HP10 0LG
www.oddsfarm.co.uk
Wide range of large and small animals, with small enclosures for feeding and touching. Easter Egg and Halloween workshops during holidays. Café and picnic areas around sand and playgrounds

**South of England
Rare Breeds Centre**   01233 861 493
Highlands Farm, Woodchurch, Ashford
www.rarebreeds.org.uk
Best to take a big picnic on a fine day and hang out with some of the most odd looking rare breeds. Indoor play areas and particularly good for parties

Willows Farm Village   01727 822106
Coursers Road, London Colney, St Albans, AL2 1BB

Wimpole Hall Home Farm   01223 207 257
Arrington, Royston, SG8 0BW
www.wimpole.org
Rare breeds farm and working estate attached to National Trust owned Wimpole Hall. Animal activites include Shire horses pulling wagons, sheep and goat feeding. Also adventure playground and barn during winter. Open 10.30-5pm (closed Mon & Fri)

ice rinks

London's ice rinks offer a combination of family skating, classes and parties. The majority offer a six-week class for children under 5. Sessions vary so check times before setting off. Prices below include skate hire

Alexandra Palace Ice Rinks 020 8365 2121
Alexandra Palace Way, Wood Green, N22 7AY
Price £3.50 for under 15s

Broadgate Ice 020 7505 4068
Broadgate Circle, Eldon Street, EC2
www.broadgateestates.co.uk
Price £4 for under 16s

Lee Valley Ice Centre 020 8533 3154
Lea Bridge Road, E10
Price £4.90 under 14s

Leisurebox 020 7229 0172
17 Queensway, W2 4QP
Price £6 – but you get to skate with the crème de la crème

**Michael Sobell
Leisure Centre** 020 7609 2166
Hornsey Road, N7
www.aquaterra.org
Price £3 – ask for parent and toddler sessions

Streatham Ice Arena 020 8769 7771
386 Streatham High Road,SW16 6HT
www.streathamicearena.co.uk
Price £2.50 under 4s. £23 for six-week classes for toddlers
up to 4yrs

museums

British Museum 020 7323 8000
Great Russell Street, WC1B 3DG
www.thebritishmuseum.ac.uk
Open 10am-5.30pm daily and to 8.30pm Thurs and Fri.
Admission free. You can't expect to do this museum in a
morning, except for the 90 minute tour which concentrate on
specific areas of the collection. But the family activities are
plentiful during the holidays, and the family backpack with
games and puzzles will help bring the ancient arts alive

Geffrye Museum 020 7739 9893
136 Kingsland Road, E2
www.geffrye-museum.org.uk
Open Tues-Sat 10am-5pm, 12pm-5pm Sun. Admission free.
The Geffrye was converted into a furniture and interior design
museum in 1914 and features room sets of different periods
from Elizabethan to the present day. They organise holiday
activities and at the weekends with family Sundays offering
model making, cooking and decorative activities. The
restaurant overlooks the gardens where you can picnic

Horniman Museum 020 8699 1872
100 London Road, Forest Hill, SE23 3PQ
www.horniman.ac.uk
Open 10.30am-5.30pm daily. Admisison free. Picnic area in
fantastic gardens, and animal enclosures are one of the many
reasons to visit the Horniman. The Dinomites exhibition is
also fantastic – featuring lifesize models and corresponding
roars. Music and musical instruments from around the world,
an aquarium and a grass-roofed house get the little one's
thinking. Great children's activites arranged for the holidays,
weekends and the new under 5's storytelling sessions, with
Auntie Dee and Nzinga Dance journeying through the stories,
games, dances and songs of Africa and the Caribbean.
Café/restaurant with highchairs, changing facilities and shop

Imperial War Museum 020 7416 5000
Lambeth Road, SE1 6HZ
www.iwm.org.uk
Open 10-6pm daily. Admission free. The IWM displays the
realities of 20th century warfare. From tanks, rockets and
fighter planes in the main lobby to a walk-in trench and secret
war gallery. There are termtime programmes as well as
holiday activities from 5yrs+ such as model-making. Café,
restaurant and shop.

Livesey Museum for Children020 7639 5604
682 Old Kent Road, Peckham, SE15 1JF
www.liveseymuseum.org.uk
Hands-on exhibition from Sept 04 exploring themes around
energy.

London Transport Museum 020 7565 7299
The Piazza, Covent Garden, WC2E 7BB
www.ltmuseum.co.uk
Open 10-6pm Mon-Thur, Sat, Sun; 11am-6pm Fri.
Admission £5.95 adults, free for under 16s. A
comprehensive look at transport in London through the ages,
where children can clamber in and out steam trains and
buses. An education centre provides drop in workshops,
craft activities as well as street safety (ie crossing the road)
and poetry on the underground.

Museum of Childhood 020 8980 2415
Bethnal Green
Cambridge Heath Road, E2 9P
www.museumofchildhood.org.uk
Open 10am-5.30pm Mon-Thurs, Sat and Sun. Admission
free. This museum contains the largest collection of toys and
games in the UK dating back as early as the 1600s. Great
range of children's activities and a good shop selling pocket-
money priced items. Café and gardens

Museum of London 020 7600 3699
150 London Wall, EC2Y 5HN
www.museumoflondon.org.uk
Open Mon-Sat 10-5.50: Sun 12-5.50. Admission free.
Colourful workshops and puppet shows bringing the Great
Fire of London to life, and mask making on Grandparents day
are some of the autumn features lined up this year. Check the
website for family events in 2005.

days out

National Army Museum   **020 7730 0717**
Royal Hospital Road, SW3 4HT
www.national-army-museum.ac.uk
Open 10-5.3pm daily. Admission free. Looking back at
1,000 years of British History there are life-size soldiers and
model battlefields to entertain your 21st century action hero.
There are weekend workshops, holiday activities,
pantomimes and Punch and Judy shows

National Maritime Museum   **020 8858 4422**
Romney Park Road, Greenwich, , SE10 9NF
www.nmm.ac.uk
Open 10-5pm daily. Admission free. Sunday family days
between 1-4pm organised party games, dancing, art and
craft activities. Drop-in activities on Tues 10.15-11.00 and
11.30-1pm for 2-6yrs. Coming in October 2004 is a new
Eco-Room exhibition covering marine environmental issues
such as climate change, over-fishing and the impact of our
lifestyle choices

Natural History Museum   **020 7942 5000**
Cromwell Road, SW7 5BD
www.nhm.ac.uk
Open 10-5.50pm Mon-Sat; 11-5.50pm Sun. Admission free.
No visit is complete without going to see the Tyrannosaurus
Rex in the Dinosaurs gallery and the blue whale in the
Discovering Mammals gallery. See also the ant colony in the
Creepy Crawlies gallery. You can follow activity trails during
half-terms and holidays as well as weekend family
workshops. Café/restaurant, nappy changing and shop

Pollock's Toy Museum   **020 7636 3452**
1 Scala Street, W1P 1LT
www.pollockstoymuseum.com
Open Mon-Sat, 10-5pm. Admission £3 adults, £1.50 3-
16yrs and free for under 3s. Museum upstairs and traditional
toy shop downstairs. Vintage teddies, dolls, Victorian
puppets and a huge range of tin toys. Great toy shop selling
traditional toys such as Jack-in-the-Box, dolls houses and
marionettes

Ragged School Museum   **020 8980 6405|**
46-50 Copperfield Road, E3 4RR
www.raggedschoolmuseum.org.uk
Open 10-5pm Wed and Thurs, first Sun of each month 2-
5pm. Once charity schools providing eduction to orphanes
this converted warehouse has been transformed into a
Victorian school where school groups are given a Victorian
lesson in a recreated classroom. Family art and craft
activities take place in the holidays such as making flags,
bags and spice jars as well as storytelling and soft toys for
the little ones

Science Museum   **020 7942 4454**
Exhibition Road, SW7 2DD
www.sciencemuseum.org.uk
Open Mon-Sat 10-6pm; Sun 11-6pm. The Launch Pad in the
Welome Wing is where you should start. It is a technical
playground where science and fun is all part of the activity. In
the basement "Garden" for 3-6yr olds there is water play, soft
play and dressing up

Somerset House   **020 7848 2526**
Courtauld Institute and Gilbert Gallery, WC2R 0RN
www.somerset-house.org.uk
Open 10am-6pm daily. In addition to three art galleries it also
host winter ice skating in the courtyard and water fountain
jets in the summer. Free family events include puppet shows,
storytelling and art workshops. Café, resturants, nappy
changing, shop and picnics in the courtyard

parks and gardens

Hampton Court Palace   **020 8781 9500**
East Molesey, KT8 9AU
www.hrp.org.uk (for all Historic Royal Palaces)
Children's trail and maze. M25 Jcn 10, A307 or Jct 12, A308

Look Out Discovery Park   **01344 868 222**
Nine Mile Road, Bracknell, RG12 7QW
Environmental family park. Combine with Coral Reef. M4,
Jct 10, A322 signs for Bagshot.

Royal Botanical Gardens   **020 8332 5000**
www.kew.org.uk
Open from 9.30am-4.30pm or later during the summer
(7.30pm). Admission £7.50 adults and free for Under 16s.
Take the rail or tube to Kew, or the river boat to Kew Pier.
This is a 300 acre garden with giant Victorian greenhouses
which contain some of the world's most tropical plants. The
new climbers and creepers exhibition has just opened (July
2004) and offers some fantastic interactive features (such as
a giant flower which your toddler can climb into). There are
also plenty of cafes dotted about to keep everyone refreshed
and a special picnic place

RHS Gardens, Wisley   **01483 224 234**
Working, Surrey
www.rhs.org.uk
Free for under 6s.

pubs with gardens or playrooms

E1
Dickens Inn   **020 7488 2208**
St. Katherine's Dock, St. Katherine's Way
Baby changing, half portions, garden area

E6
Windsor House   **020 7511 3853**
Woolwich Manor Way, Beckton

E8
Pub on the Park   **020 7275 9586**
19 Martello Street

N1
Bierodrome   **020 7226 5835**
173-174 Upper Street, Islington

Duke of Cambridge   **020 7359 3066**
30 St Peter's Street
Organic too!

N7
Shillibeers   **020 7700 1858**
Carpenter Mews, North Road

Tufnell Park Tavern   020 7272 2078
162 Tufnell Park Road
Kids' menu on Sundays

NW1
The Engineer   020 7722 0950
65 Gloucester Avenue, Primrose Hill
Colouring books, baby changing

SE1
Anchor Tap   020 7403 4637
20a Horsleydown Lane

SE10
Ashburnham Arms   020 8692 2007
25 Ashburnham Grove

North Pole   020 8853 3020
131 Greenwich High Road

SW2
Hope and Anchor   020 7274 1787
123 Acre Lane, Brixton
Play area

SW4
Bread and Roses   020 7498 1779
6 Clapham Manor Street
Back garden, toys

Windmill on the Common   020 7720 1118
44-48 Clapham High Street
Baby changing, kid's menu

SW8
Tearoom des Artistes   020 7652 6526
697 Wandsworth Road
Children's parties

SW11
The Castle   020 7228 8181
115 Battersea High Street, Battersea
Kids' menu on Sundays

SW13
Coach & Horses   020 8876 2695
27 Barnes High Street, Barnes
Separate room on Sunday in winter only. Garden packed with
playground facilities

The Red Lion   020 8748 2984
Castelnau Street
Playground and playroom

SW15
Robin Hood Pub   020 8546 4316
Kingston Vale

SW17
Leather Bottle   020 8946 2309
538 Garratt Lane
Large enclosed playground and garden

The Point   020 8767 2660
16-18 Ritherdon Road, Balham

SW19
Fox & Grapes   020 8946 5599
Camp Road, Wimbledon
Kids' portions

W6
Black Lion   020 8748 2639
2 South Black Lion Lane
Small room at back and garden

The Queen's Head   020 7603 3174
Brook Green

W13
Drayton Court   020 8997 1019
2 The Avenue

restaurants: child-friendly

Pizza Express
www.pizzaexpress.co.uk
With hundreds of branches in London and across the UK, all
pizza express stores welcome babies and children with
smaller portions and are great as a party venue.

NORTH LONDON
N1
Frederick's   020 7359 2888
106 Camden Passage
www.fredericks.co.uk

Giraffe   020 7359 5999
29-31 Essex Road
Totally child friendly, café style brassery offering good food
(and for children) – fast. Other branches across London

Santa Fe   020 7288 2288
75 Upper Street

Maremma   020 7226 9400
11-13 Theburton Street

Porchetta Pizzeria   020 7288 2488
141-142 Upper Stree

Strada   020 7704 9902
105 Upper Street
www.strada.co.uk

Tiger Lil's   020 7226 1118
270 Upper Street

Yellow River Café   0207 354 8833
206 Upper Street
www.yellowrivercafes.co.uk

N6
Idaho   020 8341 6633
13 North Hill,
www.idahofood.co.uk

N8
Florians   020 8348 8348
4 Topsfield Parade, Middle Lane

Banners   020 8348 2930
21 Park Road

N10

Caffe Uno   020 8883 4463
348 Muswell Hill Broadway
Crayons, kiddy packs.

Down the Hatch   020 8444 7782
148 Colney Hatch Lane

N16

The Cooler   020 7275 7266
67 Stoke Newington Church Street

NORTH WEST
NW1

The Engineer   020 7722 0950
65 Gloucester Avenue
Colouring books and balloons. Book early for a table in the garden

Regent's Park Café   020 7935 5729
Regent's Park Rose Garden (near playground)

Troika   020 7483 3765
101 Regent's Park Road
Russian tearoom offering children's portions

NW3

Benihana   020 7586 9508
100 Avenue Road
Clown on Suns. Also in SW3, W1

Giraffe   020 7435 0343
46 Rosslyn Hill

Manna   020 7722 8028
4 Erskine Road
www.manna-veg.com
Vegetarian restaurant offering children's portions

Maxwell's Restaurant   020 7794 5450
76 Heath Street

Smollensky's   020 7431 5007
02 Centre, Finchley Road
www.smollenskys.co.uk

NW8

Don Pepe   020 7262 3834
99 Frampton Street
Spanish tapas bar offering an authentic menu and a great children's menu

NW10

Sabras   020 8459 0340
263 Willesden High Road
Indian

SOUTH LONDON
SE1

Bella Pasta   020 7407 5267
35 Tooley Street

Pizzeria Castello   020 7703 2556
20 Walworth Road, Elephant & Castle
www.pizzeriacastello.co.uk

blue kangaroo

play time * party time * lunch time * tea time
bounce down to blue kangaroo

what can we chew blue kangaroo?

Unwind in our coffee bar downstairs in the play area, providing healthy and nutritious breakfast, lunch and teatime menus for you and your little ones.

Or relax in our restaurant where children can join their parents for a meal or run riot in the playzone downstairs whilst being watched on the big screen in the restaurant specially linked to the play area

Book your party now!
Fab and funky discos for 12yr+ too

555 Kings Road, London SW6 2EB
Tel: 020 7371 7622 • Party booking line 07979 000 832
info@thebluekangaroo.co.uk • www.thebluekangaroo.co.uk
Open every day

People's Palace   020 7928 9999
Royal Festival Hall, Belvedere Road, South Bank
www.capitalgrp.co.uk

Gourmet Pizza Company   020 7928 3188
Gabriels Wharf, 56 Upper Ground

SE5

The Sun & Doves   020 7733 1525
61 Coldharbour Lane
Large garden and children's portions

SE19

Joanna's   020 8670 4052
56 Westow Hill

SE22

Blue Mountain Café   020 8299 6953
18 North Cross Road

SE24

The 3 Monkeys   020 7738 5500
136-140 Herne Hill
www.3monkeysrestaurant.com

SOUTH WEST LONDON
SW3

Henry J Beans   020 7352 9255
195-7 King's Road

Le Shop   020 7352 3891
329 King's Road

Big Easy   020 7352 4071
332 King's Road

SW4

Bread & Roses   020 7498 1779
5-9 Battersea Rise
Infamous south London pub with garden/playroom and
regular family events

Newton's   020 8673 0977
33 Abbeville Road, Clapham Common South Side

The Pepper Tree   020 7622 1758
19 Clapham Common Southside

SW6

Blue Elephant   020 7385 6595
4-6 Fulham Broadway

Tootsies   020 7736 4023
177 New King's Road

Blue Kangaroo   **020 7371 7622**
555 King's Road
www.thebluekangaroo.co.uk
Family restaurant and play centre plus a great party venue
(See advert on previous page)

SW7

Café Rouge   020 7373 2403
102 Old Brompton Road
and other branches

Pizza Organic   020 7589 9613
20 Old Brompton Road

Francofill   020 7584 0087
1 Old Brompton Road

SW8

Le Bouchon Lyonnais   020 7622 2618
38 Queenstown Road

Café Portugal   020 7587 1962
South Lambeth Road
Fantastically busy Portuguese café between Stockwell and
Brixton where children are more than welcome

The Stepping Stone   020 7622 0555
123 Queenstown Road

SW10

La Famiglia   020 7351 0761
7 Langton Street

SW11

Dexter's   020 7924 4935
1 Battersea Rise
Organic kids menu £5.50 including drink and dessert. High
chairs, colouring, goodie bags, balloons and free baby food.

Ransome's Dock   020 7223 1611
35 Parkgate Road

The Inebriated Newt   020 7223 1637
172 Northcote Road

Le Bouchon Bordelais   020 7738 0307
5-9 Battersea Rise
www.lebouchon.co.uk
Free creche at weekends

The Boiled Egg & Soldiers   020 7223 4894
63 Northcote Road

Glaister's Garden Bistro   020 7924 6699
8-10 Northcote Road

SW13

Browns   020 8748 4486
201 Castlenau Road

Sonny's   020 8748 0393
94 Church Road

SW14

The Naked Turtle   020 8878 1995
505 Upper Richmond Road
Entertainer Sunday lunch

The Depot   020 8878 9462
Mortlake High Street

SW15

Moomba   020 8785 9151
5 Lacy Road

SW17

Chez Bruce   020 8672 0114
2 Bellevue Road
Non-smoking family restaurant with children's portions

SW18

Outback Steakhouse   020 8877 1599
Smugglers Way
Activity comic & crayons, freshly-prepared kids' food

SW19

Est Est Est   020 8947 7700
38 High Street

The Light House   020 8944 6338
75-77 Ridgway

San Lorenzo   020 8946 8463
38 Wimbledon Hill Road
Child frieldly, kids play area

WEST LONDON
W1

Browns   020 7491 4565
47 Maddox St

Giraffe   020 7935 2333
6-8 Blandford Street

days out

Hard Rock Café   020 7629 0382
150 Old Park Lane
www.hardrock.com
Very loud music which for the little ones can be a bit much.
Great for the 3yr+ age group with magicians performing
throughout

Yo! Sushi   020 7287 0443
52 Poland Street
www.yosushi.co.uk
Also at Harvey Nichols, Selfridges, O2 Centre, Farringdon
Road, Finchley Road. Baby chopsticks, crayons, kids club

Down Mexico Way   020 7437 9895
25 Swallow Street

Momo   020 7434 4040
25 Heddon Street
Sat & Sun lunchtime Kids Clubs

Carluccio's   020 7935 5927
St Christopher's Place
www.carluccios.co.uk
Winner of the Best Family Restaurant in 2002. This Italian
café serves inexpensive dishes with a particularly hospitable
welcome to bambinos.

Planet Hollywood   020 7287 1000
13 Coventry Street
www.planethollywood.com

Nadine's   020 7439 1063
23-24 Greek Street

Amalfi   020 7437 7284
31 Old Compton Street

Rainforest Café   020 7434 3111
20 Shaftesbury Avenue

W2

Mandarin Kitchen   020 7727 9468
14-16 Queensway

W4

Chiswick House   020 8742 7336
Burlington Lane
Café in the grounds of Chiswick House

Mongolian Barbecue   020 8995 0575
1-3 Acton Lane, W4
Other branches in Kensington, Wimbledon, Covent Garden

Texas Lone Star   020 8747 0001
50-54 Turnham Green Terrace, W4 1QP

W5

Pizza Organic   020 8998 6878
100 Pitshanger Lane, W5 1QX

Old Orleans   020 8579 7413
26-42 Bond Street, W5 5AA
www.oldorleans.com

W8

Sticky Fingers   020 7938 5338
1a Phillimore Gardens
American diner with family friendly weekend activities and
children's menu

Wagamama's   020 7376 1717
London House, Kensington High Street
'Extremely child friendly at lunchtimes, especially with babies.'

W11

Tootsies   020 7229 8567
120 Holland Park Avenue
and other branches

Julie's Restaurant   020 7229 8331
135 Portland Road
www.juliesrestaurant.com
Creche on Sunday lunch

WC1

Charoscuro at Town House   020 7636 2731
24 Coptic Street

WC2

Haagen-Dazs on the Square   020 7287 9577
14 Leicester Square
and other branches

Rock Garden   020 7240 3961
6 The Piazza, Covent Garden

Wolfe's   020 7831 4442
30 Great Queen Street
www.wolfesgrill.com

Maxwell's   020 7836 0303
8-9 James Street

Porters   020 7836 6466
17 Henrietta Street
www.porters.co.uk

TGI Friday   020 7379 0585
6 Bedford Street
and other branches

Café Pacifico   020 7379 7728
5 Langley Street

Brown's Restaurant   020 7497 5050
82-84 St Martin's Lane

Café in the Crypt   020 7839 4342
Crypt of St Martin-in-the-Fields, Duncannon Strt,
WC2N 4JJ

theatres

(see also arts centres and galleries, drama)

Many theatres stage shows for children, especially
around Christmas

days out

Artsline 020 7388 2227
London's information and advice service for
disabled people on arts & entertainment
Also produce a booklet caled 'Play' on activities for
disabled children (£2)

Puppet Theatre Barge 020 7249 6876
Varying locations throughout the year

N1
Little Angel Theatre 020 7226 1787
14 Dagmar Passage, off Cross Street

N7
Unicorn Theatre 020 7700 0702
St Mark's Studios, Chillingworth Road

NW1
Open Air Theatre 020 7486 2431
Inner Circle, Regent's Park
www.open-air-theatre.org.uk
August is when the Children's play is held in a 1,200 seat
theatre. Book early

NW6
Tricycle Theatre 020 7328 1000
269 Kilburn High Road

SE1
Royal National Theatre 020 7452 3000
www.nationaltheatre.org.uk
Aside from the main theatre there are children's events that
take place around fairytales, juggling, comedy magic during
the holidays

SE16
London Bubble 020 7237 4434
5 Elephant Lane
Mobile arts company

SE6
Lewisham Theatre 020 8690 0002
Catford

SE8
Deptford Albany Theatre 020 8692 4446
Douglas Way, Deptford

SE17
Nettlefold Theatre 020 7926 8070
West Norwood Library, 1 Norwood High Street
A 200 seater theatre offering a great selection of shows for
the 2-5yr old age group, including slide shows, puppetry and
theatre. The theatre is also home to the Big Foot Theatre
Company which hosts classes in drama, dance and singing
from 7yrs-12yrs

SW11
Battersea Arts Centre 020 7223 2223
Old Town Hall, Lavender Hill

SW17
Nomad Puppet Studio 020 8767 4005
37 Upper Tooting Road

SW19
Polka Theatre for Children 020 8543 4888
240 The Broadway
www.polkatheatre.com
A dedicated and comprehensive children's theatre. Daily
shows are held at 10.30am and 2pm. There is also an
opportunity to see the costumes and props from previous
shows in the exhibition centre, run around the adventure
playground or take refreshments in the cafe. Other activites
take place at the weekends and during the school holidays

W6
Lyric Theatre Hammersmith 020 8741 2311
King Street

Wembly Arena 0870 060 0870
www.whatsonwembley.com
Following the great success of Thomas the Tank Engine
comes to Wembley, they also have lined up Disney on Ice:
Toy Story 2 (19-24 October) and Milkshake! Presents Noddy
(27-29 December). Perfect for 2-5yr olds

BEST WEST END SHOWS

CHITTY CHITTY BANG BANG 0870 890 1108
Palladium, Argyll Street, W1
www.chittythemusical.co.uk
Tickets between £15.-£40. Great show with a flying car,
sweet factory and the Children's catcher. From 5yrs+

THE LION KING 0870 243 9000
Lyceum Theatre, Wellington Street, WC2
Tickets from £17.50-£40. Few children will be unfamiliar with
this classic Disney story. The ingenious costumes, lavish set
designs and the combination of puppetry and live acting with
African drumming and singing makes for a fantastic
performance. From 4yrs+

theme parks

Alton Towers 0870 520 4060
Alton, ST10 4DB
www.altontowers.com
Price £21 4-11yrs. For white knuckle water rides head to this
theme park and model farm. Using the Parent-Q-Share pass
you can help minimise waiting in long queues with young
children.

**Chessington
World of Adventures** 0870 444 7777
Leatherhead Road, Chessington, KT9 2NE
www.chessington.com
Price £18, 4-12yrs. Theme park and zoo. Jct 9 off M25 or
A3.

Thorpe Park   0870 444 4466
Staines Road, Chertsey, Surrey
www.thorpepark.com
Price: £18.50, 4-12yrs. More suitable for the Under 5s to visit the Farm, whilst older brothers and sisters can have their stomachs turned inside out on the Nemesis Inferno..

Legoland   0870 504 0404
Winkfield Road, Windsor, Berkshire
www.legoland.co.uk
Price: £19, 3-15yrs. This year they have installed the miniature Millennium Eye and Buckingham Palace, but young ones will be amazed to see what they can build with the basic lego brick. Go outside school holidays to avoid the queues which can be colossal

Beckonscott Model Village   01494 672919
Warwick Road, Beaconsfield, HP9 2PL
www.bekonscot.com
Price £3, 3-16yrs. Miniature village, playground and ride on steam railway

Diggerland   0870 034 4437
Whitewall Road, Strood, Kent ME2
www.diggerland.com
Open 10-5pm during holidays, this theme park is a must for Bob the Builder enthusiasts. Includes diggers, fork-lift trucks, dumpers and tractors

trains

Bluebell Railway   01825 723 777
Sheffield Park Station, East Grinstead, Sussex
www.bluebell-railway.co.uk
Price £4 3-15yrs. Steam engine takes you along the old Lewes to East Grinstead line. Family events including Thomas the Tank Engine days and Santa specials. Check the website for opening times

Didcot Railway   01235 817 222
Didcot, Oxfordshire
www.didcotrailwaycentre.org.uk
Price £4.50, 3-15yrs. Take a ride on the old steam engine line. For seasonal family events check the website.

Kent & East Sussex Railway   01580 765 155
www.kesr.org.uk
Open between Apr-November daily 10.40am-3.30pm. Admission £9 and free for under 3s. Beautifully restored engines and carriages running between Tenterden and Bodiam stations. Check the website for when Thomas the Tank Engine has his special outing

Miniature Steam Railway
Brockwell Park, Brixton
Price £1 return. The line runs along the east side of the park (Herne Hill side) and trains run on Wed, Sat & Sun when dry

zoos

Be aware that the majority of the zoos below close their doors at around 4.30pm as a last entrance for tickets

Battersea Park Zoo   020 8871 7540
North Carriage Drive, SW11
As we go to print the future of Battersea Zoo looks better than for a long time. Plans to develop the area seem to have stalled so three cheers for parent pressure!

Birdworld and Underwater World   01420 22140
Holt Pound, Farnham, GU10 4LD
www.birdworld.co.uk
Open Feb-Oct 10am-6pm. Price £6.95, 3-14yrs

Cotswold Wildlife Park   01993 823006
Burford, OX18 4JW
Open 10-6pm. Price £5.00 3-16yrs. Camels, zebras, reptiles, penguins and rhinos

Drusilla's Park   01323 874100
Alfriston, East Sussex BN26 5QS
www.drusillas.co.uk
Open 10-6pm Apr-Oct. Price £8.50, free for under 3s. The low-level windows allow even the smallest toddler to peer at an exotic range of wild animals, followed by a terrific adventure playground and steam railway. A great day out

Howletts   01227 721286
Bekesbourne, Canterbury, Kent
www.howletts.net
Open Apr-Oct 10-6pm. Gorillas, elephants, tigers amongst other small, wild animals

London Zoo   020 7722 3333
Regents Park, NW1 4RY
www.zsl.org
Open Apr-Oct 10-5pm. Price £9, 3-15yrs

Marwell Zoological Park   01962 777407
Golden Common, Winchester, SO21 1JH
www.marwell.org.uk
Jct 11, M3. Open Apr-Oct 10am-6pm. Free for under 3s

Whipsnade Wild Animal Park   01582 872171
Whipsnade, nr Dunstable, Beds, LU6 2LF
www.whipsnade.co.uk
Open Mar-Oct 10am-6pm. Price £9.50, 3-15yrs. Elephants, tigers, bears, giraffes and hippos

Woburn Safari Park   01525 290407
Woburn Park, Beds, MK17 9QN
www.woburnsafari.com
Open Mar-Nov 10am-5pm. Price £10.50 3-15yrs. Bears, monkeys, tigers, wolves and rhinos.

adoption

To adopt you need to be approved by the British authorities [4-6mths]. The first step is to contact your local authority where a social worker will assess your suitability to adopt and perform the necessary checks. To adopt overseas the Department of Health has to formalise the paperwork [6-9mths] and send the papers to the British Embassy in your chosen country

Adoption UK   0870 770 0450
www.adoptionuk.org.uk

After Adoption   0161 839 4930
www.afteradoption.org.uk

BAAF   020 7593 2000
www.baaf.org.uk
British Association for Adoption and Fostering. Information and advice for prospective parents; list of UK children looking for families [normally 5yrs+]

OASIS   0870 241 7069
www.adoptionoverseas.org.uk

Overseas Adoption Helpline   0870 516 8742
www.oah.org.uk

Post-Adoption Centre   0870 777 2197
www.postadoptioncentre.org.uk
Daily advice line which offers advice , information and support to all affected by adoption.

councils

Your local council is an excellent source of information. Ask for the Children's Information Service department for enquiries about play centres, parks etc, the Early Years department for childcare and early education. Some produce little booklets about what's on offer for children in the borough, although it can sometimes be out of date. In the main we have provided the main switchboard numbers as the individual departments do get moved around during the year

Barking & Dagenham   020 8270 4882
www.barking-dagenham.gov.uk
Barnet   020 8359 2000
www.barnet.gov.uk
Bexley   020 8303 7777
www.bexley.gov.uk
Brent   020 8937 3001
www.brent.gov.uk
Bromley   020 8464 3333
www.bromley.gov.uk

Camden   020 7278 4444
www.camden.gov.uk
Corporation of London   020 7606 3030
www.cityoflondon.gov.uk
Croydon   020 8760 5453
www.croydon.gov.uk
Ealing   020 8579 2424
www.ealing.gov.uk
Enfield   020 8578 6154
www.enfield.gov.uk
Greenwich   020 8854 8888
www.greenwich.gov.uk
Hackney   020 8356 5000
www.hackney.gov.uk
Hammersmith & Fulham   020 8748 3020
www.lbhf.gov.uk
Haringey   020 8801 1234
www.haringey.gov.uk
Harrow   020 8424 1307
www.harrow.gov.uk
Hounslow   020 8583 2000
www.hounslow.gov.uk
Islington   020 7527 5959
www.islington.gov.uk
Kensington & Chelsea   020 7937 5464
www.rbkc.gov.uk

Westminster Children's Information Service

Information and advice on childcare and early years education.

- Nurseries
- Childminders
- Out of school clubs
- How to get help with childcare costs
- Starting a career in childcare

020 7641 7929

Phone line open 9-5 weekdays
Voicemail at all other times.
cis@westminster.gov.uk

for the most important things in your life

City of Westminster

Kingston upon Thames www.kingston.gov.uk	020 8547 6582
Lambeth www.lambeth.gov.uk	020 7926 1000
Lewisham www.lewisham.gov.uk	020 8314 8556
Merton www.merton.gov.uk	020 8543 2222
Newham www.newham.gov.uk	020 8430 2000
Redbridge www.redbridge.gov.uk	020 8708 3145
Richmond upon Thames www.richmond.gov.uk	020 8891 1411
Southwark www.southwark.gov.uk	020 7525 5000
Sutton www.sutton.gov.uk	020 8770 5000
Tower Hamlets www.towerhamlets.gov.uk	020 7364 5000
Waltham Forest www.walthamforest.gov.uk	020 8527 5544
Wandsworth www.wandsworth.gov.uk	020 8871 6000
Westminster www.westminster.gov.uk	020 7641 6000

ex-pat advice

American Women's Club of London 020 7589 8292
68 Old Brompton Road, SW7 3LQ

Focus Information Services 020 7937 0050
13 Prince of Wales Terrace, W8 5PG

fatherhood

Families Need Fathers 020 7613 5060
134 Curtain Road, EC2A 3AR

www.fathersdirect.com
The UK's national information centre for fatherhood

financial advice

Having a baby has both short- and long-term financial implications and it is wise to plan for both. If you haven't already done so you should consider making a **Will,** and taking some life assurance, critical illness cover or mortgage protection

Investments for Children: Friendly Society plans, Deposit Accounts, National Savings Children Bonds and Premium Bonds can be started for children where interest payments are tax-free. Other investment schemes can prepare you for school fees or future expenditure. Children can't own stocks or shares in their own name. It may also be worth looking at Trusts, where grandparents or parents can assign property or money to children for inheritance tax purposes

The Children's Mutual 0800 138 1381
Abbey Court, St John's Road, Tunbridge Wells, Kent, TN4 9TE
www.thechildrensmutual.co.uk
The UK specialist dedicated to savings for children

Foreign & Colonial Management Ltd 0800 136 420
Exchange House, Primrose Street, EC2A 2NY
www.fandc.com/sfc
Savings plans for children from F&C. First in investment trusts

helplines

Action for ME Pregnancy Network www.afme.org.uk	01749 670799
Action for Sick Children	020 8542 4848
Action on Pre-Eclampsia	020 8427 4217
Anaphylaxis Campaign www.anaphylaxis.org.uk	01252 542029
Anti-Bullying Campaign	020 7378 1446
Assoc for Improvements in Maternity Services www.aims.org.uk	020 8390 9534
Association for Postnatal Illness www.apni.org	020 7386 0868
Baby Milk Action www.babymilkaction.org	01223 464420
Bedwetting Education Advisory Line www.bedwetting.co.uk	0800 085 8189
Birth Crisis Network	01865 300266
Birth Defects Foundation	08700 707020
British Allergy Foundation www.allergyfoundation.com	020 8303 8583
British Association for Early Childhood Education www.early-education.org.uk	020 7539 5400

Looking for quality registered childcare in North London?

Contact your local Children's Information Service

Barnet on 0800 389 8312
Email: childrens.info@barnet.gov.uk

Enfield on 020 8482 1066

Haringey on 020 8801 1234

or
visit the website at
childcarelink.gov.uk

Interested in working in childcare, early years or play?
Telephone the local recruitment Helpline on the number shown above.

Putting the Community First

British Dyslexia Association   0118 966 8271

British Epilepsy Association   0113 210 8800
www.epilepsy.org.uk

British Institute for Brain
Injured Children   01278 684060
www.bibic.org.uk

British Institute for
Learning Disabilities   01562 723010
www.bild.org.uk

British Stammering Association   020 8983 1003
www.stammering.org

Caesarian Support Network   01624 661269

Cerebral Palsy Helpline (SCOPE)   0808 800 3333
www.scope.org.uk

Child Bereavement Trust   01494 446648
www.childbereavement.org.uk

Child Death Helpline   0800 282 986

ChildLine   0800 1111
www.childline.org.uk

Children's Information Service   0800 960296
www.childcarelink.gov.uk

Cleft Lip And Palate
Association (CLAPA)   020 7431 0033
www.clapa.com

Coeliac UK   01494 437278

Contact-A-Family   020 7383 3555
www.cafamily.org.uk

Cot Death Helpline   0845 601 0234

Cot Death Society   01925 850086
www.cotdeathsociety.co.uk

Council for Disabled Children   020 7843 6000
www.ncb.org.uk

CRUSE Bereavement Care   020 8940 4818

Cystic Fibrosis Trust   020 8464 7211
www.cftrust.org.uk

Daycare Trust   020 7840 3350

Diabetes UK
(ex-British DiabetesAssociation)   020 7323 1531
www.diabetes.org.uk

Disability Alliance   020 7247 8763

Down's Heart Group   01525 220379

Down's Syndrome Association   020 8682 4001
www.dsa.uk.com

Dyspraxia Foundation   01462 454986
www.dyspraxiafoundation.org.uk

Enuresis Resource &
Information Centre (ERIC)   0117 960 3060
www.eric.org.uk

Families Need Fathers   020 7613 5060
www.fnf.org.uk

Foundation for the Study of
Infant Deaths   020 7233 2090
www.sids.org.uk/fsid

Fragile X Society   01424 813147

Group B Strep Support   01444 416176
www.gbss.org.uk

Herpes Viruses Association   020 7609 9061

Home Education   01707 371854
Advisory Service
www.heas.co.uk

Home-Start UK   020 7388 6075
www.home-start.org

Hyperactive Children's
Support Group   01903 725182
www.hacsg.org.uk

ISC: London & South East   020 7798 1560
www.isis.org.uk/southeast

Kidscape   020 7730 3300
www.kidscape.org.uk

LOOK (National Federation of
Families with Visuall   0121 428 5038

Mediation in Divorce   020 8891 6860

Meet A Mum Association
(MAMA)   01761 433598
www.mama.org

Meningitis Research   08088 003344
www.meningitis.org

Meningitis Trust   0845 600 0800
www.meningitis-trust.org.uk

Miscarriage Association   01924 200799
www.miscarriageassociation.org.uk

Multiple Births Foundation   020 8383 3519
www.multiplebirths.org.uk

National Advice Centre for
Children with Reading D   0845 604 0414

National Asthma Campaign   020 7226 2260
www.asthma.org.uk

National Autistic Society   020 7833 2299
www.nas.org.uk

National Childbirth Trust   0870 4448707

National Council for
One-Parent Families   0800 185026
www.oneparentfamilies.org.uk

National Deaf
Children's Society   020 7250 0123

National Eczema Society   020 7388 4097
www.eczema.org

National Endometriosis Society   020 7222 2781
www.endo.org.uk

National Family Mediation   020 7383 5993

National NEWPIN   020 7358 5900

NHS Direct   0845 4647
www.nhsdirect.nhs.uk

NSPCC Child Protection   0800 800 500

Parentline Plus   0808 800 2222
www.parentlineplus.org.uk

Parents At Work   020 7628 2128
www.parentsatwork.org.uk

Parents for Inclusion   020 7735 7735
www.parentsforinclusion.org

Positively Women   020 7713 0222

Relate:
National Marriage Guidance   020 8367 7712
www.relate.org.uk

RNIB   020 7391 2245

Sexual Abuse   020 8950 7855

SCOPE   020 7619 7100
www.scope.org.uk/

Serene (incorporating Cry-sis)   020 7404 5011

Sexual Health &
National Health Helpline   0800 567123

Stillbirth And Neonatal
Death Society (SANDS)   020 7436 7940
www.uk-sands.org

TAMBA   0870 770 3305
www.tamba.org.uk

The SHE Trust
(Simply Holistic Endometriosis)   01522 519992
www.shetrust.org.uk

Women's Domestic
Violence Helpline   0161 839 8574
www.wdvh.org.uk

Women's Health   020 7251 6580
www.womenshealthlondon.org.uk

Gingerbread   020 7488 9300

Kids No Object   01243 543685
Lymington, Farwell Avenue, Eastgate, Chichester, West
Sussex

Single Parent Travel Club   01243 543685
   0870 241 621

naming ceremonies

If you want a secular naming ceremony, as
opposed to a christening, then you have many
options available to you. If you choose to focus the
event on naming the child and making a public
declaration of the commitment of parents and
godparents then the following organisations will be
able to guide you with a selection of formats (formal
or informal)

Baby Naming Society   01905 371 070
Yeoman's Cottage, Kerswell Green, Kempsey,
Worcestershire, WR5 3PF

British Humanist Association   020 7430 0908
47 Theobald's Road, London, WC1X 8SP

Welfare State International   01229 581 127
www.welfare-state.org

parenting classes & courses

These courses can help parents expand their
knowledge and techniques for effective parenting,
as well as know how to set limits, foster self-
esteem and maintain a happy equilibrium in the
home

The Parent Company   020 7935 9635
6 Jacob's Wells Mews, W1H 5PD
www.theparentcompany.co.uk
Evening seminars on discipline, self-esteem, sibling rivalry,
raising boys/girls

Parentline Plus   0808 800 2222
www.parentlineplus.org.uk
12 week parenting course or in modules

Parent Talk 020 7450 9073
www.parenttalk.co.uk
Website has useful tips on getting the most out of
relationships with your children

The New Learning Centre 020 7794 0321
www.parenting-skills.com
Learn how to develop confident and motivates children.
Focus in on 0-4yrs

The Family Caring Trust 02830 264 174
www.familycaring.co.uk
6-8 week course for parenting children up to 6yrs

paternity testing

Cellmark Diagnostics 01235 528000
PO Box 265, Abingdon, Oxfordshire
www.cellmark.co.uk
5-day DNA test. Phone customer services for confidential advice

working opportunities

Sing and Sign 01273 550 587
www.singandsign.com
Run your own music groups teaching established baby
signing programme (see advert on page 85)

**The Virgin
Cosmetics Company** 020 8580 1975

Usborne Books at Home 01825 769 515
www.usborne.com
Flexible job selling books. TAke your children with you. Career
prospects.

Working Options 020 8932 1462
www.workingoptions.com
Using your professional skills in a part-time way

useful tradesmen

Architects
Simon Miller (RIBA) 020 8201 9875
This architect's mantra is "The good new is you've had a
baby. The bad news is you've got no space"!

George Powers Associates 020 7498 5927
The Studio, 9a Emu Road, SW8 3PS
george.powers@tiscali.co.uk

Cleaners
As soon as your first child arrives you will realise
that you cannot possibly attain the previous levels
of tidiness and cleanliness in your home. These
agencies are well aware of your requirements and
have reputable services providing staff of a high
quality and efficiency. I don't think you can ever
have too many helping hands in this department,
and if you've DIY-ed most of your life, then this is
the time to let go...

A Bit of Help 020 7476 0020
Help with cleaning, ironing services, party helpers and
nannies on call

**Mrs Browns
Staff Agency Ltd** 020 7736 0080
149 Wandsworth Bridge Road, SW6
mrsbrown@staff149.freeserve.co.uk,
Adaptable, capable and kind help with children, elderly or home

Selclene Ltd
North of the River 0800 781 8080
South of the River 0808 698 7777
www.selclene.co.uk

Simply Domestics 020 8444 4304
65 Colney Hatch Lane, N10
www.simplydomestics.com
For all your childcare and domestic needs

Nesting?
Want to tinker with the internal layout of your property?

George Powers Associates specialise in
maximising the use of space.

We can visualise interiors in a way clients
might not have imagined and have proven
ability in getting planning permission.

We offer a friendly helpful service geared to
meeting your individual needs.

George Powers Associates ASID.
Tel: 020 7498 5927
Over 30 yrs qualified experience.

The Studio, 9a Emu Road, London, SW8 3PS
george.powers@tiscali.co.uk

Clutter Clearers

Whatever you feel about someone telling you how to put things away, I think pregnancy is the time in your life where your natural nesting instinct should be exploited so that you get things well organised for a busy few months ahead. Or maybe you've got 4 children already and no one can agree on what should go where…

No More Clutter   07974 076 675
www.nomoreclutter.co.uk

Clear Space   020 7233 3138

Simply-Sorted   020 8769 7276

London Home Organizers   0776 112 8059
enquiries@londonhomeorganisers.co.uk
Unpacking, inventories, hodoctor… We organise all your house problems. Ring us and see?

House and Garden

Polly the Flower Lady   07880 882 645
Fresh, cut flowers every Wednesday (Streatham & Balham)

Richard the Handyman   020 8672 3555
Get Richard in for _ a day for plumbing, electrical, carpentry, locks, pointing and plaster patching

0800 Handyman   0800 426 3962
Hang blinks, fix leaky taps, assemble furniture, install a shower, lights, tiling and painting

Floor Trade Direct   01256 880 253
home service offering big savings on all types of carpet, wood stone, laminate and vinyl

Garden Designers   07977 125 677
Have your garden redesigned with kids in mind by Annabel Foster

Plews Garden Design   020 8289 8086
www.plewsgardendesign.co.uk

Austins Painters & Decorators   020 8671 4221
Interior and exterior redecoration.

Window Cleaning: SJ Bridgeman   020 7404 5011
High recommended for be reliable and trustworthy.

Pet Nanny   020 8875 0341
www.petnanny.co.uk
For those going on holiday and worrying about what to do with cats and dogs, call Serena and she will arrange for one of her carers either to visit your cat on a daily basis, or care for your dog in their home.

Video Magic   020 7585 1139
www.videomagic.co.uk
Set your videos to music and transfer it to CD DVD or VHS tape

Advertisers are highlighted in blue

1.2.3 sol	161
1.2.3. Soleil	160
9 london	43
abbeville nannies	**81**
active birth centre	1
active kids	102, 162
acupuncture	9
adoption	192
adventure playgrounds	154
albany midwifery practice	1
alexander technique	9
alison evans	81
all seasons nursery shop	58
allsorts	159
alton towers	190
amanda's action kids	102, 169
angela & urchins	47
angelcare	48
annie haak	**39**
announce it!	**22**
antenatal classes	1
antenatal scans	2
antenatal tests	2
aquababies	**179**
arabella b	44
aromatherapy	10
art 4 fun	101, 154
art centres & galleries	180
aspace	**36, 52**
asprey & garrard	29
asquith court schools	**117**
au pair international	**76**
au pairs	76
autosafe	**25**

babes in the wood	81
babies r us	41, 58
babiTENS	8
baby accessories	21
baby closet	34
baby concierge	57
baby equipment (see nursery goods)	57
baby equipment hire	21
baby heirlooms	**29**
baby jogger	69
baby london	52
baby list company	**39, 52, 57**
baby massage	16
baby organix	37
baby play	16
baby research	10
baby showers	21
babybond	2

babydan	41
babygoes2.com	98
babygoodsdirect	67
babyhut	25
babylab	**10**
the baby show	**back cover**
babysitters childminders	**77**
babyviewcam	48
back2front	61
ballet classes	156
barbican centre	180
battersea arts centre	180
battersea zoo	191
baybiz	57
bea's baby music school	**169**
bebe confort	26
bebetel	48
beckonscott model village	191
beds & cot beds	36
bestbear.co.uk	83
bibs & stuff	41
big hugs	42
birth announcements	22
birth centre	**5, 81**
birthbody	1, 15
blooming marvellous	**43**
blue kangaroo	**106, 166, 187**
blueberry playsongs	**102, 169**
board bug	48
bodium castle	181
body painters	3
bodywise	43
bonne nuit	**42**
bookclubs	25
bookshops for children	22
breastfeeding	2
bright horizons	**109**
bringing up baby	**121**
britax	26
british museum	184
brush strokes	101
bugaboo	68
buggysnuggle co	69
bump to 3	59
bushbaby	26
business bump	44

cake dreams	**102**
cake store	102
camden arts centre	180
camping	98
canapes gastronomiques	102
car safety	25
carolyn cowan	**3, 61**
carolyn weller	**61**
carriers, slings & backpacks	25
castings: hands & feet	27

catherine owens	16
cells 4 life	**6**
ceramic cafes	155
changing the guard	181
chatterbox cards	22
cheeky monkeys	72
chelsea baby hire	21
chemists: late opening	10
chess	155
chessington world of adventures	190
chicco	26, 67
childalert	12
childbase	**116**
childcare	76
childminders	**77**
children's cottage company	39
children's furniture co.	**36, 52**
christening gifts	29
christening gowns	29
christine hill associates	2
cinema clubs	182
circuses	182
clapham picture house	182
clare byam-cook	3
clementine toys	75
clothing shops: boutique	29
clothing shops: cheap & cheerful	34
clothing shops: high street	32
clothing: mail order	34
club petit pierrot	160
clutter clearers	197
complementary health	11
cookery	155
cornerhouse day nursery	**143**
cornwall beach house	**95**
cosatto	67
cotton bottoms	51
councils	192
courtauld institute gallery	180
cow jumped over the moon	**50**
cranial osteopathy	17
craniosacral therapy	18
crazee kids	157
creative wiz kids	**102, 154**
crechendo playgymns	**162**
cribs & cots	36
cute as a button	22
crescent kindergartens	**134**
cycling & scooters	156

daisies day nursery	**127**
daisy & tom	40
damask	42
dance	156
debenhams	35
debra sequoia	**1**
department stores	35

diana vowles **61**
diggerland 191
discover story garden 154
doctor's laboratory 2
doulas 78
dragons of walton street 52, 60
drama 159
dressing up 37
drusilla's park 191
dulwich picture gallery 180

east coast nursery 41
easy 2 name **50**
eat yer greens 34
eden nannies **78, 81**
electric cinema 182
elisabeth smith model agency 169
elite nannies **78, 81**
elj design **50**
ella van meelis 2
emmaljunga 67
exercise 12
ex-pat advice 192
ezee-reach 21

families magazines **47**
family portraits **61**
family ski companies 98
family villages & resorts 98
fancy dress 37
farms: city 182
farms: out of town 183
fatherhood 193
favourite things 21
fig 42
financial advice 193
first aid 12
first impressions **27**
florence de crevoisier-fedder 18
foetal medical centre 2
food (organic) 37
football 161
foreign language classes 160
formes 43
fowey hotel **95**
french classes 160
french nursery schools 144
fulham osteopathic practice **17**
future health technologies **6**

garden toys 38
geffrye museum 184
german classes 161
giftboxes for newborns 39
gifted children 153
gifts, personalised 39
gillian wood ceramics **27**
golden hands, silver feet 27
graco 26
great little trading company **59**
greatcare **81**
green baby copany 58
green people 43
greycoat placements **81**
grobag 42
gwendolen house **133**
gymboree **102, 162, 169**
gyms-mini 162

H&M mama 43
hairdressers 40
hampton court palace 181
happy times **145**
happyhands **22**
haringey council **194**
harrods 35
hauck 68
haydn photography **61**
health clubs with creches 14
helplines 193
**heritage personalised
stationery** **22**
hever castle 181
hickory fiddle violin club 169
hickory jig music **169**
highchairs 41
hippychick 25, 36, 70
historystore **22**
holidays (UK) 95
home delivery 37
home from home **129**
homeopathy 14
homeswaps 98
hopes & dreams **77, 81, 113**
hopscotch dressing up 37
horniman museum 184
hospitals: NHS 4
hospitals: private 5
hotels (UK) 95
howletts 191
huggababy 25, 60
hullabaloo kids 40
hyde park international **81**
hyperbubba 22
hypnotherapy 15

iana 31
ice rinks 183
ickworth hotel **98**
ideal nannies **81**
immunisation 15
imperial nannies **81**
imperial war museum 184
imprints **27**
in trust 77
independent schools council **149**
indoor playcentres 165
infertility 15
international star registry 40
isabella oliver **44**
islington ballet school **157**
iyengar yoga institute 19

jackie coote 9
jackson's lane centre 180
JAGS sports club **14**
jane car seats 26
jazz-mataz 169
jo newman **61**
joe lacey 15
joga junction 19
john lewis 35
johnston prams 67
jojomamanbebe **35, 41, 44, 52**
judy difiore 13
julia laderman **3**
just help **76, 82**

kane & ross clinics 18
kate magson **61**
kensington nannies **82**
kew gardens 185
kiddipics **61**
kiki's clinic 18
kindergartens nurseries **134**
kiwiOz nannies **82**
knightsbridge nannies **82**
knoll house **96**
kundalini yoga **19**
kushies 51

la conception 44
la leche league 3

langdon photography	**61**
lapin & me	75
laurie temple	**103**
le club francais	160
le club tricolore	160
leapfrog nurseries	**119**
learning difficulties	153
leeds castle	181
left-handedness	153
legoland	191
les petits lapins	160
libella bedwear	42
libraries	166
life centre	12
lifestone	27
lilliput	21, 58
lindam	48
linen	42
linen merchant	**42**
lionwitchwardrobe	52
litte green earthlets	60
little acorns	**169**
little angels nursery	**115**
little darlings	29
little darlings photography	61
little kickers	**161**
little gym	**162**
little noggins	40
little stars	21
london academy of	
personal fitness	**12**
london intl gallery of children's art	180
london nanny company	**82**
london prams	58
london transport museum	184
london zoo	191
london's child	**47**
lotions & potions	43
lucky me	35, 40
luxury family hotels	**insert**

maclaren	67
magazines	47
Mama TENS	8
mamas & papas	26
marie askin first aid	12
maris practice	18
mar's au pair agency	**76**
martien jonkers	17
marwell zoo	191
marylebone ballet school	**157**
massage for baby	15
massage for mums	16
maternally yours	**78**
maternity bras	44
the maternity co	**44**
maternity connections	**78**
maternity nurses & nannies	78
maternity wear	43

maternus	**44**
mattresses	36
maxi-cosi	26
maxine hamilton stubber	17
miche gray-newton	61
midwives: independent	81
mighty ducks swim	**178**
mili mouse	**21**
mini crotchets	**169**
minor mail	22
model agencies	169
monitors	48
monkey music	**102, 169**
monkey sites	22
moonfleet manor	**97**
mothercare	59
mountain buggy	69
mountfitchet castle	181
movie magic at the NFT	182
mozzee	41
mulberry bush	75
mulberry house school	**147**
mums 2 be	**44**
museum of childhood	184
museum of london	184
museums	184
music for the young	**169**
music groups	169
music house for children	169
musical bumps	169
musical express	**169**
muzsika	**170**
my nanny network	**12**
my puku	35

name tapes	50
naming ceremonies	196
nannies incorporated	**78, 82**
nannies of st james	**82**
nannies one	82
nanny agencies	81
the nanny agency	**82**
nanny match	**82**
nanny payroll services	93
nanny search	**82**
the nanny service	**82**
nanny tax	**93**
nappies	51
nappy express	21
national army museum	184
national childbirth trust	8
national gallery	180
national maritime museum	184
national portrait gallery	180
natracare	43
natural history museum	184
natural mat	**36, 52**
natural mother	**11, 15, 19**

nearly new	52
neil's yard remedies	43
new baby company	**1**
nicola hippisley	**61**
night nannies	**82**
nina west nurseries	111
norfolk holiday cottage	98
nursery furniture	52
nursery goods	57
nursery goods: mail order	59
nursery interior design	60
nursery schools	107-146
nursery window	**52**
nutrition	17

occasional &	
permanent nannies	**78, 82**
one o'clock clubs	173
one small step,	
one giant leap	**71**
organic food	37
organic paints	60
osteopathy	17

paddling pools	174
paint pots art classes	**155**
paint pots holiday classes	**165**
paint pots montessori	**129**
pamela lloyd-jones	**61**
parent company	**196**
parenting classes	196
park & gardens	185
park nanny agency	82
playgrounds	175
party entertaining	103
party equipment	104
party food	101
party ideas	101
party organisers	105
party shops	105
party venues	106
patricia wigan designs	29, 31
payroll café	93
penny poppins	154
peques nursery	**129**
perfectly happy people	60
pesky kids	35
peter jones	35
petit bateau	34
phil & teds	69
photographers	61
physiotherapists	18
platinum nanny service	**78**
playdays nursery	**138**
playhouse nursery	**129**

polka threatre 190
pollock's toy museum 185
pom pom **60**
portland hospital **11, 13, 15, 16**
portraits 61
pots for tots 37
pottery café 102
pram & buggy repairs 66
prams, pushchairs 67
pubs with gardens or playrooms 185
pulsar sembley medical 8
puppet theatre barge 190
push maternity 44

quinny 67
quo vadis? family travel 98

ravenstone house **137**
rebeccalouise photographics 61
reflexology 18
restaurants: child-friendly 186
revolution health **12**
riding stables 178
riverside childcare **82**
robin farquhar-thomson **61**
rocking horses 70
rub a dub dub 58
rucksack music **170**

safe & sound 12
safety advice 12
saplings nurseries **124**
sara langdon photography **61**
sarah page sculpture **27**
schools, pre-prep 146-153
science museum 185
second hand 52
selfridges 35
seraphine **44**
shoe shops 70-71
shoes 70
silver cross 68
simon horn **36, 52**
simply childcare **78**
sing and sign **170**
skiing companies 98
sleeping bags 42
smart cells **6**
somerset house 185
south bank centre 180
south of the river 82
spanish nursery schools 146

speech therapists 153
st john's wood ballet **157**
stacey mutkin **61**
stagecoach **156, 159**
starchild **70**
stem cell collection 6
stokke 41
stork news 22, 40
storkparty 21
stuck on you 50
sue lewis antenatal **1**
swansons **82**
swimming classes 178
swimming pools: outdoor 179
swimwear & sun stuff 72

tate britain 181
tate modern 181
taxing nannies **93**
teddies nurseries **139**
tennis - mini 179
TENS hire 6
the little gym **162**
the nanny service **78**
the nesting company 60
the parent company **12**
theatres 189
theme parks 190
thorpe park 191
three bags full 42
tia may **61**
tiffany & co 29
tinies childcare **78, 82**
tinies paediatric first aid 12
tiny beats 170
toddler activities 154
togz 34
tommee tippee 48
tomy 48
top notch doulas **78**
top notch nannies **83**
tournicoti 32
tower of london 181
toy shops 72
toys for the garden **38**
toys: mail order 74
trains 191
transformations **50**
travel 95
travel cots 75
travelling with children 75, 98
tricycle theatre 181
tripp trapp 41
tuition (extra) 153
tumble tots **162**
twinkel on the web 51
twizzle parties **105**
two left feet 60

urban detour 69
urchin 60
usbourne books 197
useful tradesmen 197

vaccinations - yes or no? 15
vanblanken 67
vibeke dahl photography **61**
vicki scott - baby confidence 3
victoria page tuition **153**
vital touch 10
volga linen company 42

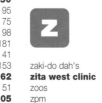

walleroo nannies **83**
waterbirth 8
watermans arts centre 181
wellcare, wellness, well-being 43
westminster city council 192
whippersnappers **102, 170**
whipsnade wild animal park 191
white company 42
white rabbit england 21
why cry analyser 48
wilkinet baby carrier 25
wingreen 39
woburn safari park 191
wonder woman fitness **12**
woolley grange hotel **98**
working opportunities 197
wrightson & platt **27**

yoga 19
yoyabananas 19
yoga for pregnancy 19
yogabananas 104
yogahome 19
young england **31**

zaki-do dah's 40
zita west clinic **2, 9, 15, 17**
zoos 191
zpm 21

order form

To order by telephone call: **020 8678 9000**
or order via our secure website at **www.babydirectory.com**
or send this order form with your cheque to:
The Baby Directory, 7 Brockwell Park Row, London SW2 2YH

Title	Price	Qty	Postage	Total
The London Baby Directory	**£8.99**		**£1.50**	
The South East Baby Directory (Surrey & S. Middlesex, Hampshire, Sussex & Kent)	£5.99		£1.00	
The Central Baby Directory (Oxfordshire, Berks, Bucks, Northants, Beds & Herts)	£5.99		£1.00	
The East Baby Directory (Essex, Cambridgeshire, Suffolk & Norfolk)	£5.99		£1.00	
			Total Order Value	

Please print clearly

Name . . . .

Address . . . .

. . . .

. . . . Postcode . . . .

Tel . . . . E-mail address . . . .

METHOD OF PAYMENT (please tick appropriate box)

Cheque/Postal Order ☐   Credit Card ☐

Please make cheques payable to **The Baby Directory Limited**

Card Number ☐☐☐☐☐ ☐☐☐☐☐ ☐☐☐☐☐ ☐☐☐☐☐ ☐☐☐☐

Issue No ☐☐   Expiry Date ☐☐ ☐☐   Valid from ☐☐ ☐☐

Signature . . . .

How did you hear about the Directory?. . . . . Leaflet Code ☐☐

If you would like to receive our monthly e-newsletter please tick here ☐

ADVERTISERS

If you provide a service or product we should know about, drop us a line, fax or e-mail.

☐ This is a new product, service or facility.

☐ Please send me a media pack.

☐ Oops! You've missed this.

☐ Change of address, new branch, etc.

Category of product (eg, park, restaurant, nursery) ....

Name of product, service or facility ....

Address ....

....

Postcode .... Tel No ....

E-mail address .... www ....

Contact name and tel no (if different from above)

....

READERS

We would very much appreciate your comments. Errors, omissions, or poor service, please let us know. **A free copy of next year's book for the most useful comments!**

Feedback ....

....

....

....

Your own name, address, 'phone number, e-mail address (all optional)

....

....

Many thanks for taking the time to fill in this form

Please send completed form(s) to:

The London Baby Directory, 7 Brockwell Park Row, London SW2 2YH
Tel: 020 8678 9000   Fax: 020 8671 1919   E-mail: editor@babydirectory.com

Luxury Family Hotels

All our hotels are different in character and location. What unites them is the warmth of welcome to families, allowing busy parents to enjoy quality time with their children. Parents can relax knowing that their children are being entertained and watched over by our free childcare facilities.

In the evening parents can enjoy dinner in the restaurants, all of which serve excellent food and offer a superb choice of wines whilst the children are monitored by our baby listening service or one of our hotel baby sitters. The hotels are individually styled with luxurious interiors and every comfort in mind and bedrooms are roomy and accommodating with sofa beds and cots available.

So relax and enjoy a luxury break the whole family can delight in!

Woolley Grange	Moonfleet Manor	Fowey Hall	The Ickworth
Wiltshire 01225 864705	Dorset 01305 786948	Cornwall 01726 833866	Suffolk 01284 735350

For more information call one of our hotels or visit:

luxury family hotels

www.luxuryfamilyhotels.com